The Boy's Dream

Request permissions by contacting Christian Clement at
theboysdreambychristianclement@gmail.com

Hard Cover: ISBN-978-1-7379329-1-8
Paperback: ISBN-978-1-7379329-0-1
Digital Online: ISBN-978-1-7379329-3-2
EBook: ISBN-978-1-7379329-2-5

Library of Congress Number: TXu 2-269-460 and TXu 2-115-640

First paperback, hard cover, and e-book editions: 2021

Printed by: RJM in the USA

Dedicated
To
My Mother
And
My Father
For Bestowing Upon Me
This Wonderful Gift
Of
Human Existence

TABLE OF CONTENTS

Chapter One: "The Dream"

Chapter Two "The Interview"

Chapter Three: "Science"

to even consider ***JESUS' SCIENTIFIC*** **teachings** does seem to be based upon an arbitrary, disingenuous, and atypical criterion.

P.84.... Consciousness could not possibly exist, *solely*, because of the electrical activity of many neurons oscillating together as they share and integrate ***all*** incoming sensory information throughout the ***entire brain network*** because consciousness and self-awareness are not, in any way, diminished (even in instances when . . .)

P.86.... My conclusion is that (1) mental function and consciousness are entirely different and that (2) consciousness in not dependent upon a properly functioning brain in order to exist ***somewhere.*** Even though Alzheimer's disease causes consciousness to disconnect from an Alzheimer sufferer's brain and body, it is unlikely that the sufferer's spiritual uniqueness is damaged and ceases to exist.

P.89.... Agnostics, atheists, and the scientific community conclude that Alzheimer's disease causes consciousness to die forever. In contrast, *Christians* (who fully understand the scientific conclusions presented in this chapter) *prefer to believe Jesus' explanation* (that souls do survive the deaths of bodies) is, ***more likely than not***, the correct explanation.

P.91.... The successful effort by Nobel laureates to convince the United States' Supreme Court to ***outlaw*** Christian beliefs in public-school classrooms was not a demonstration of the Nobel laureates' genius but, instead, was, merely, an example of the narrow-minded bigotry of a small group of *non-Christian* and/or *anti-Christian* dogmatists who chose to *misuse* their Nobel-award status for the purpose of forwarding their, pre-existing, *anti-Christian prejudices*.

P.92.... Public education's core objective has always been to stimulate students' intellectual growth (to the best of their abilities) by teaching them how to develop higher-level, analytical thinking skills (not to either (1) appease anti-Christian bigots or (2) brainwash impressionable young minds with *imperfect and quasi-factual **theories***, solely, for the purpose of undermining the majority population's value and belief system by indoctrinating Christian children to turn against their traditional culture and religion).

P.93…. Jesus' explanation (the remarkable, abstract, scientific theory which foreshadowed, by two thousand years, the conclusions of several, recent, breakthrough scientific theories) does enhance scientific instruction….

P.97….When a ***single***, *lower-court*, Federal District judge concluded that Intelligent Design cannot be taught as a complement to evolution in the public school, his biased decision created a, nearly, impossible legal hurdle for Christians to overcome. Fortunately, that decision was not appealed to the Federal Circuit Court and, then, to the Supreme Court.

P.99…. Toward the end of his life, retired Supreme Court justice, Harry Blackmun, (a justice who provided one of the anti-Christian votes in both the abortion case of *Roe v. Wade* and the Creationist case of *Edwards v. Aguillard*) admitted that some of his decisions were not based upon the law, Democratic principles, or the United States' Constitution but, instead, upon his own personal philosophies. In other words (just prior to his death), this *never-married* Justice felt compelled to reveal his *deviant intentions* by gloating about how he had *exploited* his position of ultimate power to, ***tyrannically***, ***force*** unwarranted transformations upon an, unsuspecting, Christian country.

P.99…. America's founding fathers did not favor a religious test for judicial appointments because they wished to avert the antagonism, and frequent wars, that continually erupted between Catholics and Protestants; however, when they made that determination, the founding fathers never envisioned the possibility that anti-Christians would ever be in the position to *censure and eliminate Christian beliefs* (in this Christian country).

P.100... Too many non-Christians, anti-Christians, and make-believe Christians (without any forms of scrutiny and accountability) have *continually* failed to maintain proper judicial objectivity.

P.101… Seizing control of the judiciary is the primary way, in a Democratic form of government, to effectively unleash tyranny upon a free citizenry.

P.101… Since the media (as well as the legal and political communities) so convincingly categorize *each and every Judge* as being "honorable" and "above reproach" professionals, all present Supreme Court justices (as well as future judicial nominations) will, ***no doubt*** [*sic*], hereafter, quite willingly, ***contractually*** *consent* to (corruption-proof) polygraph testing (1) for the purpose of verifying their "above reproach" integrity and (2) for the purpose assuaging the majority culture's concerns regarding potential impropriety.

P.103… Any suggestions by Christians that it is time for the United States to return, once again, to a ***Democratic, majority-ruled society***, after more than one-half century of patient acquiescence to the non-stop societal atrocities perpetrated by members of America's non-Christian, and/or anti-Christian minorities, Christians are now scorned as merely being bigoted (and racist) supremacists.

P.104... The time has arrived for Christians to expose ingratitude, hatred, and savagery by, finally, confronting ***evil-hearted hypocrites*** in a way that is comparable to Jesus' confrontation of the moneylenders in the temple. This can best be done by ***demanding that a TRUTHFUL American history*** be taught to all American public school children.

P.105… There is no justifiable Constitutional reason to exclude ***any Christian scientific*** theory that (1) has advanced scientific understanding and/or (2) can be shown to help facilitate the development of higher-level thinking skills. The most significant ***Christian Scientific*** theories follow:

Chapter Four: "The Modern Era"

P.130… It is ironic that atheists, and others who do not believe in a spiritual existence are those who are most willing to terminate a life when they know the child will *never* have another opportunity to ***live.***

P.133… Chemical substances have a direct influence on a human's soul.

P.133… It is foolhardy to play games with the gift of consciousness and existence.

P.133… Drugs make it difficult (if not impossible) for anyone to *properly align* one's best thoughts, feelings, and impulses with that person's spirit.

P.133… Of course, not all chemical substances have equal negative effects.

P.134… The primary spiritual risk associated with the use of any chemical substance results from the fact that the substance can strengthen connections to evil spiritual tethers which may be present in a person's spiritual frequency yet remain dormant and inaccessible until alcohol or drug use activates that person's connection to those evil tethers.

P.135… Despite claims to the contrary, narcotic use has the potential to be far more damaging than alcohol use.

P.136… An addict's spiritual frequency can be so damaged that the addiction *just might turn that person into a lost soul.* If so, drug abuse is, far more, a spiritual issue than most humans realize. It is tragic enough when an addict destroys his or her mind and body; it is quite another matter when an addict destroys his or her soul and the pathway to spiritual salvation.

P.137… The problem which results when an *overwhelmingly large percentage* of modern-day adults are, at the very least, allowing themselves to be addicted to painkillers is that such drug abuse turns them into creatures whose senses are so deadened that nothing ever matters. To them, "anything goes". They separate themselves from love, **truth**, goodness, empathy, order, balance, and all other, meaningful, values and principles. The only human talent they struggle to preserve is that skill which enables them to maintain an ***untruthful*** façade.

P.138… It is clear that a very large number of Americans have allowed themselves to become drug dependent. The "elephant in the room" is the fact that a significant portion of those Americans also perceives themselves as being good Christians; and that, too, is an improbable incongruity.

P.138... God tolerates drug proliferation for the same reason that He allowed Eve to bite into the forbidden fruit: God's love has granted all humans the opportunity to possess the freewill to do whatever they desire. Ultimately, of course, humans will have to assume responsibility and accept the consequences for their "**choices**".

P.139… The proper title for a drug dealer is either "drug predator" or "drug terrorist".

P.140… Rash young persons who allow themselves to be conned (by media inducers and drug predators) into sampling drugs have always been the most easily manipulated, foolish, and valueless of all, weak-minded, human beings. For their own good, those gullible youths must be ***shamed for their stupidity*** because they need to be *protected* from drug predators--not *encouraged by media to "**experiment**" with drugs.*

P.141… A frighteningly large number of the wrong-types of people are, presently, in positions of responsibility and trust. Despite superficial appearances, it is obvious that far too many of those people do not live as Christians (or are, even, concerned for their own spiritual salvation).

P.141… The conundrum is that, even, the *United States' government* will not allow decent American Christians to isolate and protect themselves and their children from the most evil humans in society.

P.142... Drug predators would have never found most of the communities that are now plagued by drug abuse problems if ***our government*** had not made all of the arrangements for housing and paid all of the expenses for those drug predators and their families.

P.143… *Mainstream Media and* **corrupt** *governmental officials* have succeeded in obliterating the *basic principles of the* **Christian Democracy** that has always prevailed in ***our United (Christian) States***. This, too, must immediately be confronted and stopped because, throughout history, this type of evil has only been allowed to prevail in countries where tyranny has reigned.

P.143… Drug-dealing criminals are ***urban terrorists*** who are far more dangerous than radical Muslim terrorists; thus, there is no sane, moral, or justifiable reason to continue to extend citizenship to such monsters and their accomplices. In a nutshell, *America's mainstream media and government* have chosen either to facilitate (and/or to virtually ignore) the mayhem and harm that "drug predators" and their ilk have unleashed against *defenseless citizens* of this, overwhelmingly, Christian country. Why?

P.144… Obviously, it is the Christian way to help those who are ***truly*** *needy and deserving*. However, at Matthew 7: 6, Jesus clarifies His meaning by warning: "Do not give what is holy to dogs or toss your pearls before swine. They will trample them underfoot, at best, and perhaps even tear you to shreds".

P.144… Paul elaborates this principle at 1 Corinthians 2: 15-16 when he explains that "the spiritual man…can appraise everything…;" thus, the spiritual man has the ability to *identify* the "dogs" and "swine" through a *discernment* which results from knowing the mind of Christ. ("*Discernment*" means keenness of insight and the ability to perceive. It stresses the power to distinguish and select what is **true** and appropriate from that which is not). Christ clearly instructs that there is a difference between *discernment* and *judgment*, and Christians are obligated to utilize their

Christian discernment to help all Christians identify and protect themselves from the "*dogs*" and the "*swine*".

P.144… Regrettably, too many powerful non-Christians, anti-Christians, and make-believe Christians control and manipulate America's media and educational system, so completely, that, despite their obvious contempt for Christian beliefs, the Christian way of life, and Christian children, they have assumed the role of indoctrinating and teaching Christians what Christians should tolerate and believe. At Matthew 7:15-16, Jesus warns: "Be on your guard against false prophets, who come to you in sheep's clothing but underneath are wolves on the prowl. You will know them by their deeds".

P.145… Media and advertising strategies are (1) utilizing consumer motivational research to ***subliminally*** *influence* ***unwitting*** *consumers* to buy products they don't want or need and (2) employing psychologically manipulative techniques in order to convince unenlightened and unsuspecting people to tolerate and accept beliefs that are not in their best interests.

P.146… Although any statement which claims that mainstream media is in the business of brainwashing and corrupting Christians is obviously extreme, brainwashing and propaganda techniques have been employed, for example, in order to persuade this predominantly Christian country to transform into a country which has legalized gambling, drug use, and homosexual marriages. (Euthanasia is next).

P.148… Of course, there are other contributing factors which make the brainwashing of the general population so easy. First, rather than teach children (1) to reason and analyze properly and (2) to develop higher-level thinking skills that will enable them to discern for themselves, schoolchildren, for more than the past forty-five years, have been ***programmed*** to accept whatever they are told to believe ***without question***.

P.148… Second, unchallenged commercial advertisers have been so totally effective at incorporating subliminal suggestions, as a way of influencing consumers to buy their products, that those subtle influences have, successfully (yet unscrupulously), ***conditioned*** the general population to be susceptible to (and to be easily controlled by) ***all other*** *subliminal message cues* as well.

P.148… Finally, far too many adults are, frequently, under the influence of some form of chemical substance. Sadly, *impaired humans* are far more easily manipulated and, as a result, are far less likely to be guided and influenced by moral principles (especially religious values and beliefs) than they would be if they were to remain sober.

P.149… Christians who publicly explain or defend Christian beliefs are not only being portrayed, by mainstream media, as bigots and haters, they are, now, also being labeled as "extremists" and "radicals" (even though *those Christians* are expressing the beliefs of the *majority* population in the United States).

P.149… It is clear that these non-Christian propagandists have been fighting and, thus far, winning an ***undeclared war*** *against an unsuspecting Christian majority* in a manner that is best explained by the words expressed in the motto of Mossad (the National Israeli Intelligence Agency): "By deception, we will do war"; in other words, "as we smile in your faces, we will stab you in your backs". The last time such an undeclared war against the Christian majority (by a non-Christian minority) was successful (beginning in the 1930's in the Ukraine), more than seven million innocent Eastern European Christians were, within less than a decade, ultimately *murdered.* This is the worst Holocaust in the history of the world (Christians were victimized because they were Christians); yet, this horrible event has been totally concealed from the American public by a totally treacherous American media that, presently, is controlled by non-Christians, anti-Christians, and make-believe Christians. Why?

P.150… The non-stop assault on America's Christian culture (and democratic way of life) is frightening; yet this onslaught can easily be thwarted by any *intelligent and **unified*** Christian response which ***honestly and correctly*** *identifies and exposes* all non-Christian, anti-Christian, and make-believe Christian miscreants for the types of ***evil*** *human beings they* ***truly*** *are.*

P.150… A small number of very dangerous (non-Christian, anti-Christian, and make-believe Christian) bigots are, clearly, the *wrong people* to be controlling this country's access to free speech.

P.152… While mainstream media has been very quick to blame law-abiding, gun-owning citizens for high school massacres, they have consistently refused to *honestly* report (and, thus, teach) the **truth** about what happened to defenseless Christians in countries (such as the Ukraine in the early 1930's) after all of their weapons had been seized. Media has also failed, for example, to **truthfully** relate the most significant details regarding the ***first*** (modern era) high school *massacre* (that was *sensationalized* by national mainstream media) at Columbine High School in Littleton, Colorado on April 20, 1999.

P.153… The primary reason this modern society has become so corrupt is that the massive sums of money earned from illegal activities (starting with Prohibition, gambling, and prostitution and continuing with illegal drugs and Wall Street and Governmental corruption) are presently the financial engines that are controlling American society (the bad guys now control everything); nevertheless, Christians can easily overcome this evil by uniting (because there are so many Christians yet so few bad guys).

P.154… Returning to the drug abuse discussion--in truth, doesn't the willingness to share illegal drugs help less attractive males to be more alluring to attractive females; and isn't this the primary reason that so many young people choose to use drugs?

P.154… The surest means by which an unmarried man is able to achieve sexual intimacy with an attractive woman (in this modern era) is by, first, sharing drugs and/or alcohol with her. This approach (a far cry from the flowers and candy gifts provided by suitors of previous generations) does enhance a less attractive male's prospects for having intercourse with a more attractive, drug-craving female.

P.155… Commitment and integrity are two concepts that do not exist in the minds of drug users; thus, it follows that God, most likely, is disappointed with those of His offspring who will not allow themselves to be sufficiently satisfied with the joy of drug-free sexual intercourse (and **true** affection). Even when husbands and wives are not drug users, the absence of commitment and integrity (as well as the betrayal of vows and trust in a marriage) are, also, significant causes for spiritual frequency problems.

P.155… Nevertheless, most of the Old Testament's prohibitions guiding sexual interactions were, most-likely, practical rules created by humans (to enable barbarians to live peacefully, safely, and healthfully together in civilized communities) rather than mandates ordered by God.

P.156… Originally, God created all mammals to have an overwhelming urge to procreate. It is clear that, at a time when the world was dangerously underpopulated, nothing was more important to God than the survival of as many members of the human species as possible.

P.156… As humans transitioned from being hunters and gatherers into people who lived in communities, it became clear that laws were necessary in order to maintain stability and peace within those communities; thus, two of the Ten Commandments focused on family relationships. Apparently, adultery was rampant during the Biblical Era because the Sixth Catholic and the Seventh Protestant Commandment admonishes sexual relations with anyone outside of a marital union. It is, also, obvious that other forms of barbaric behavior prevailed because the Ninth and Tenth Catholic

Commandments and the Tenth Protestant Commandment instructed that a man should not covet his neighbor's wife or any of his neighbor's possessions.

P.157… For a substantial period in human history, *societal necessity*, also, best explains the reason why a woman's virginity has been such a significant moral and religious issue. People who lived during Biblical times had very little knowledge or understanding of venereal diseases such as gonorrhea and herpes, yet they were aware that the only ways to avoid such venereal infections were to either abstain from intercourse entirely or to be sexually involved with only one virginal woman. It was easy for the people living in those eras to conclude that ***God's** intention* was to severely punish philandering humans; thus, from the beginning of the Biblical Era until the present day, it has been logical for all humans to conclude that, because *feminine promiscuity* (too often) causes serious health problems (including premature death), it has always made sense to regard a woman's wonton sexual behavior as sinful behavior.

P.159… It is quite obvious that God never intended to create Heaven on Earth. God has always utilized temptation and turmoil in order to sufficiently test His children so that their **true** identities would be defined and revealed to Him. Most likely, after programming humans to have strong urges to procreate, God was not pleased with the behaviors of those prehistoric rapists because they lived lives that caused them to sculpt spiritual frequencies which were unsuitable for ascension to *Heaven.* For the same reason that God cast Adam and Eve out of paradise, God's solution to this dilemma was to cause prehistoric savages to endure the pain, suffering, and regret associated with venereal diseases in order to help them acquire the sensitivity and humility necessary to sculpt *acceptable spiritual frequencies* and, in the process, to learn how to become civilized human (and spiritual) beings.

P.161… Regardless of whether syphilis mutated as a result of evolution or as a result of divine intervention, the history of venereal disease and the role it has played in the transformation of human behavior demonstrates how God does work in mysterious ways.

P.173... Decades ago, students would have been well versed in Christian moral teachings; and *Tess* would have provided an effective, higher-level, intellectual counterpart. Regrettably, for more than forty years, most references to Christian beliefs and morality have been either (1) condemned or (2) excised from both undergraduate and college-level educational programs.

P.173... Presently, college students are being taught, ***only***, a dumbed-downed, one-sided, propagandized, anti-Christian point of view. No longer is any effective attempt being made to help students develop sound moral foundations and higher-level skills.

P.173... With *Tess* (and with far too many other areas of college curricula), the only indoctrinating message a college student is required to retain is that people who earn diplomas should be both suspicious and contemptuous of Christian religious beliefs. As a result, unfortunately, too many college graduates are no longer allowing themselves to be guided by Christian values.

P.174... The problem with *The Crucible*'s lessons, for example, is that the allegory misrepresents history. Although it is **true** that Senator McCarthy's tactics were dishonest and heavy-handed, his improper behavior was minor (and forgivable) compared to the significant issues that modern revisionists have chosen to erase from historical records. Not a single reference to the mass murder, less than two decades earlier, (by way of starvation, torture, and firing squads) of between seven and ten million Eastern European **Christian** landowners is ever included in *The Crucible*'s lessons; nor is there a single acknowledgment that the **truthful** purpose for the McCarthy hearings was to assure that such mass murder would not be duplicated in the United States. McCarthy's purpose was to identify, and thwart, the conspiratorial intentions of those influential and powerful members of America's non-Christian and anti-Christian minority who advocated (and, *secretly*, worked to instigate) similar political upheaval and mass murder in this country.

P.175… American students have been successfully brainwashed into believing that (1) the excesses of the McCarthy hearings and (2) the improper execution of ***twenty*** *Puritan innocents* in 1692-1693 are noteworthy illustrations of extremism, yet ***the mass murder of between seven million and ten million Germanic and Slavic, Christian, innocents*** **in the 1930's,** ***by non-Christians, is insignificant***. ***WHY***?

P.176… *Tess D'Urbervilles* is a *work of fiction*--a *tale* that was ***entirely contrived*** by Thomas Hardy. Properly educated humans must be taught to be able to recognize the differences between (1) fiction and reality *and* (2) **truth** and propaganda. Regrettably (and **puzzlingly**), far too few students who have earned ***advanced*** *degrees* in recent decades have been taught how to develop that ability.

P.179… Hardy's method of, convincingly, transforming facts into a *contrived fiction* is not dissimilar to the way American and world history have been transformed (since the 1960's) into a series of dishonest and incomplete tales which have been fabricated for the purpose of (1) fermenting unjustified social changes, (2) forcing the majority Christian culture to tolerate non-stop, inexcusable, barbaric misconduct in American society, (3) stripping Christian children of their traditional beliefs and values, and (4) demanding that the majority Christian culture condescend to the transfer of massive amounts of their accrued financial wealth and security to others. A properly educated young person must be taught how to *perceive the* ***truth***; sadly, that is no longer happening in public schools, colleges, and universities in the United States. Regrettably, the United States has, as a result, been forced to re-enter a (modern-era) "Dark Age".

P.179… Victorian Christian behavior requires far less defense than any other societal behaviors which existed elsewhere in the world, at that time, because Victorians formulated a value system which molded the most moral, advanced, and civilized Nineteenth Century society. That morality was based more on Old Testament wisdom (which originally was a canonical collection of Holy Hebrew Scriptures) than it was based on the teachings of Jesus.

P.180... The objective of the stern interpretations of those Old Testament instructions was to save "the many" even if it were at the expense of "the few". That approach is just the opposite of modern-day thinking where, non-Christian, socialist activists choose to put "the many" at risk even where there is only a slight likelihood of saving "the few".

P.181... While Hardy was correct to criticize mean-spirited, hypocritical, and prideful people who used Christian morality as a *weapon to, unfairly, abuse distressed humans*, Hardy (as well as other anti-Christians) was wrong to be critical of stern Victorian values which were based on Hebrew teachings and traditions. Those moral rules successfully uplifted the lives and souls of most Victorians because ***truthful*** *Christian values and behaviors* were far less sinful (and far more enriching) than any of the alternative values, behaviors, and imperatives that predominated, throughout the world, during that Era.

P.182... My dream's concept of sin *runs parallel* to Christian philosophies.

P.183... My dream has taught me, however, that God does not want His children to fear Him. God would prefer that His children *demonstrate their gratitude for their spiritual consciousness by* ***choosing*** *to live decently*. My dream has also revealed that God is not a vengeful God because vengeance does not exist in Heaven; thus, it has been my belief that God seldom, if ever, negatively judges His children. Instead, each individual has the free will to be solely responsible for his or her own eternal spiritual destiny.

P.184... More than anything, it is thoughts and emotions which exercise the greatest influence upon a person's link to God and Heaven.

P.185... Decent humans must, then, be *prudent* in the manner by which they choose to activate and utilize spiritual energy; hence, Christians have always been encouraged to express, *only*, feelings of love, kindness, goodness, respect, **truth**, and decency when they make love (or think about making love).

P.185… Those countless sexual thoughts, urges, and behaviors which are not generated by thoughtfulness, respect, and affection must be some of the most sinful influences upon spiritual frequencies because it is the ***character*** *of a person's thoughts and feelings* that **truthfully** defines that person's spiritual identity.

P.186… It, usually, takes a lifetime to sculpt a personal spiritual frequency; thus, *rarely* will one act or time period be determinative in the creation of a spiritual connection with Heaven. God knows that, because of Original Sin, most people will behave improperly during their lives; as a result, God's plan (and God's teachings) do allow for those sinners to transform themselves for the better (should they choose). The problem is that far too many people, consciously, choose not to be good or to transform themselves for the better; this is *particularly* ***true*** when they are attempting to satisfy their sexual urges.

P.186… The dilemma for those humans who choose to secretly succumb to sexual activities which involve ***evil*** thoughts, urges, and actions is that such behaviors (which usually remain unchanged and, thus, typically define those individuals for their entire adult lives) are not secrets on the spiritual plane.

P.186… If, for example, (1) some persons take pleasure in dominating others by inflicting pain, torture, and/or humiliation while engaging in sexual activities, or (2) if they choose to fantasize about sadistic and other hurtful deeds, there is no other endeavor that more clearly defines their spiritual identities than ***those types*** *of sexual thoughts and behaviors*.

P.192… A sexual desire or act, in and of itself, cannot be a sinful activity. Instead, thoughts, feelings, and behaviors (which are devoid of love, goodness, kindness, **truth**, respect, and decency--yet energized and magnified by sexual energy) *can be* sinful and, thus, *can*, *possibly*, cause significant damage to any person's connection to Heaven. There is no need to feel guilt, or seek forgiveness, for having sexual desires as long as love, kindness, goodness, respect, **truth**, and decency are the strongest types of feelings and spiritual thoughts that accompany those sexual urges.

P.193… Any question concerning homosexuality requires a lengthier explanation than might readily be expected because there are far too many distinct homosexual behaviors, thoughts, and urges; and each of those distinct manifestations of homosexuality is accompanied by its own unique measure of sin or goodness.

P.193… God would have never condemned, or punished, two human beings who ***loved*** *one another* merely because they engaged in same-sex intimacies.

P.193... Since homosexuality is, now, being praised as a desirable lifestyle and, as a result, there has been no *honest* public analysis of those aspects of homosexual behavior which are sinful, it could prove helpful (and instructive) to examine and understand the, most likely, reasons why God and Jesus would be disappointed with any contemporary culture that chooses to be steered by an immorality which is comparable to the decadence that consumed Sodom and Gomorrah. Just because modern media and governmental influences have ***forced*** society to accept the belief that *aberrant lifestyles* should no longer be regarded as improper, that does not mean that God concurs. God's disenchantment with such activities results from the fact that too many of the thoughts, urges, and behaviors sculpted by such transgressors fail to connect with the frequencies which guide humans to spiritual salvation; thus, any valid examination of homosexual behavior requires an analysis of those thoughts and urges:

P.195... The most serious, unintended, consequence which results from the validation of homosexual marriages is that the accompanying marriage licenses create a permanent homosexual identification registry in the public records.

P.196… An additional reason Christians have always had doubts about the wisdom of validating homosexual marriages is that Christians have been aware that the overwhelming majority of homosexuals (including those who have lived together under the same roof for extended periods of time) have, repeatedly, confessed to their non-homosexual family members that they have no intention of restricting their sexual activities to monogamous relationships. The desire to have sexual trysts with scores of partners of the same sex has always been the focus of, *virtually all, sexually active homosexuals*. Regardless of whether a union is heterosexual or homosexual, *betrayal and absence of* ***truth*** *in any relationship* have always been sinful. Homosexual adultery is no less sinful than heterosexual adultery. That reality makes it difficult for Christians to understand the wisdom, morality, and the societal need to legitimatize the *majority* of homosexual marriages when the overwhelming number of partners in such unions has no intentions of remaining faithful. Virtually all propagandized claims to the contrary are dishonest.

P.197… The ***impetus*** *that triggered a* ***successful*** *homosexual revolution* originated on college campuses in the 1960's and 1970's. Students were manipulated into believing that, in order to be "evolved and well-educated humans", their minds had to be reasonable, balanced, moderate, and (above all) *tolerant* toward all unpopular issues; thus, efforts were continually made to convince college students that *the "well-educated" did not condemn* ***anything*** that was, at that time, considered aberrant by the moral majority. (Those young minds were *brainwashed* into believing that "evolved and properly educated" college graduates were totally accepting and "tolerant" of *all* behaviors--particularly those which had not, historically, been fully embraced by Christians).

P.197… I finally, realized that such a belief system was nothing other than a *propaganda scheme*. The, underlying, reasoning principles for that *ruse* require a total absence of all, higher-level, analytical thinking skills. That "non-questioning" process could not possibly have produced an "evolved or well-educated" person because it has always advocated ***blind obedience***, and ***mindless acceptance***, of virtually everything mandated by others (particularly non-Christians, anti-Christians, and make-believe Christians).

P.197… At 1 Corinthians 2:15-16, Paul taught that a *spiritually* well-educated human, by knowing the mind of Christ, can *discern* spiritual truth: "the spiritual man…can appraise everything…." All properly educated college students (regardless of whether they are Christians or not) should be taught *comparable secular abilities* in order to cultivate sufficient keenness of perception so that they can, also, develop higher-level skills which enable them to, ***correctly***, *distinguish and select* those ideas which are **true** and appropriate from those which are not. When this type of discerning analysis is applied to the homosexual revolution, doubts arise as to whether society's acquiescence to the embracing, and mainstreaming, of the homosexual lifestyle is in ***anyone's*** *best interest*.

P.198… ***Prior to the 1970's***, most homosexuals *claimed* that they were gay because they had an *innate sexual revulsion* toward the opposite sex. Over the ensuing years, that explanation has transformed into the (more politically correct) *claim* that most homosexuals had been born with genitalia that was incompatible with their (psychological and emotional) *gender identities*. If that were, indeed, correct, why, then, did homosexual behavior mutate into *sadistic and masochistic* homosexual behavior (and worse) at the very moment in history when homosexuality had achieved widespread tolerance?

P.200… Since the 1970's, I have suspected that homosexuals are, indeed, born with different impulses and urges; however, I have long doubted that those, innate, impulses are limited, merely, to sexual behavior. I have ***feared***, *instead, that far too many homosexuals* are, actually, born with a compulsive need to be deviant (or, in some cases, even evil) and that living ***clandestine*** homosexual lives had been, until the 1970's, the most effective way for those persons (with *an **obsessive** need to be different*) to satisfy that compulsion. If my suspicions are correct, that would mean that, at the very moment homosexuality was no longer regarded as being a deviant activity, many homosexuals would have felt compelled to pursue an, even more extreme, alternative lifestyle (with new, and distinctly unacceptable, social behaviors) *in order to continue to satisfy their **innate** aberrant urges*. It should not seem surprising, then, that a very large percentage of the homosexual community has recently moved to the forefront of many radical movements which attack and attempt to eliminate all Christian influences and institutions--as well as all other stable, just, and moral aspects of our society. Christians must realize that people who share these types of mental disorders have, repeatedly, worked to destroy stable societies *for centuries* because they have always been more driven by their deviant compulsions than they have been motived by any type of moral principles.

P.201… The first disturbing example, also, began during the 1970's (at the very same time that (1) the homosexual lifestyle was gaining widespread acceptance and at the very same time that (2) numerous leather bars were coming into existence). A significant number of homosexuals were booking ***sex**-junket vacations* to Haiti for the purpose of engaging in sexual acts (and quite possibly sadistic acts) with, under-aged, African-Haitian ***boys***.

P.201… Society needs to, openly, ask this question: if homosexual men had, indeed, been born with, ***only***, a predisposition which compelled them to engage in same sex copulation, how, why, and when did (1) the urge to sexually pursue young boys and (2) the urge to engage in sadistic acts originate?

P.201… Soon thereafter, a new (mysterious--yet deadly) venereal disease began ravaging the North American homosexual community. By 1980, that disease was isolated and identified as Acquired Immune Deficiency Syndrome (AIDS).

P.201… As the epidemic grew, it was clear that the best way to stop the spread of the disease was to quarantine those with AIDS because the majority of those infected (**sinfully**) refused to curb their *promiscuous lifestyles* in any way.

P.202… In the heat of the quarantine discussion, an AIDS infected (closeted) Florida dentist, Dr. David J. Acer, committed one of the most evil acts of domestic terrorism (and serial murder) in the history of this country. He, ***intentionally***, gave AIDS to six of his dental patients (including a teenage girl). His acts were clearly intentional because there is no way that an *accidental transmission* could have possibly occurred (even once) based upon the type of treatment he had provided his patients. Since he knew that he would soon die from AIDS, his purpose was to send a *terrorist's message* to this entire country by making everyone aware that there were numerous other *closeted homosexuals* who were ready, willing, and able to cause a widespread AIDS epidemic among the general population if any, state or Federal, governmental agency were to *quarantine even one homosexual*. As a result of that blackmail, homosexuals were allowed to continue to widely spread their diseases to ***hundreds of thousands*** *of innocent victims* despite the fact that, in the beginning, the disease could have, easily, been *eliminated* by quarantining ***a few thousand*** *infected* **homosexuals**.

P.202… By 2013, the Center for Disease Control estimated that 1,194,039 United States citizens had been diagnosed with AIDS and that 658,507 people with an AIDS diagnosis, subsequently, died (**at the expense of billions of *non-homosexual taxpayers' dollars*** for research and treatment costs).

P.203… The ***primary reason*** that AIDS jumped, so quickly, into the general population is that it was *maliciously disseminated by AIDS infected homosexuals and bisexuals (whose evil and maniacal intentions were the* *same as Dr. Acer's).* It is, then, fortunate that AIDS is not as easily transferred to unsuspecting victims during heterosexual, vaginal, sex as it is during homosexual, anal, sex (because anal abrasions and ruptured hemorrhoids more readily facilitate the virus' entry into the bloodstream). Had AIDS been as easily transferred heterosexually, the number of infected Americans would, by now, be in the tens of millions (if not hundreds of millions).

P.204... "The road to hell is paved with good intentions" may not be a Biblical passage.... If people choose to support a social movement, they have an *obligation* to know what they are, actually, supporting. There has ***never*** been a balanced discussion or analysis of the homosexual revolution. Anyone who might have a dissenting point of view, no matter how valid, has been confronted and silenced by a propaganda machine that makes those which existed in Communist U.S.S.R. before and during the Cold War seem amateurish. Why? It is unlikely that the majority of people (including most lesbians and many male homosexuals who support homosexual rights) are even aware of the **true** history of AIDS.

P.205... Sadly, sadism, Haitian sex-junkets, the blackmailing of America, and the intentional dissemination of AIDS are not the only examples of improper homosexual behaviors that have aroused Christian concerns; and *none of those concerns are based upon,* ***irrational, homophobia***.

P.205... Beginning in the late 1960's, America's youth was bombarded with propaganda from media, college campuses, musical idols, and cinema which proved to be very alluring society-altering influences. That movement, cleverly orchestrated by non-Christians and anti-Christians (who were *directly linked* to that Fifth Column which Senator McCarthy had failed to, successfully, thwart in the early 1950's) encouraged American youth to protest against the United States' involvement in the Viet Nam conflict, support civil rights and anti-apartheid activities, accept socialism, use drugs, embrace promiscuity, and reject their parents' cultural, religious, and moral values. It proved to be a total success at undermining and replacing the principles and beliefs of the *Christian* generation that had fought for this country and won World War II. The societal transformation that resulted could not have been any greater (or more damaging) if the United States had lost the World War to the Communist U.S.S.R. and been occupied by a tyrannically hostile enemy army.

P.206… Prior to1968, most American soldiers who served in Viet Nam (***truth*****fully**) were Christians of European descent. During that time, America fared well. After 1969, a necessary, all-inclusive, multi-cultural military draft proved disastrous for America's military efforts because too many of those drafted soldiers (1) preferred getting high on hardcore narcotics and (2) are known to have, frequently, killed their platoon leaders while on patrols (by "fragging" them--killing them with fragmentation grenades for the purpose of making the murders appear to be the results (1) of accidents or (2) of engagements with opposing forces) rather than risk the possibilities of encountering and fighting Viet Cong guerrillas.

P.207… The Christian community should obligate itself to either prove or disprove the **truthfulness** of those (wide-spread) allegations of *traitorous behavior* because, if **true**, the United States' military (by (1) concealing ***most*** accounts of the assassinations of those Christian officers and (2) not pursuing and prosecuting their murderers) has, thus far, been able to avoid paying ***appropriate*** lifetime earnings-compensation damages to the entitled families of those murdered Christian officers.

P.210… Once the Viet Nam conflict came to an end, many of those *instigating socialist, Marxist, and Communist activists* searched for the optimal new arenas from which they could continue disseminating their socialist, Communist, and anti-Christian agendas. Many pursued careers in areas such as media so that they could acquire the power to both limit and maintain control of all national discussions (fake news). Others chose educational administration so that they could continue to propagandize and brainwash children by controlling the educational process; or publishing so that they could put themselves in the position to rewrite history; or law so that they could rewrite America's laws. Those who pursued careers in finance, constantly, conceived and implemented ploys (such as the Derivatives and Sub-prime mortgage schemes) that succeeded in separating massive amounts of accrued Christian earnings and retirement savings from those trusting Christians who had gained their financial stability by way of hard and decent work.

P.211… Still, other activists (despite the fact that they were not very religious) realized that the best way to continue spreading their ideology was by taking advantage of the prosperity, authority, and influence that Christian ministries would provide them. It was so easy to disguise socialist propaganda as Christian belief; thus, from then until now, far too many sermons (which seem to have been written more by *secular* humanists than Christians) have instructed that good Christians, unquestioningly, should give *all* that is theirs to others (regardless of whether those beneficiaries are *deserving*).

P.212… The *primary* church purpose should have always been (1) to help its own "hungry", "thirsty", and "naked" members make *the very best connection* ***with their spiritual frequencies*** and (2) to help those ***sincere Christians*** accomplish that goal by focusing, primarily, on ***strengthening Christian families and Christian communities***. Regrettably, that has not been happening for decades; thus, it is not surprising that, because of *far too many* ***dubious*** *modern church agendas*, the number of Christians who have remained active churchgoers has declined. Decent Christians should have never been "exploited", "trampled underfoot", or "torn to shreds"; but that is what has been happening since the 1970's.

P.212... Sadly, too, it was during that time period when an even more extreme level of homosexual impropriety succeeded in damaging both (1) the lives of many innocent Christian victims and (2) the stability of the Christian church.

P.212… The *primary event* involved the Catholic Church, which was rocked by one of the most damaging scandals in its history. Numerous priests (1) were accused of having sexually molested young boys and girls (yet overwhelmingly ***boys***)--national media has (puzzlingly) chosen not to report accurate percentages of male-female molestations; and, thus, has chosen to conceal this scandal's most relevant fact); and the Catholic Church (2) was accused of having covered-up those molestations for decades. Victims were awarded billions of dollars in legal judgements or settlements; and, with each legal result, more victims came forward to reveal their victimizations (and to collect their financial rewards--an amount which, by now, has been estimated to be *far in excess* of three billion dollars). The financial costs to the church were so great that parishes and schools had to be closed; and many Catholic charitable services had to be curtailed or terminated.

P.213… It is worth restating that during the entire time of the scandal, mainstream media (fake news) chose to ***ignore*** and, thus, ***conceal*** *the most significant factual detail*: the rogue priests guilty of the molestations (and the church officials responsible for cover-ups--in instances where cover-ups had occurred) were, almost entirely, homosexuals.

P.213… Remarkably, during that time-period when media was condemning the ***entire*** *Catholic Church rather than, merely, the guilty four percent of homosexual priests and church officials* (a number that, coincidentally, closely parallels the percentage of ***admitted*** homosexuals in the general population), media was also engaged (puzzlingly) in a parallel propaganda campaign that *supported homosexual agendas* such as those which demanded, for example, (1) that, openly gay, homosexuals be ordained as Protestant ministers and (2) that, openly gay, homosexuals be permitted to serve as Boy Scout leaders.

P.214... In all fairness, the Catholic Church had *no way of knowing* that (1) the *intentions* of a sizable number of "post-Hippie Era" priests were very different from those of previous generations or that (2) many had chosen to join the priesthood more for socialist and Communist ideological reasons than religious reasons or that (3) some were not even religious or that (4) a small percentage had no intention of remaining celibate regardless of their vows to the Church and God.

P.215... The real question that should have been asked (but never was) is: How could ***so many*** *boys have been sexually molested, yet* ***so few*** *of them had ever sought help from their parents or the police when the molestations were occurring*?

P.215... The generally accepted answer is that ***all of the boys*** *were so traumatized* (and were caused to feel so ashamed) that their extreme emotional injuries made them too fearful to seek help from anyone. In all instances where this had been the ***truth*****ful** reason, multi-million dollar awards *were appropriate*.

P.215... However, *one* of the primary reasons that so many *Hippie-Era*, non-religious, homosexuals chose to join the priesthood was because the duty of hearing young boys' confessions provided them opportunities to identify and make personal connections with those adolescents who confessed to either having homosexual interests or having engaged in homosexual activities; thus, in many instances, the homosexual-molesting priests confined their sexual pursuits to those boys who had, during confessions, indicated that they, too, had homosexual inclinations. This is particularly **true** when higher Church officials, *actively, made attempts to cover-up reported molestations*, solely, because those officials were also homosexuals.

P.217... Thus, those *homosexual* boys who *falsely* claimed to have been victimized (in order to gain millions of dollars in payments) could, quite conceivably, have caused greater damage to their own frequencies than any other participants. Their spiritual behavior could, possibly, be likened to the behavior of those females who (1) falsely accuse blameless men of rape, (2) are believed, and, thus, (3) succeed in destroying the lives of those innocent men. In *almost all instances*, mock victims are spiritual transgressors.

P.218… There was one significant childhood event which has *provided* ***insight*** and helped me to conclude that the compulsive need to be deviant could, possibly, be the prevailing impulse which controls the behavior of a substantial number of homosexuals. That experience began when, at the age of fifteen, my mother decided to send me to the YMCA to, belatedly, learn to swim.

P.219… At that time, I was aware that some of my YMCA friends had attracted older mentors who befriended and demonstrated great interest in the welfare of those friends. To a degree, I was, somewhat, jealous because I wished that I, too, might have demonstrated the type of qualities that would have attracted the interest of an older, caring, mentor; but that never happened. Since I was already aware of my friends' good qualities, I, fully, understood why older men would have recognized their outstanding attributes as well. I, merely, concluded that I was not, yet, perceived as being the same caliber of person as my friends; and I accepted that fact.

P.219… More than forty years passed before I noticed a newspaper *editorial obituary* summarizing the life of one of my older friend's mentors (whose lifelong success merited a picture and a tribute of nearly one thousand words). The obituary motivated me to, finally, locate that friend and offer my condolence. His response to my well-meaning intentions, however, proved to be the most startling, and unexpected, confession I have ever had admitted to me.

P.220... He revealed that when he processed his mentor's personal effects, he discovered a treasure-trove of pictures and movies of his mentor engaging in homosexual intimacies with numerous men and boys, love letters to and from many men, and a large collection of sadistic and homosexual sex toys. When I, innocently, asked my friend how he had not been able to recognize his mentor's homosexuality for more than fifty years, he confessed that the two of them had been sharing an *open* homosexual relationship since the 1960's (when he was still a very young teenager). While struggling to conceal my shock, I inquired about those other teenage friends who had, also, attracted mentors at the YMCA. He disclosed that they, too, were homosexuals.

P.221… I, next, inquired about my best friend (and role model) since, as a teenager, that friend had vented, non-stop, disapproval toward all homosexuals (and often expressed a desire to engage in "gay bashing"). In response, I was informed that his anti-homosexual behavior had merely been a charade.

P.221… That ***truth*ful** explanation has caused me to reconsider the statistical basis for the nineteen percent of all, alleged, hate crimes that are being committed against homosexuals. I, now, must wonder how many of those attacks are actually being committed either by closeted homosexual sadists or by consenting partners who had participated in sadistic homosexual "games" (or other deviant activities) that went too far.

P.222… Regrettably, the revelation that was most disappointing to me came next. I was informed that several of those homosexual boys whom I believed were my friends, had been, anonymously, selling their sexual services to, countless, older homosexuals on a regular basis; and, when they did, all had agreed to assume my name and reveal details of my life as a way of, convincingly, concealing their own identities (for no other reason than the fact that I was one of the few among them who was not homosexual). If this revelation were **true**, that would mean that their inability to be faithful friends, or to live **truthful** and decent lives, had, apparently, caused my reputation to be destroyed (without my knowledge) for no other reason than I had ***not** chosen* to participate in their ***evil*** *life choices*. If the types of boys who had been involved with homosexual priests behaved similarly, it is unfathomable to comprehend why *any of them* would have been deserving of multi-million dollar payoffs from the Catholic Church since it would be difficult to comprehend how any of them could have, possibly, been victims.

P.222… Until the 1970's, most urban YMCA's and YWCA's *required same-sex* ***nude*** *swimming*; in retrospect, it is obvious that it was the nude swimming policy that attracted *those types of mentors*; thus, it is regrettable that, despite the presence of the word "Christian" in the name of the organization, YMCA swimming pools and shower areas were allowed, for decades, to be *prime hunting grounds* for homosexuals and pedophiles.

P.223… Despite the fact that I will always be grateful for the help and kindness I had received at the YMCA, I have, unnecessarily, been made to realize that the, ***inbred,*** *sexual urges and emotional compulsions* of those friends had prevented them from, ever, being capable of trustworthiness or decency (even when being guided by a positive YMCA influence).

P.223… It would seem as if their needs to maintain secret and dishonest lives were just as compelling an inclination as their homosexual urges. This realization, *thus*, is one of the primary reasons I have concluded that many homosexuals are driven as much by a compulsive need to be deviant as they are by their sexual desires.

P.224… It is regrettable that far too many homosexuals have fronted for both corrupt and/or criminal organizations either because (1) they had pursued lifestyles that, readily, made them prone to blackmail victimization or (even more likely) because (2) they (much like Hollywood actors and actresses) had proven to be far more willing (and capable) of living duplicitous lives than most other humans. Sadly, *such deviant impulses are never harmless but, in fact, are the triggers for the aberrant behaviors of troubled humans* who take pleasure in deceiving, betraying, and harming those persons who had, *unwisely*, placed trust in them. Although *Timothy* was speaking of all types of evil humans, it would be mindful to be guided by 2 Timothy 3:4 where he warns, "They will be treacherous, reckless, pompous, lovers of pleasure rather than God as they make pretense of religion but negate its powers. Stay clear of them". By means of Timothy's advice, insightful Christians have not been irrational "homophobes" (as accused) but, instead, have always understood that it is unwise to place *complete trust* in humans who have, willfully, chosen to live *deviant and deceptive lives*.

P.225… I have long wondered why (because of the massive amount of violent and sadistic homosexual rape that, *allegedly*, has been taking place in some prisons) no one has examined the obvious connection which exists between homosexual and criminal behavior. The first question that must be asked is: are those inmates committing violent homosexual attacks because such acts are, merely, additional means by which they choose to vent their innate sociopathic and psychopathic hostilities; or, instead, are such criminal behaviors, merely, out-of-control expressions of innate, yet often suppressed, homosexual urges? In other words: where (in the minds of aberrant humans) do homosexual compulsions end, where do the urges to commit criminal acts begin, and to what degree might these two inborn, deviant, compulsions overlap?

P.226… Since ***admitted*** homosexuals compose little more than three percent of the population, this statistical data, shockingly, reveals a dramatically disproportionate percentage of criminal behavior among homosexuals and, thus, explains *the most obvious reason* why Christians have remained somewhat skeptical about, mindlessly and unquestioningly, ***embracing all aspects*** *of the homosexual lifestyle*.

P.228… While Constitutional protection facilitates freedom of the ***printed*** press, it is remarkably puzzling that (1) all (but, *possibly*, one) major media outlets are presently controlled by a single non-Christian influence and that (2) there has been, virtually, *no* ***effective*** *mainstream media voice (for more than fifty years) which has fairly and clearly represented any aspect of the* ***intelligent*** *Christian perspective.*

P.228… It is this anti-Christian mainstream media voice, for example, which has, most recently, been brainwashing young girls by fabricating and, then, perpetuating the lie that ***all*** "modern" adolescent girls ***must*** experience a "teenage lesbian stage".

P.228… The problem which results from the broadcasting of this dishonest indoctrination (as with the glorification of teenage drug use) is that most young girls never emotionally recover from exposure to such damaging (formative years) sexual experiences and, thus, find it difficult (if not impossible) transitioning into the roles of *well-adjusted and capable* wives and mothers. The acts of encouraging young girls to experience such corrupting and harmful influences, at such young ages, is nothing other than a clear attempt to destroy young lives and, thus, destabilize the foundations of the Christian family structure.

P.229… Nationwide, a united Christian community has to expose, confront, and stop ***all*** *non-Christian, anti-Christian, and make-believe Christian media agendas* which are so devoid of fairness that they suppress honest debate and the expressions of legitimate ideas. The Christian community must make certain that those persons, institutions, and ***advertisers*** responsible for such damaging propaganda are ***no longer allowed to control, and dictate, any societal beliefs and norms in a democratic country that is populated, overwhelmingly, by a Christian majority***.

Chapter Five: "The Seven Deadly Sins"

P.230… I am aware of how easy it is for any person to appear to be a great humanitarian when condemning the sins of others while concealing his or her own misconduct; so, please be assured, it has never been my intention to be that hypocritical….Because I have been guided by such a powerful, spiritually instructive, dream since the age of seven, I have far fewer excuses for any of my sins because I cannot use spiritual ignorance as an excuse. At Luke 23: 34, Jesus urged God to: "Forgive them, Father; for they know not what they do". I cannot expect such absolution to excuse any of my transgressions. It is most likely that all of *my* sins will be judged far more harshly than those sins committed by the "unknowing"; thus, it should be obvious that I have no ordained right to judge anyone.

P.231… As for those of my deceased YMCA friends who may have lived closeted-homosexual lives, I doubt that they had abandoned very many of the *better human qualities* that I had always known them to possess; so it is doubtful that their homosexuality, *alone*, would have prevented them from having achieved ascension to Heaven.

P.231… To briefly summarize: those human qualities which sculpt the best human frequencies **(truth, love, goodness, humility, and peace)** are the spiritual qualities which, most often, were missing in the previous homosexual discussions; and it is the absence of those qualities in human living experiences which makes the possibility of ascension to Heaven more problematic.

P.232… The reason for the thorough review was to illustrate how difficult it can be for most humans, in this modern-era, to recognize where, how, and when goodness ends and sin begins. Such knowledge is *paramount* because the ***only way*** humans are going to be able to sculpt the best possible spiritual frequencies is by understanding God's expectations and, thus, the manner by which God (*not contemporary culture*) approves or disapproves of various human thoughts, impulses, and behaviors.

P.232… The best way for humans to develop the spiritual insight that will guide them *to avoid damnation* was explained by Paul in 1 Corinthians 2: 1-16 (particularly at verse 10) when Paul taught that: "God has revealed this wisdom to us through the Spirit"; thus, Paul at 1 Corinthians 6: 19 made clear that *God's **true** intentions* can be found in the innermost recesses of *our own minds and our own souls* once we have developed the ability to hear God's voice.

P.233… The purpose of the extensive homosexual discussion was to illustrate how ***worldly*** *preoccupations* have the potential to create enmity with God; thus, whenever, for example, human beings choose to, *primarily*, identify themselves as homosexuals, they are indicating that they have succumbed to their bodies' impulses and cravings and, thus, have foolishly caused themselves to be "*in the flesh*" **and not** "*in the spirit*".

P.234… In summary, the goal of my thorough explanation is merely to provide a *first example* of the manner by which God, *most likely*, scrutinizes all human follies and sinful behaviors (*not just* ***some*** *homosexual behaviors*). Regardless of how readily any society is willing to, superficially, praise and embrace worldly foolishness, Matthew 7: 13-14 makes clear that God expects more from those of his children who seek ascension to the most desirable "rooms" in Heaven. God expects his children to ***attempt*** *to live more like Jesus in every possible way* (not as deviants).

P.235… The pursuit of internal peace is not only a significant Christian objective; such peace has also been one of the primary objectives for virtually all of the great religions. Christians who strive to achieve internal peace, thus, can greatly benefit, for example, from the Buddhist wisdom which teaches that peace is best achieved when humans succeed in freeing themselves from greed, hatred, fear, delusions, ignorance, and all other worldly *cravings*--passions--and--attachments. Peace is the calm which emerges in the presence of balance and order.

P.235… The most effective means (by which to achieve such peace, order, and balance) results when Christians master the ability to ***recognize and avoid sins*** **(particularly the notorious Seven Deadly Sins: gluttony, lust, greed, pride, sloth, wrath, and envy)** ***at their inceptions*** because all seven of those sins are examples of excessive desires and indulgences which attract and motivate Satan and can, *unwittingly*, convert what would, otherwise, be *peaceful*, normal, and acceptable behaviors into sinful activities.

P.236… My dream has taught me that the reason why these seven sins are so significant is because all seven are behaviors which are the fuels that extinguish goodness and ignite transgressions. (The Seven Deadly Sins, therefore, are the building blocks upon which most other, more grievous, sins arise); thus, it makes sense for righteous Christians to develop the ability to, instinctively, *recognize* ***that moment*** *when sin originates* so that they can prevent sinful tethers from exercising control (and creating "a false spiritual *balance*" within them).

P.236… This is the primary reason why Christians have utilized corporeal punishment (not as an excuse for venting animalistic aggressions against weaker and more defenseless humans but, instead,) as a means of teaching their children (and misguided adults) the importance of, *immediately*, identifying and avoiding sin. In contrast, rather than supporting and recognizing the importance of corporeal discipline, modern secular society's prohibitions against such punishment have proven to be extremely damaging to the young. By preventing parents from ***training*** *their children to* ***INSTINCTIVELY recognize appropriate limits***, it is secular society's total lack of standards and values which are the primary causes that steer the young to drug and alcohol addiction, promiscuity, reckless and criminal behavior, non-learning, apathy, selfishness, materialism, sloth, and countless other forms of *imbalanced*, sinful, and out-of-control behaviors that disappoint God.

P.237… **1. Gluttony** is included as one of the Seven Deadly Sins because ***excessive*** yearning for food (and other worldly pleasures) leads to *over*-consumption….

P.238… **2. Lust**, therefore, transforms acceptable sexual desires into sinful behavior because the pursuit of *immoral urges* often leads to, out-of-control, activities which ignore all harmful consequences….

P.238… **3. Greed** is a similar sinful compulsion; however, greed is more a lusting for worldly possessions such as money and material objects...

P.240… **4. Pride**: While some have claimed that **Pride** might be the most serious of the Seven Deadly Sins, pride is, also, one of the trickiest sins to identify and understand….

P.243… **5. Sloth**: When Pope Gregory, in AD 590, revised and consolidated earlier recognized vices into what are presently The Seven Deadly Sins (for the purpose of identifying those human behaviors which most frequently--*yet unwittingly*--trigger more grievous sin), **Sloth** focused on humans (1) who chose to avoid *essential* work and obligations, ***and*** (2) who chose to refrain from utilizing their minds (and the gift of *consciousness*) in an appropriate manner that would please God….

P.246… **6. Wrath**: One of the most significant reasons humans must be, steadfastly, aware of the distinctions between good and evil results from the fact that we are all spiritual beings who exist within primate bodies which are controlled by animalistic instincts, urges, and desires. God's purpose for creating such a reality for us is to help God determine which impulses dominate and, thus, define our identities. God's hope is that we develop such ***spiritual strength*** that we are able to utilize and control our life-essential animalistic talents rather than be ruled by them; as a result, when we allow ourselves to succumb to our body's impulses and cravings (and permit them to sculpt our identities), we sin and fail God's test. Few savage compulsions dominate humans more than *anger*. While the venting of anger (in the absence of sin) *can be* an essential way for all humans to (periodically) effectively release an excessive buildup of aggressive feelings, *uncontrolled* and continuous anger has the potential to be one of the most extreme, unhealthy, and harmful of all animalistic impulses. James 1: 19-20 advises: "Know this my beloved brothers: Let every person be quick to hear, slow to speak, and slow to *anger*; for the *anger* of man does not produce the righteousness of God". This is particularly **true** when that anger is of a **wrathful** nature: a strong, stern, and fierce type of anger that is so deeply resentful that it demands vengeance and punishment….

P.252… **7. Envy**: **To** begin, it is noteworthy that envy is the only Deadly Sin which is also included as two of the Ten Commandments by the Catholic religion and one of the Ten Commandments by the Protestant religion. Deuteronomy 5: 21 instructs: "You shall not *covet* your neighbor's wife. You should not *desire* your neighbor's house or field … nor anything that belongs to him"; thus, by having been included as (either one or two) Biblical Commandments, it is clear that **Envy** has remained one of the most persistent "unwitting" sins in Judeo-Christian societies since before the time of the Great Exodus. The primary reason that Envy is included as one of the deadly sins is because it is motivated, almost entirely, by malicious and animalistic impulses which cause spiritual imbalance and disorder; thus, the more envious a person chooses to be, the greater the chasm between that person and the spirit within. Envy is an uncomfortable urge which causes both a strong resentment toward another person's assets, qualities, advantages, accomplishments, reputation, or good fortune and an unreasonable desire, *triggered by malevolence*, to unjustifiably take possession of those benefits for oneself.

P.254… Christians must remain mindful, however, that the hardships (and levels of desperation) faced by the poor, during the time of Christ, were dramatically more severe and less justified than those difficulties faced by modern-era poor who are free, are allowed equal opportunity, and are given *more than sufficient* governmental aid by the richest country in the history of the world. In fact, those who are now regarded as being the most impoverished have a far more advantaged existence (in every way) than the wealthiest humans who lived during Jesus' era. It is difficult, then, to understand why anyone would demand that charitable Christians (who had, willingly, created a Democratic and free society) should, additionally, *be forced to give* ***equal*** *amounts of what is theirs to others* who have deliberately chosen to live decadent and slothful lives rather than have properly utilized their God-given abilities to adequately provide for themselves and their families. The ***envious*** motivational urges (which insist that all humans are ***equally entitled*** to everything a society can provide) derive from some of the most sinful and malevolent human impulses imaginable.

P.257… Instead of uplifting humans, *Socialism and Communism* facilitate and encourage the perpetuation of the lowest forms of human behavior; thus, these types of governmental systems could not possibly be God's favorites. While it is **true** that any society which allows a privileged class to exploit and restrict the freedoms and opportunities of the poor is a tyrannical and indecent society, there is no more tyrannical and evil form of government than a Communist system which allows the most sinful members of society to exploit and, essentially, enslave its most decent, hard-working, and talented; thus, neither Socialism nor Communism can ever successfully prosper (in the long term) because, ***in all instances***, the primary intention of the largest percentage of its more sinful citizens is, solely, ***to enviously ill-use and plunder the work-results of others***.

P.258… To summarize this "Seven Deadly Sins" discussion: it must be noted that although most insightful Christians have always known that living ***moderate*** lives is the best way for them (1) to maintain spiritual order and balance and (2) to avoid sin, Christians must, nevertheless, also be aware that if they are going to *fully succeed at avoiding "unwitting" sin*, it is essential for them to, likewise, continually remain conscious of that *exact instant* when they might disconnect from the Holy Spirit within.

Chapter Six: "The Ten Commandments"

P.259… It would be presumptuous and haughty for me to ever represent myself as being a Christian expert or advisor. For more than two thousand years, ***numerous*** *inspired humans* have *devoted their lives* to the effort of fully grasping and, then, revealing the meaning of God's and Jesus' teachings. I could never pretend to possess their degrees of insight, spiritual guidance, devotion, and goodness. My in-depth discussion of the Seven Deadly Sins was for the purpose of *emphasizing the importance of being able to,* ***immediately*****,** ***recognize that instant*** *when harmless behavior transforms into sin* so that all decent humans might utilize their spiritual strength to avoid as many transgressions as possible.

P.262… The willingness to steal and, thus, commit a *more significant sin* results when several ***Deadly*** Sins intertwine and create an even stronger (and more controlling) evil compulsion. To explain: thieves, typically, allow themselves to be driven by ***gluttonous*** and ***greedy*** hungers which cause them to crave materialistic items beyond basic survival needs (yet thieves are too ***lazy*** and impatient to work for what they desire); thus, rather than be conscientious and self-disciplined for the purpose of avoiding both mental and physical ***sloth***, thieves choose, instead, to ***enviously***, malevolently, unjustifiably, and criminally take possession of those items even if (in some more extreme instances) they must utilize ***wrathful*** and destructive violence in order to succeed in their sinful endeavor. The willingness to steal, then, is an illustration of how easy it is for humans to commit *grievous sin* when they allow themselves to be dominated by ***a combination of*** (otherwise less controlling) ***animalistic urges at the same time***.

P.264… I am certain that God is even more enraged with this modern society's *lusting for drugs* than He had been with the sexual practices of the sodomites at Sodom and Gomorrah. Despite the fact that God must be disheartened for every soul that is lost because of addiction, God does not exercise control over the manner by which human beings (as a result of free will) sculpt their spiritual frequencies. Humans are masters of their own fates *and* the captains of their souls. The spiritual downfalls of addicts, thus, can, also, best be understood by recognizing the role that a comb*ination of the Seven Deadly Sins* plays in enabling ***weak-minded*** *individuals* to, willingly, succumb to drug addiction.

P.265… Rehabilitation enables addicts to improve but never recover

P.265… The Catholic Eighth Commandment (and the Protestant Ninth Commandment) decrees that Christians should not bear false witness against their neighbors because that Commandment is still another significant means by which God has conveyed the importance of ***truth*** to His children.

P.266… Brain scans have revealed that the amygdala region becomes less sensitized after every falsehood (no matter how inconsequential the dishonesty may seem) to a point where the brain becomes indifferent (and ***deadened***) to the absence of **truth**.

P.267… Far too many modern-era transgressors, nevertheless, deceive themselves into believing that it is, merely, forgivable human nature which causes them to *greedily* pursue material items and worldly benefits they desire (by *any* means necessary) including by bearing false witness. It is unfortunate they do not realize that when they succumb to their body's impulses and cravings (and *permit their sins to sculpt their identities*), they fail God's test.

P.269… It is, then, worth recalling the warning from Matthew 7: 13-14: "The gate that leads to damnation is wide, the road is clear, and many *choose* to travel it. But how narrow is the gate that leads to *life*, how rough the road, and *how few there are that find it*"; thus, the practical reason why *free-thinking* Christians should avoid worshipping and connecting with *false gods* is because ***righteous*** Judeo-Christian convictions are the beliefs which ***best*** guide them to the "gate that leads to *life*".

P.270... You stated that The Ten Commandments are the foundation upon which both Jewish and Christian beliefs arise. Despite the fact that the two religions are the most similar of the world's greatest religions, Christianity and Judaism, nevertheless, have dramatically different belief systems. How does your dream knowledge reconcile the *distinctions* between the two religions?

P.270… Briefly, Christians believe that Jesus is the **Messiah** who fulfills the Old Testament's *Messianic Prophesies* (Isaiah 7: 14; Psalm 22: 14-19, etc.); but Jews, *generally*, are not willing to recognize the possibility of Jesus' divinity because (1) Jews do not believe the Messianic Age has yet arrived (just as Christians do not believe that Christ's second coming has arrived) and (2) Jews believe Jesus to have been a human being who was only one of several *false prophets* who had claimed to be the Messiah.

P.271… Judaism, also, does not recognize Jesus as the Messiah because Jews do not believe (1) in the *Holy Trinity*, (2) in abstract spiritual beliefs and thoughts such as the ***nature*** of God and the ***afterlife*** (Jews have no definitive or official beliefs regarding any such abstract subjects but, instead, are concerned, primarily, with human *action*--based upon 613 commandments given by God in the Torah--as well as long- standing Jewish customs) or (3) that humans are born *with original sin* and are, thus, inherently evil and in need of salvation. Jews believe in Maimonides's Second Article of Faith which states that *their God is an absolute and unparalleled* ***unity***. In addition, they have faith in *the Torah's translation* of Deuteronomy 6: 4 which states: "***Hear Israel***, Hashem is our God, ***Hashem is one***" and trust that this verse, *correctly*, echoes the intention of the First Commandment and, thus, eliminates the possibility for accepting a *Trinitarian Doctrine* which recognizes the Father, Son, and Holy Ghost as being "**one**". Most notably, Jews, steadfastly, insist that ***no***

human, including Jesus, (1) should claim to be God *or*, more importantly, (2) should be worshipped as an idol.

P.273… Christians, thus, fail to understand why any **truly** religious human would choose to ***totally*** *disregard the* ***truth****, wisdom, and value of Christ's message.* If Judaism had merely been willing to *unseal and read Jesus' scroll* rather than, steadfastly, observe the precepts of men, how could any "son or daughter of Abraham" not have recognized that Jesus' inspired words (at least, in part) fulfill God's promise?

P.273… The Third Catholic Commandment (and the Fourth Protestant Commandment), "Remember the Sabbath Day to keep it holy"….

P.277… The reasons why The Second Commandment is not the same for both the Catholic and Protestant religions…

P.281… An interpretation of the Second Catholic Commandment (and the Third Protestant Commandment) from Exodus 20: 7: "You shall not take the name of the Lord, your God, in vain, for the Lord will not leave unpunished him who takes His name in vain"….

P.284… The reason why the Fourth Catholic Commandment and the Fifth Protestant Commandment (which is proclaimed at Exodus 20: 12: "*Honor your father and your mother that you may have a long life in the land which the Lord, your God, is giving you*") has been included as one of The Ten Commandments….

P.303… An explanation and justification for some of the final observations and tones that provide the foundation for ***true*** Christian activism)….

P.304… Despite the fact that Jesus made clear that His intention was not to condemn the world but, instead, to save it, both Jesus and God are, nevertheless, sufficiently omniscient to perceive all **truth**; therefore, ***my primary intention has been to reveal THAT REALITY which Jesus, God, and the Holy Spirit***

actually perceive. Two additional purposes for my analyses have been (1) to explain why Matthew warned at 7: 13-14: "The gate that leads to damnation is wide, the road is clear, and many *choose* to travel it. But how narrow is the gate that leads to *life*, how rough the road, and *how few there are that find it*"; and (2) to clarify why it is senseless for humans to connect with tethers which lure them to damnation rather than those righteous Judeo-Christian tethers that shepherd them to the "gate that leads to life".

P.304... In summary, my analyses has attempted (1) to provide the best reasons for humans to examine and reflect upon the ways that they have chosen to live their lives and (2) to help them realize that Jesus' greatest gift to humanity has been to show humans "***the way***" to their spiritual salvations (by revealing those human qualities and behaviors which best assure Heavenly ascension). My hope (like those of the Doomsday Prophets) is that I have, successfully, (1) reminded all humans of their primary spiritual purpose, (2) provided them the insight and motivation to live the remainder of their lives in "ways" that would please God, and, thus, (3) helped *all humans* to better understand how to, continuously, harbor God's goodness within their hearts and souls. My prayer is that God will be so pleased with the life choices of ***all*** of His children that He will be able to bestow His love and blessings upon ***everyone*** because He will, finally, be able to recognize that ***all*** human souls are vibrating on the same wave-lengths as the ***peaceful Christian TRUTH frequencies*** which are tethered directly to the most desirable Heavenly rooms.

FOWARD

It is my belief that the Holy Spirit has *inspired me* to safeguard the long-term viability of the Christian faith by *revealing* those insights which explain (1) why Christians should not abandon their beliefs and traditions--regardless of the intensity of modern-day, non-stop, anti-Christian propaganda that is successfully causing so many to lose faith and (2) why it makes sense for all Christians to, once again, be guided by the teachings of Christ. It is my hope that (by sharing the insights that were stirred by my dream experience) I will be able to teach all humans how to strengthen and/or reestablish their own connections with the Holy Spirit. As a result, I am asking that you help me share this Christian message.

My childhood dream's vision of Heaven is the most noteworthy portion of this manuscript. Despite the absence of all fairy-tale-type elements, my dream experience will enable Christians to, finally, recognize what *is*, ***in fact***, ***the true description of Heaven***.

Within Chapter Three, I explain how most, currently accepted, scientific theories regarding human existence are, *merely*, restatements of Jesus' teachings; thus, by merging Jesus' words with accepted (and recently ***proven***) scientific ***theories***, I convincingly reveal (1) ***how***, ***more-likely-than-not***, human souls will survive the deaths of their physical bodies and (2) ***how*** it is possible that Heaven ***does*** exists. My explanations are so clear, concise, and (most importantly) ***correct*** that even intelligent atheists and agnostics will, hereafter, be forced to reassess their non-religious and anti-religious biases.

Chapter Three also contains (in plain English) the legal argument which will effectively enable Christians to overturn the Supreme Court decision that prohibits all lessons *with Christian antecedents* in the classroom *(Edward v Aguillard,* 482 U.S. 578 (1987). After this book's publication, there will, no longer, be a single, justifiable, ***legal*** reason to, ever-again, bar Jesus' ***scientific*** lessons from ***any*** classroom.

Other topics covered in the first three chapters provide the ***correct*** *explanations* for many "New-era" spiritual queries such as: (1) the most precise ***scientific*** (***and Christian***) definition for the concept of ***time***; (2) the ***true*** nature of human consciousness; (3) God's preferred governmental system; (4) the existence of ghosts; (5) and, even, past-life experiences.

Darwin's Theory of Evolution is not disputed in Chapter Four; however, since evolution does not account for the development of human consciousness and spiritual uniqueness, it is very easily supplanted by ***my***, more-*appropriate, explanation* (Christian Mammalian Differentiation Theory) which derives ***equally*** from (a) *recent* scientific events *and* (b) Jesus' wisdom.

The remainder of this manuscript discusses and analyzes modern examples of sinful behavior such as the Seven Deadly Sins, abortion, drug use, murder, sadism, homosexuality, (and more) for the purpose of teaching humans how to identify ***that precise moment*** when innocent behavior can transform into actions that are spiritually damaging.

In some instances, my insights vary from Christian beliefs because this manuscript is more concerned with identifying that ***precise*** human impulse which triggers sin. For example, while I make clear that God would never frown upon two people who *truly* love one another (even if both are of the same sex), I devote multiple pages to an examination of those other behaviors that are associated with the homosexual lifestyle which are sinful. Hence, while *The Boy's Dream* will prove to be very popular with Conservative Christians, it is non-Christian and anti-Christian curiosities that will, very likely, cause this publication to fully achieve its purpose.

In conclusion, if (1) the topics covered in *The Boy's Dream* intrigue you, invest a few hours of your time; you will be *very* pleased that you did.

God Bless!

Christian Clement

CHAPTER ONE

THE DREAM

For the past two millennia, a succession of self-appointed prophets has come forward to predict that "the end of the world" is near. Since the world has not yet ended, such predictions have always seemed silly. I, initially, became aware of those people in the early 1950's, soon after I learned to read. Numerous cartoons and comic strips depicted the prophets as being old, long-bearded, robe-wearing men who carried signs that often would warn, "Repent, The End Is Near!" The punch lines of the cartoons, although funny, would invariably cause the prophets to appear foolish.

Those cartoons helped me to make some of my earliest inferences about what kind of human being I should be. I realized that I wanted to be normal, to fit in, and to be accepted. I understood that I would never be accepted if I were to be perceived as some type of religious zealot; thus, for more than the past six decades, I have kept my religious insights to myself.

Over the decades, I have, nevertheless, become, somewhat, more understanding of the objectives of those prophets; and I, now, realize that they were not *that silly*. "The End" was, indeed, near for over eighty-five percent of all of the human beings who were alive in the early 1950's; thus, the prophets were correct to remind all humans of their fleeting mortality. I, now, understand that Doomsday

Prophesies are merely spiritual exercises. Their singular purpose is to provide everyone a good reason to examine and reflect upon the ways they have chosen to live their lives. Those prophets demonstrated that they understood Jesus' greatest gift to humanity was teaching "the way" to spiritual salvation by revealing those human qualities which best assure ascension to Heaven. In a nutshell, those prophets were *merely* ***attempting*** (1) to remind all humans of life's *primary* ***spiritual*** *purpose* and (2) to motivate everyone to live the remainder of their lives in a manner that would please God.

I mention those prophets because I, too, might seem *rather silly* for choosing to share some insights that I acquired from a dream that I dreamt in early October, 1953--just two months after my seventh birthday. Although I am seldom able to recall *any of my dreams*, this, *particular*, dream has maintained such a powerful hold that I have, continuously, remained conscious of it (every waking minute) for more than six decades. I realize that wisdom acquired during a boy's dream could seem to be just as incredulous as those doomsday prophesies; nevertheless, the understandings I gained have been so beneficial that I know they can also be fruitful for all Christians who are striving to live good lives. As a result, a ***brief*** summary and explanation of the boy's dream follows:

The Dream

I remember having been quite ill; thus, I had stayed home from school that Monday. My dream could have only lasted for a few minutes, yet it has proven to be the single most influential event of my life. I found myself in a place that was totally black and vastly different from any earthly location. Nevertheless, I felt very alive and secure; and I knew that I belonged there. It seemed very much like outer space because there was only emptiness. I was conscious and felt at peace, yet I did not have a body. I knew that I was in a place where I would not experience hunger, thirst, pain, or fear. I, now, believe that I had entered an existence that was very similar to either an ethereal Eden or Heaven. Once I *believed* that I fully understood where I was, I thought about a spiritual friend; and she responded, telepathically, in an instant. She asked where I had been. I told her that I returned one last time to inform her that I had been living as a human and that I had decided to continue doing so because I had become fond of my mother. That decision upset her because she, repeatedly, advised that living as a human was not a good idea. She kept reminding me that I had promised her that I was not going to remain on Earth for very long. She repeated, "You promised! You promised!"

Her concern amused yet pleased me; thus, I attempted to reassure her by letting her know that I had preloaded my body, my glands, and my nervous system with all of the correct instructions to (1) safeguard that I live a proper life and to (2) ensure that I would not do anything that might prevent me from being able to return when my physical-world existence ended. She, nevertheless, remained very concerned. At that point, I advised her that she should not worry despite the fact that I would be away from her for a while.

I proceeded, then, to embark upon my return journey. Even though I was leaving a place where I had been unable to perceive human-type feelings, I, nevertheless, *began* to experience a continually increasing sensation that indicated I was plummeting at an ever-accelerating speed; and that fall seemed to last for a very long time. The descent was so *frightening* that it remains the most terrifying experience of my entire life, and the horrifying feelings became so intense that I believed I was sinking to hell. Eventually, the descent slowed.

I was, finally, able to realize that I had returned because I saw myself approaching *three* Earths, and I recognized The Cisco Kid (a 1950's cowboy hero) riding figure eights around the *three* Earths on his palomino stallion, Diablo. By then, I clearly knew that I had returned to normal dreaming. Almost immediately, I was awakened by a hand that was gently shaking my shoulder. My mother and my older sister (who had just returned home from school) were sitting alongside of me. My mother said that I had been screaming, so she rushed to my bedside. My illness soon disappeared, and I resumed being a child.

CHAPTER TWO

THE INTERVIEW

That dream did change me; and, from then until now, I have been inspired by a type of insight that has been more meaningful than any other influence. Although my memories are not, totally, consistent with *all* Christian beliefs (they, instead, are the recollections of a seven year old who had not yet attended church), they have provided me with sufficient understanding to be convinced that Christ's teachings are mankind's greatest gift. Because more and more people from Christian backgrounds are being cleverly duped into abandoning their faith, I realize that the time is right to present a contemporary and straightforward explanation as to why it is in their best interest to, once again, live as Christians. The most effective way to share all that I have learned from my dream is to present, and then answer, those questions that any rational, and skeptical, mind would require me to answer. That question and answer session follows:

***

Your dream is distinctively different from the accounts of other persons who have provided in-depth descriptions of their visits to Heaven. Why didn't you share more details about your experience?

The obvious explanation is that my dream lasted for such a short period of time that there is neither (1) basis nor (2) justification for an in-depth description. My dream's purpose was to instill the ***correct*** spiritual wisdom within me so that (should I choose) I would be able to effectively teach both (1) devout believers and (2) cynical doubters how to strengthen and/or regain their abilities to believe in God and Heaven. My dream provides ***THE CORRECT*** **description of Heaven**. For now, that is all that is essential. Shortly, however, I will present (*by a preponderance of* ***all presently accepted scientific evidence***) a ***combined scientific and Christian explanation*** which ***VALIDATES*** the correctness of (1) Jesus' teachings ***and*** of (2) my description of Heaven--so, *be patient*.

Virtually all other versions of visits to Heaven (and conversations with God) are merely fictional accounts (*too often* published by non-Christian, anti-Christian, and/or make-believe Christian publishers) which cause more harm than good because those stories, cunningly (yet incorrectly), *convince* rational minds to conclude that Heaven, Jesus, After-life, and **Santa Clause** are nothing other than *comparable fairy-tales*.

Despite the fact you are claiming that what you experienced was only a dream, are you not really portraying yourself as being a modern-day prophet?

A prophet is a person who (1) is under divine influence and (2) is directed by God to teach God's will to others. I have been guided only by my spiritual self (which I have always interpreted as being a miniscule spark generated by the Holy Spirit) to follow a certain path in an effort to ensure a successful return to the place of my origin. I am aware that (1) I was provided with a very incomplete picture (and recollection) of that spiritual existence (and a *very brief glimpse* of the ***divine***) during my dream and that (2) I was allowed to retain just enough insight to, effectively, pilot me through life. Since this guidance has been very beneficial to me, I hope that it might be helpful to others as well. In addition, for most of my life, I had been programmed to recognize that there is nothing about me which is different from any other person; thus, I have always believed that if I had had such a dream, everyone else must have had a similar dream as well. I have presumed the only difference is that *I still remember my dream*; and that, *probably*, is because my dream occurred at a much older age. I trust that this is what Jesus meant at Matthew 11:25-26 when he prayed, "I praise you, Father, Lord of Heaven and Earth, because you have hidden these things from the wise and learned, and revealed them to little children".

You are talking about your place of origin. Are you suggesting that you existed elsewhere (on some spiritual plane) prior to your birth?

Since my dream, I have always believed that I had a spiritual existence prior to my birth. As a result, I have never doubted Jesus when He made clear that He existed prior to His birth and that He was a part of God and that He knew God's will. Jesus taught us that there is, indeed, a Heaven; and His purpose on Earth was to show us how our souls can survive the deaths of our bodies. Because of my dream, I have always been certain that I can trust Jesus' teachings.

At John 3:13, Christ said, "No one has ever gone into Heaven except the one who came from Heaven--the Son of Man". Are you suggesting that you are the Son of Man?

I am not claiming to be the Son of Man; however, at John 6:46 Jesus was more specific about what He meant: "No one has *seen the Father* except the one who is from God; *only He* has seen the Father". I did not have an interaction with God during my dream; therefore, I am aware that I did not experience the same Heaven from which Jesus came.

Heaven is, usually, depicted as being bright and colorful and vastly populated. Your description is nothing like the representations of others who claim that they have been to Heaven and returned. How do you explain that?

I have always understood that my recollections of Heaven could have been intentionally altered so that I would only remember that there is a Heaven (without being provided additional details). I realize that I may have been in some darkened Heavenly closet. However, as I aged, I gradually recognized that my vision of Heaven is, most likely, correct. The earthly light which humans see, for example, is a by-product of burning hydrogen in a nuclear reaction that is only perceived by humans because *physical-world eyes* are sensitive to, and react to, that burning hydrogen. All human perceptions of light are ***physical-world*** phenomena that are dependent upon the existence of mass and matter. There was no mass or matter in the Heaven depicted in my dream. It was as dark as an outer space that is devoid of stars, planets, and space debris. There were no fluffy white clouds and blue skies or spiritual beings dressed in robes because all of those types of descriptions could only, possibly, exist in the physical world. I did not have a body, so I could not speak aloud, see colors, hear vibrations, feel anything, walk, eat, drink, or perform any other functions that the physical body can perform. I experienced being a ***spiritual consciousness***; thus, I have always been *rather certain* that Heaven is devoid of all *physical- world* properties.

As far as I have always understood, it has never been God's intention to reveal too much about Heaven to humans. Jesus' message was sufficient; thus, people who claim that they had a conversation with God (and returned) or visited a colorful and worldly Heaven (and returned) are very likely (at best) merely recalling a vivid dream (just like me)-- nothing else.

Christ taught humans that those persons who are saved will be brought into the light, but sinners will face the eternal damnation of darkness; thus, at first glance, it would appear as if your dream suggests that hell is your place of origin. Are you claiming that you are correct and Christ is wrong?

Christ is correct; nevertheless, I do not believe that what I remember from my dream is incorrect (or in opposition to Christ's teachings). Most Christians should recognize that Christ, often, made use of *figurative language* and, clearly, *utilized imagery when depicting Heaven.* ***Light***, always, represents goodness; and ***darkness***, always, represents evil. More specifically, most Christians should recognize that the ***light*** to which Christ was referring represents the spark of eternal consciousness while the ***darkness*** refers to a permanent cessation of consciousness (or worse). At John 8:12, Jesus said, "I am the ***light of the world***. Whoever follows me will never walk in darkness, but will have the ***light of life***". I do not believe that it was ever Christ's intention to mislead humans to believe that massive balls of burning hydrogen, fueled by nuclear fusion, exist in Heaven.

In fact, at Mark 13: 24-25, Jesus presented an apocalyptic vision of what will remain after the end of this world. His description seems foreboding (but really isn't): "During that period after trials of every sort, the sun will be darkened, the moon will not shed its light, stars will fall out of the skies, and the Heavenly hosts will be shaken". Despite the fact that later scribes may have created a more ominous tone for these verses than was intended, Christ was only describing a

Heaven that is devoid of mass and matter. Heaven is not a scary place; it is, merely, different from this physical world.

You are already creating the impression that, like the Doomsday Prophets, you are some sort of self-styled expert about the Christian religion. What makes you such an expert?

I do not believe that I am any type of Christian expert. Having grown-up in a neighborhood where, nearly, all of the other children attended parochial schools while my family seldom attended church, I had always presumed that *virtually anyone else* was more knowledgeable about the *Christian religion* than me. Despite that, my parents' primary objective to guide me to be a decent human being has led me to be very concerned about the long-term viability of the Christian faith; thus, I am presenting heartfelt reasons why I think that Christians should not abandon their beliefs and traditions regardless of the intensity of the modern-day, non-stop, anti-Christian propaganda that is, successfully, causing so many to lose faith. I am revealing the bases for my reasons to believe that it makes sense to be guided by the teachings of Christ. Most humans have an innate belief in the existence of God and Heaven; and it is quite possible that they do either because (1) they had once had a similar early childhood dream and/or because (2) they sense the Holy Spirit within themselves. It is my hope that, by sharing my dream experience, I can help them regain some recollection of their own dream experience and/or of their connection with the Holy Spirit.

You have explained that there are no bodies in Heaven that are similar to our physical bodies; but, then, you claimed that you had a conversation with a woman. Is not that a total contradiction?

I sensed that my friend behaved toward me in the same way that a woman would interact with a man. In other words, even though we both lacked bodies and sex organs, we, nevertheless, possessed a spiritual connection which helped us to complete each other. I have always believed that the existence of a *feminine* **consciousness** in Heaven, merely, verifies Genesis's explanation of the creation of life. We have been taught that, in the beginning, God created both a man and a woman in Eden.

Do you not realize how odd it appears when you claim that everyone was speaking English in your dream?

I am certain that English was spoken so that I could have the opportunity to remember what had transpired during the time I was there. For humans, language begins as vibrations that are received and recognized by the eardrums. Those sounds are then interpreted by the brain and converted into meaning. In my dream, there were no sound vibrations or ears; there was, merely, comprehension. Omniscience was a quality possessed by all in my dream Heaven.

If you could not eat or drink, how could you (or any other spiritual being) have survived in that environment?

Although my dream did not *directly* provide me with an answer to that question, I have been able to i*nfer* how spiritual beings are able to sustain themselves. At that very moment when I willed myself to accelerate, I, immediately, became aware that I was surrounded by a nourishing form of energy. It is my belief that spiritual beings are able to sustain themselves merely by willing themselves to accelerate within that energy for the purpose of *recharging* themselves. Since there were no human body parts which could age or deteriorate, I realized, also, that I was in a spiritual realm where there was no possibility of a death that, in any way, could be similar to human death. The best analogy would be the Hindu concept of a "Supreme-Soul" and the Transcendentalists' belief in a "Great over Soul" (a spiritual existence where we are all *unique* aspects of an all-encompassing Spiritual being). From then, until now, it has always been my belief that (as long as I do not stray too far from Heaven's pathway) my spiritual consciousness has the *potential* to remain a glimmer of the Holy Spirit's, Jesus', and God's goodness; and it is that spiritual goodness which nurtures and sustains all spiritual beings in Heaven.

You describe a Heaven that is totally dark and lacking any form of matter. Now that you have discussed many things that are missing in your dream Heaven, can you provide any details that could make Heaven seem enticing?

I am certain that most of the very best aspects of Heaven were beyond my *human* ability to comprehend and, thus, were hidden from me. I, nevertheless, do recall some details. To begin, there was peace and contentment and an awareness that there is no death. As far as specific talents are concerned, there was the ability to establish an instant telepathic connection. All I had to do was think of another person, and that person was in immediate, spiritual contact. It was such a pleasant experience that the modern-day popularity of cell phones has never surprised me.

Since humans have been made in *God's* ***spiritual*** *image*, I have always recognized and accepted the fact that my *spiritual consciousness* seemed to possess some omniscient talents as well. For example, I had, obviously, known what had been happening on Earth the entire time that I was in Heaven prior to my birth. Additionally, it has always made sense to me that if there are other worlds where intelligent life exists, my spiritual-self must have been able to view those worlds too.

It appears as though I, also, manifested some form of omnipotence since I was able to insert myself into a human body and, freely, travel back and forth between my human body and my spiritual existence without, apparently, needing to ask for permission. I have always believed that God's Heavenly children possess and control omniscience, omnipotence, telepathy, free will and more; thus, I have always believed that these types of talents are examples of the **true** reflections of God's image.

Most Christians believe Genesis 1:26 which quote God as stating: "Let us make man in our own image, after our likeness", and 1:27 which confirms that, "God created man in His image"; thus, most Christians perceive God as a human form. You, instead, claim that man is, solely, a reflection of God's spiritual image. How did you arrive at such a conflicting conclusion?

Since God exists entirely in the spiritual world, He has no need for human body parts because the sole purpose of those parts is to facilitate survival in the *physical world*; thus, the *most obvious inference* is that our souls, our consciousness, our goodness, our humility, our **truthfulness**, and our individuality (not our physical bodies) are those aspects of God's image which will define and distinguish our identities after the deaths of our bodies. It must, therefore, be concluded that those human characteristics which have the potential to survive death, and ascend to Heaven, must be those qualities that are the ***true*** *reflections of God's image*.

Since you are claiming that you were omnipotent and had the ability to travel back and forth between your human and spiritual bodies, it can easily be inferred that you had

the ability to place yourself in the best human situation possible. Did you?

From a material point of view, I did not. My parents earned very little money, had very little education, and lived modest lives; thus, I have long pondered why my spiritual-self would have chosen such a life experience. The only, slightly negative, observation my father ever made about my mother was that she had "never fully grown up". She lived her life as an innocent and, rarely, fully engaged in most adult behaviors. She did not plot or scheme or sue or confront or drink alcohol; she always accepted losing, graciously.

In 1915, at the beginning of World War I, my father, a five-year-old son of German and Scottish immigrants, had his skull shattered by a baseball bat that was wielded by an older English boy (who was never punished for his vicious, anti-German attack). My father was blinded in one eye and lived his entire life with a metal plate in his skull protecting a portion of his brain. Dad never exhibited a desire to inflict similar types of harm on anyone else. Instead, he remained aloof and preferred to avoid complications and involvements with bad people.

Neither of my parents were active Christians, yet they both, ***innately***, behaved as Christians. Despite their human imperfections, they were *instinctively* humble, non-aggressive, and merciful; thus, their examples guided me to maintain a, **peaceful**, **spiritual** nature for *most* of my life. Even though I developed worldly talents, I often (although, regrettably, not always) found myself being influenced more by my parents' behaviors than by my adult abilities to compete, succeed, and win. Their *modest* lifestyle influences helped to keep me on a better and more correct ***spiritual*** *path*; thus, they were the proper parents for me. Proverbs

16:19 reminds us that: "It is better to be humble with the meek than to share plunder with the proud".

Besides, I was born just after the United States had won a world war; and I lived in one of the largest cities in the richest country in the history of the world. I remember a time when most people did not own refrigerators, modern washing machines, air conditioners, central heating, telephones, televisions, or automobiles; all that, of course, has changed during the course of my life. Antibiotics had just been discovered, and the polio vaccine was soon to be as well. Earning money and living comfortably (without the need for spiritual compromise) have, continuously, been easy during my lifetime. I have always been pleased with my body, mind, appearance, goodness, health, and fitness. I do not believe that I could have chosen a better time, place, mind, or body for the purpose of experiencing life on Earth.

Most Christians believe that the Garden of Eden existed somewhere on Earth. You believe that Eden exists within some alternate spiritual dimension. Are there any other ways that your religious theories vary from Christian teachings?

There are four. The first addresses the way some Christians choose to interpret the Bible. Since Jesus often identified many Old Testament stories as parables (stories which *illuminate* a moral attitude or a religious principle), I have always concentrated on the *message* conveyed in the Garden of Eden story rather than the *factual* ***truthfulness*** of the story. I have believed that after God came into existence (perhaps by way of some primordial Big Bang, billions of years ago) and, then, decided to create additional life in His own ***spiritual*** *image*, He was faced with an unexpected dilemma. By giving His children both freewill and individuality (rather than make them automatons), His children were sufficiently free to choose to be either good or evil. God soon recognized that His good children could not easily thrive in a Heaven overrun by evil children. I have, thus, always believed that Eve had not really been tempted by an actual snake (snakes cannot talk). Instead, I have believed that the snake, Satan, and evil (in general) are, merely, various forms of the same bad spiritual energy that is not compatible with good spiritual energy; thus, it soon became obvious to God that God needed to generate some form of testing facility to learn the ***true*** *nature* of all of His children so that they would, ultimately, find that place where they actually belong. It is for that reason that God created the physical world and the human plane of existence. Had God wanted Eve to be totally obedient, He could have easily designed her that way; however, for the sake of creating His children in ***His*** own image, ***God's love*** caused Him to, intentionally, choose to bestow freewill upon His creations; thus, He has willingly chosen to exercise no control over ***that*** *aspect* of His offspring's existences. He, merely, sits back and observes the degree of goodness or evil by which His creations choose to define themselves and, then, allows them to either ascend or descend to that spiritual dimension (afterlife) where they ultimately belong.

All humans must, then, be sufficiently vigilant (and wise) to recognize that the snake is merely an allegorical representation of modern society's temptations and *other* corrupting influences. The Biblical lesson to be learned from Adam's and Eve's parable is that it does not matter if modern sinners (1) do not realize they are transgressing and/or (2) are merely allowing themselves to be persuaded by clever societal enticements. God's children should always know that ***they***, alone, will be held accountable for ***their*** choices and lifestyles. As was the case for Eve, *willful ignorance* [sic] can never be an effective *spiritual* defense for sinful behavior.

Before you explain your other three theories, there are two major issues that many Christians would not like to be glossed-over. Many Christians trust that every word in the Bible must be literally accepted because the Bible is the inspired word of God; thus, they believe that any real Christian must have faith that all Biblical events are literally true. You, however, are claiming that many accounts in the Old Testament are merely stories. How does this help anyone to be a better Christian, and how does this stop many people with a Christian background from abandoning their faith?

Whenever a person questions the **truthfulness** of some facet of a Biblical story (for example, a snake talking to Eve), that person *might*, sometimes, be advised that he should not question any aspect of the Holy Scriptures; and he should *blindly accept* that which cannot be explained. Such an edict creates problems for the Christian religion because few people are willing to, *blindly*, believe anything. Parables must be recognized as being instructive stories--not factual accounts; thus, I have always believed that the two primary objectives for all Christians are (1) to fully understand and internalize ***Christ's*** *teachings* for the purpose of making them an automatic part of one's nature as completely as possible and (2) to, so completely, understand the ***lessons*** taught elsewhere in the Bible that it is easy to make that *wisdom* an instinctive part of one's nature as well. No good Christian objective can be achieved by debating whether a snake, in the Garden of Eden, really did speak to Eve and tempt Eve to be evil. No good Christian purpose can be achieved by suggesting that such Biblical stories are not parables. *Silly belief* does nothing to convince anyone either to become or to remain a Christian. At Mark 7:6-13, Christ quoted Isaiah's prophesy by stating, "These people honor me with their lips, but their hearts are far from me. They worship me in vain; their teachings are but rules taught by men. You have let go of the commands of God and are holding on to the traditions of men."

Many of the faithful may state that they believe that a snake spoke to Eve, but few can ***truly*** believe that it did. What is most important is that *the Garden of Eden **parable** teaches a significant lesson.* All insightful Christians (1) recognize that the *snake* is, merely, a metaphorical symbol and (2) understand that, sinful, modern cultural influences are the present-day representations of that snake; hence, Christians should also **know**, ***with certainty***, that, regardless of the allure of those modern-day temptations, no humans will be excused by God if they, foolishly, (like Adam and Eve) allow themselves to be seduced.

While it is **true** that some more "fairy tale-like" aspects of the Christian story might have, throughout history, convinced many lesser-educated sinners to convert to Christianity, modern-era transgressors can no longer be converted (or even influenced) by those same "fairy tale-like" explanations; as a result, the modern Church's focus should, instead, be on helping sinners (1) embrace the lessons taught by Jesus and (2) understand that Jesus' reason for sharing His spiritual wisdom was to reveal how all humans can locate and travel that Heavenly pathway which leads to eternal salvation. Christ's teachings, *alone*, provide sufficient reasons to choose to live as good Christians. The ***literal*** *interpretation* of every word in the Bible (particularly in the Old Testament) does not.

The second issue concerns your perception of Satan. Most Christians perceive Satan as a grotesque human form. You, on the other hand, claim that Satan is nothing other than a manifestation of evil spiritual energy. Will you please explain?

If Heaven is, indeed, devoid of all physical world matter, that, *most likely*, is **true** of hell as well. It is not possible, then, that a red-skinned, human-shaped creature with horns, a tail, and a pitchfork could be presiding over hell. Satan, as Christians most frequently identify him, is, therefore, nothing other than a ***personification*** *of evil spiritual energy*. It, also, is not possible that the unpleasant aspects of hell could be defined as a tortuous environment consumed by burning fires and unbearable heat because all are terrifying, metaphorical, ***physical world*** *descriptions created by humans* in the same manner (and for the same reasons) that Hollywood horror movie images are crafted: to produce a powerfully frightening and lasting image of how dreadful an eternity in hell will actually be. Satan's worldly appearance is merely a composite of ancient illustrations of evil from multiple cultures; hence, the pitchfork is a representation of Poseidon's trident; red skin comes from the shape-shifting evil Egyptian deity, Set; and the horns come from both the Greek god Pan and the terrible, netherworld Canaan demon deity, Habayu, who had both horns and a tail.

It is **true** that humans are constantly being tempted by satanic energy forces, but that temptation never occurs in the manner depicted, for example, in Washington Irving's delightful moral tale, "The Devil and Tom Walker"--a story in which Tom is initially tempted by "Old Scratch" to sell his soul and then is, finally, kicking and screaming, carried off to hell by "Old Scratch" as payment. That story and all similar, highly entertaining and instructive, fables are merely fictions.

Satan's evil energy is, nevertheless, around us, all of the time. It is present *every single instance* any human has to make a choice between a good decision and an evil decision. Whenever that individual deliberately chooses the evil path, that person has, at the same time, willfully welcomed Satan into his or her soul by connecting with an evil spiritual tether.

I have often recognized Satan, just below the surface, in the faces of those humans who have, unnecessarily, chosen to betray me or harm me even when they were aware that I had trusted them and that there was no justifiable reason for their betrayal and/or harmful intentions. Any time a person makes such a willful evil choice (and finds pleasure in doing so), that person has contracted a spiritual debt with Satan that, at some future time, will have to be paid. This is the New Testament explanation for Judas' betrayal of Christ. Luke 22: 3 teaches: "Then Satan Took possession of Judas…" and John 13: 27 explains that immediately after Jesus shared bread with him, Judas allowed Satan to enter his heart.

In ***most*** instances, one such evil decision could not possibly be *sufficiently* ***damning***; however, a lifetime of such choices would, surely, create some form of binding connection with (and commitment to) Satan's evil energy. Although the horror and torture which await those souls who will eventually descend to hell cannot possibly be comparable to *any form of recognizable physical world torment and pain*, it is certain that the type of suffering which awaits in hell will be *appropriately matched* with a human's lifelong accumulation of sin.

At times, you seem almost cynical of the manner by which some Christians practice their faith. What is your second theory that challenges the way, at least, some Christians understand their religion?

I am respectful of the way Christians practice their faith-- not cynical; nevertheless, I have always been amazed at the number of Christians who are not aware (1) of the fact that a recognizable English language had not yet come into existence during the time that Christ lived on Earth or (2) of the fact that Christ, *most likely*, spoke Aramaic (because the town of Nazareth, the town where Jesus spent the most significant part of his life, was an Aramaic speaking community).

The language most often spoken when we recite The Lord's Prayer (*Our Father who art in Heaven*) is, actually, Early Modern English (the form of English spoken in England in the early 1600's) because that was the time-period when the King James Version of the Anglican Bible was first, officially, translated into English. Prior to 1066 A.D. (the year of the Norman Conquest), Old English (and the languages that preceded Old English) were *mostly* Germanic (not English) dialects; and the first line of The Lord's Prayer in Old English clearly demonstrates those obvious differences: *Faeder ure, thu the eart on heofonum.*

The problem with attempting to, literally, understand even the 1600's King James Version of the Bible results from the fact that much of Early Modern English is also a (somewhat) unfamiliar language. There has been such a significant shift in syntax (and in the meanings of words) over the past four hundred years that the assistance of a linguist and interpreter would be helpful in order for us to *even approximate* an accurate modern-day understanding of *too many passages* from that Biblical translation. When we consider that (1) the King James Version was translated from the Classical Greek language and that (2) a written version of the New Testament had not been started until decades after Christ's death (approximately between 50 A.D. and 140 A.D.), it is obvious that the most meaningful Christian focus should not be on the ***literal meaning*** of one word (or one story) but, instead, on the ***lessons*** *revealed in those stories*.

We are taught, for example, that God made the Earth in six days. What does that mean? Heaven is timeless, so what is a day in God's life? The word "day" is a *human translation* for a Heavenly event that was accomplished in a manner that is beyond human comprehension. For humans, a day is the amount of time it takes Earth to revolve one complete turn; but there is no mass or matter in Heaven. It should be obvious that God's "day" is not dependent upon the Earth's rotation. What is *most important* is that God did choose to create this world (not the number of ***earthly*** *days* it took him to complete the job).

What is your third concern regarding the manner by which most Christians perceive their faith?

Christians must realize that there is a dramatic difference between the Old and New Testaments. The Old Testament provides a compilation of spiritual wisdom and inspired words written, approximately, between the years 900 B.C. and 160 B.C. for the purpose of teaching savages and barbarians how to live peacefully together in civilized societies. The Old Testament is the foundation for most, functioning, modern legal and social systems. Those good persons who choose to live, solely, by the principles taught in the Old Testament *could, quite possibly*, realize spiritual salvation--regardless of whether they believe in (or even know of) Christ.

The New Testament, in contrast, focuses on Christ's teachings. Although Christ was also concerned with taming the savagery in human beasts, *His* ***primary*** *purpose* was (1) to assure all humans that there is a spiritual reality and (2) to teach everyone "the way" to achieving the optimal, eternal, spiritual life.

From this perspective, Christians should realize that Old Testament teachings are worldly and practical but are, sometimes, spiritually deficient. For example, the Old Testament teaches that it is acceptable, necessary, and utilitarian to take an "eye for an eye". If that were not the case, none of us would be able to live as good human beings. If the actions and intentions of evil persons were not confronted and stopped, there would be only hell on Earth.

In contrast, Jesus teaches that we should turn the other cheek. At Matthew 5:38-39, Christ says, "You have heard that it was said, 'Eye for an eye, and tooth for tooth'; but I tell you, do not resist an evil person. If someone strikes you on the right cheek, turn to him the other also." Christ's reason for issuing such an instruction is that it is better to endure worldly harm than to compromise the goodness in our souls because our human existence is illusory, yet our spiritual existence is eternal.

Despite Christ's teachings, even Christ resorted to Old Testament solutions (including violence) and chose not to "turn the other cheek" when He perceived the need to confront evil. Matthew 21: 12-13 informs us that "Jesus entered the temple area and drove out all who were buying and selling there. He overturned the tables of the moneychangers and the benches of those selling doves. 'It is written,' He said to them, 'My house will be called a house of prayer, but you are making it a den of robbers'" (*organized crime*).

The dilemma of this *apparent contradiction* is that both teachings are correct because they address different aspects of human existence. In times of peace, Christians are best served by emphasizing and adhering to the teachings of Christ rather than those of the Old Testament. In times when that peace is threatened, Christians, reluctantly, have no other choice than to rely upon Old Testament solutions.

I have believed that God has always *utilized turmoil as a tool* to help our Creator effectively evaluate the degree of goodness in each of His children; thus, I have realized that it never has been (and never will be) God's intention to allow humans to experience Heaven on Earth. Instead, His intention has always been (1) to see how well His children are able to prevent hell from existing on Earth and (2) to prevent evil from dominating their souls. President Donald Trump emphasized this Christian belief in his speech to the United

Nations on September 19, 2017, when he reminded the entire world: "If the righteous many do not confront the wicked few, evil will triumph". It is for this reason that Jesus chose not to "turn the other cheek" but, instead, elected to *violently confront* the moneylenders in the temple.

You have just suggested that humans who live good lives yet do not believe in Christ or, perhaps, have never even heard of Christ could, nevertheless, enter Heaven. Many Christians, however, would contend that belief in Christ is an essential prerequisite for anyone to enter Heaven. Does this distinction have anything to do with your fourth concern regarding how Christians perceive their faith?

Yes, it does. Originally, Christians were named "Followers of the Way" because they believed that if they lived their lives pursuant to Jesus' teachings, they could realize eternal life. Throughout history, however, many non-Christians and pagans have, instead, chosen to worship various idols, symbols, and/or forces of nature. The only way Christian Evangelists could entice and convince *those types of humans* to embrace the teachings of Christ was to demonstrate, and emphasize, His superhuman (idol-like) qualities. For two thousand years, that approach has been proven to be the most successful sales program in the history of the world. Those Evangelists' ***sole purpose***, however, has, always, been to convince all people to live their lives in such a good way that they will, upon death, have earned eternal life.

Although it is **true** that there are examples in the Bible where Jesus states that those who believe in Him shall achieve eternal salvation, I have always known that what Jesus had, *really*, meant is expressed at John 5:51 when He advised, "I tell you the **truth**, if anyone *keeps My word*, he will never see death," and John 14:23 when He said, "If anyone loves Me, he will *obey My teaching.* My Father will love him, and We will come to him and make Our home with him." At Matthew 7:21, Jesus warned, "Not everyone who says to Me, 'Lord, Lord,' shall enter the kingdom of Heaven, but *he who does the will of My Father....*" At verse 24, Jesus adds, "Therefore whoever hears the *sayings* of Mine, and does them, I will liken him to a wise man who built his house on the rock...."; and at verse 26, Jesus concludes, "But everyone who hears these *sayings* of Mine and does not do them, will be like a foolish man who built his house on sand...".

Any human who has lived his life in a manner that is ***reflective of Jesus' teachings*** (regardless of whether that person is Christian or non-Christian) would have "built his house on the rock" and, thus, will certainly be "loved by Jesus' Father in Heaven". Christians should, then, be able to acknowledge that God, also, has the greatest love for those (post-World War II) *Japanese* individuals, for example, whose lives are guided by the honor, humility, goodness, and decency of their Buddhist and Shinto beliefs (despite the fact that they *may have* little, or no, knowledge of Jesus) because, ***righteous***, *non-Christian, Japanese souls* do, ***nevertheless***, *live moral existences which are reflective of Jesus' teachings.*

For example, because Shintoism (way of the Gods) is a polytheistic religion which recognizes the presence of God's spirit (Kami or Shin) *everywhere* in nature (including the forces of nature) such as mountains, streams, trees, wind, rain, etc., Shintoists, humbly, venerate *nature* spirits and perceive God as a "spiritual essence" and energy which, by generating ***all*** *things,* exists everywhere; thus, Shintoists believe that *everything* in the world (animate and inanimate) has a soul (and should be revered). Resultantly, those ***reverent*** religious beliefs (toward *all* things) are highly effective at guiding earnest Shintoists to "built their houses on the rock" as well as (or, perhaps, even better than) the lessons and approaches presently being advocated by ***too many*** *misdirected* Christian sects. *All Christians* could greatly benefit, then, from (1) studying how Shintoists and Buddhists teach children about sin and the importance of ***truth and goodness*** and (2) identifying the optimal age when those lessons should begin.

Christians recognize, however, that the obstacle for, ***too many****, non-Christians* is that it remains difficult, if not impossible, for non-Christians who have never learned of Christ's teachings to nurture the abilities to build their "houses on rocks" and, thus, successfully enter the "pathway" which leads to Heavenly ascension. This belief is amplified by Paul in Romans 3:20 when he taught that, by observing God's laws, we are provided *a* ***tool*** to help us recognize our sins so that we may attempt to repent for those sins. Without the benefit of such a ***tool***, Christians know that it is more difficult for non-Christians to find, and enter, the "Heavenly pathway".

Nevertheless, far too many Christians, also, mistakenly believe and teach that *worshipping Christ as an idol* is all that is necessary to please God; thus, too many Christians are willing to convince themselves that eternal salvation is automatic as long as they believe that Jesus is God (regardless of how they live their lives and) despite the fact that Jesus had warned that not everyone who believes in Him "shall enter the kingdom of Heaven". This misconception has caused serious problems.

One such instance results from the way that some Christians interpret what Jesus (allegedly) said to the eleven, *after* resurrection, at Mark 16:17-18: "And these signs will accompany those who believe: In My name they will drive out demons; they will speak in new tongues; they will pick up snakes with their hands; and when they drink deadly poison, it will not hurt them at all; they will place their hands on sick people, and they will get well." The earliest versions of the gospel of Mark do not include Mark 16:9-20 (most likely (1) because these verses appear to have been added by a later scribe *who had no* ***direct*** *knowledge of the Resurrection* and (2) because these words were not spoken by a living Christ but, instead, are *alleged* to have been spoken by a resurrected Christ).

More importantly, these passages are able to reinforce Christ's teachings which guide and reveal the pathway to eternal life ***only if they are interpreted figuratively***. In most instances, snakes, demons, and poisons are ***metaphorical SYMBOLS*** of various types of evil that can exercise no control or influence over ***true*** *followers of the way*. Also, despite the fact that many different languages were spoken during the time of Christ, believers in Christ were (and still are) able to bridge all language barrier through *caring expressions of their goodness*. Finally, since goodness is a universal language, Christians are able to take the hand of the *spiritually* ill and (with the guidance of Christian righteousness) lead those damaged spirits onto the healing salvation pathway. This *non-literal* (yet more meaningful) interpretation, then, is, essentially, a more specific ***restatement*** of Luke 6: 18 which explains that "Those who were *troubled with* **unclean spirits** *were cured*; ...because power went out from Him which *cured* all".

Despite the fact that this ***figurative*** *interpretation* makes better sense (and is more consistent with Christ's teachings), too many Christians have chosen to interpret these passages ***literally*** and trust that by, merely, believing in Christ, they, too, will be granted ***super human powers*** while still living in the physical world; thus, there are, for example, Christians who include poisonous snake-handling as a means of demonstrating that their ***true faith*** will protect them from physical world harm. They do this while, apparently, being oblivious to the fact that God has allowed thousands (if not millions) of his most ardent and decent ***believers*** to suffer and die horribly throughout history. If God did not save countless devout saints, monks, nuns, and other innocents from barbaric attacks, why would modern-era snake-handlers (some of whom have not lived pious lives) believe that God would be willing to intervene and protect them? Christians must ask: (1) is it conceivable that such activities as snake-handling, speaking-in-tongues, and laying-on-of-the-hands can, *in any way*, reveal pathways which guide Christians to spiritual salvation, (2) is it possible, instead, that these types of activities are quasi-Christian substitutions for pagan idol-worshipping, and (3) is it likely, then, that such endeavors countermand the Second (**Protestant**) Commandment which instructs that *Christians should not worship **false idols*** (either literally or figuratively)?

Christians must recognize that, although it is **true** the Bible is a compendium of wisdom inspired directly by God, *the Bible cannot be entirely infallible* because that wisdom has been interpreted, translated, and written by human beings (and humans are capable of errors). One *obvious example of Biblical fallibility* exists at Exodus 35: 2 where *Moses* (not God) orders: "…the seventh day shall be sacred to you as the Sabbath of complete rest to the Lord. ***Anyone** who does work on that day **shall be put to death***". It would be difficult for ***anyone*** to believe (regardless of what a single verse might instruct) that it is God's intention that all humans who work on the Sabbath should be executed because that would mean that everyone on Earth would have to, immediately, die. If the Bible is to be helpful in leading humans to the most desirable Heavenly "room", *Christians must be **wise enough** to be guided by the Bible's goodness* (and most significant principles) rather than picking and choosing and, then, allowing themselves to be ***misguided*** by some of the most questionable (and out of context) verses.

Are there any other ways that your dream beliefs vary from conventional Christian beliefs?

I realize there is a great likelihood that most Christians will find many more distinctions between their Christian convictions and the beliefs which have guided me since the time of my dream. It should be realized that the wisdom I gained from my dream was instilled in me at a very young age (*before* I had been exposed to most Christian teachings). Despite those differences, I am hopeful that my views will provide ***some*** *insight and clarity* for those Christians who might be struggling with aspects of their Christian faith.

Most of Christ's teachings regarding spiritual salvation are presented as parables which employ figurative language. This has made it difficult for many Christians living in this modern-era to decipher Christ's meanings. Why, in your opinion, did Christ not use language that is more straightforward?

Throughout history, most people never learned to read. During Christ's lifetime, for example, most Jews could not read Hebrew. That is why the first version of the Christian Bible was written in the (universally understood) Classical *Greek* language. The *conventional way* that great ideas were passed from generation to generation was by **orally** incorporating those great ideas within a story, a fable, or a parable because it was easier to remember and retell a good story.

In this modern-era, however, most Christians can read; yet few have mastered the skills required to either utilize or interpret analogies, allegories, metaphors, similes, fables, and parables effectively. In addition, despite the fact that Christ uttered millions of words during his life and ministry, only approximately forty thousand of his words have been preserved. It can be readily surmised that ***most** of Christ's teachings regarding salvation* have been lost. This does create confusion for all well-intending Christians.

Is there any way that your dream might provide clarity to help make it easier for Christians to follow "the way" to their personal salvation?

At the beginning of Chapter Two, I said, "I have been guided only by my spiritual-self to follow a certain path in an effort to ensure a successful return to the place of my origin". I am willing to share what I learned from my dream about that process.

Christians have believed that as long as a person lives a good life, that person will, most likely, enter Heaven. Why would you think that you might not be able to return?

Heaven and hell are vast areas that have the capacity to accommodate an *infinite number* of spiritual beings. Since the age of seven, I have been less concerned about whether I would return to Heaven but more concerned about the location to which I might return. Naturally, I would want to return to the existence that I visited in my dream because there was peace, goodness, and truly caring and loving, familiar, souls there; but living as a human for multiple decades has changed and corrupted me so much that I may, no longer, be the same spiritual being that I was at age seven. If that is the case, I will return to another part of Heaven (or hell) where I will no longer be able to *readily* stay in contact with my Heavenly family. This is *one* reason why my *dream friend* was so very apprehensive about my decision to live as a human.

If you return to Heaven, why would you not be able to communicate with anyone you choose?

At John 14:2-4, Jesus shared one of the most significant (yet misunderstood) passages in the entire Bible: "In my Father's house are many 'rooms'.... I am going there to prepare a place for you". I am certain that Jesus explained much more about those "rooms" to His followers during His ministry, but this passage is His only Biblical reference. My dream taught me that not only is the eternal world divided between Heaven and hell; but Heaven, also, is *partitioned* into many (distinct) "rooms"; thus, those persons who are fortunate enough to ascend to Heaven will find themselves in that "room" where they ***spiritually*** *belong*; and that "room" will be occupied, ***only***, by other souls who exist on that same *spiritual* "*frequency*". Communication with souls in other "rooms" is as difficult as communication is with humans on Earth; thus, contact, although not impossible, would be more difficult.

You are making it sound as though God is the ultimate segregationist.

Christians have always recognized that God is, indeed, the ultimate segregationist. Since evil persons will never be capable of deceiving God, God will always separate the good from the bad and make certain that miscreants and reprobates spend their eternities together in hell or cease to exist entirely. This is the reason why Christians have always recognized the need to separate and protect themselves from savages, sociopaths, psychopaths, and, even, non-believers.

Can you explain what you mean by Heavenly "frequencies"?

The best way for me to explain ***my*** understanding of Heaven is to compare Heaven to a television. Although the television screen occupies one area in space, it can, nevertheless, broadcast a large number of entirely different television networks from that same screen. When a viewer changes the channel, that person is merely switching to another frequency. All of the stations are distinct and do not interact in any way even though they all *appear* to be coming from (and exist) at the same location. That is what Heaven is *truly* like. Each Heavenly frequency is separated by distinct levels of goodness, love, peace, humility, and **truth**--from the purest form of spiritual energy to the most evil form of spiritual energy. By employing scientific terms, one could easily explain that Heaven is composed of an infinite number of distinct "dimensions". *How we live, our lives,* will determine the "room" or "dimension" that is most appropriate when we either ascend or descend to our Heavenly existences.

Earlier, you said that you had safeguarded your return by preloading your body, glands, and nervous system with the proper instructions. What does that entail?

There is, obviously, some form of connection between our *physical* bodies and our *spiritual* souls; and it is the interaction between (1) our human thought, feelings, urges, instincts, values, and actions, ***and*** (2) our spiritual souls which, ultimately, determines our *eternal spiritual frequencies and identities*. Since our souls (and our Heavenly frequencies) are devoid of mass and matter and are composed of a form of energy that is unlike any physical world energy (in the Bible, this energy is, most frequently, referred to as the Holy Spirit within us), the question is how and where does this interaction take place?

From the time of my dream, I have felt as though a spiritual tether has kept my Thymus gland and my Thyroid gland (and, to a lesser degree, other glands located within my brain--as well as the amygdala region of my brain), continuously, on the same frequency as the frequency of my dream Heaven; thus, I have always regarded my Thymus gland, my Thyroid gland, and my amygdala region as being my body's *primary* ***spiritual*** *brains* and the locations where the interaction between the human-self and the spiritual-self takes place. In essence (in modern language), Christ taught us that we should live our lives in such a way that the "frequency" which defines who we are should be the same frequency as the Heavenly "room" to which we aspire to ascend; and His teaching of "the way" has taught us how to reach that very best (and most desirable) Heavenly "room".

I have always believed this is what Paul meant when he explained at 1 Corinthians 2: 10, "God has revealed this wisdom to us through the Spirit"; thus, Paul at 1 Corinthians 6: 19 made clear that *God's* ***true*** *intentions* can be found in the innermost recesses of *our own minds and our own souls* once we have developed the ability to hear God's voice: "You must know that *your body is a temple of the Holy Spirit,* ***who is within****--the Spirit you have received from God*".

What may be different for me than others is that my spiritual tether is an incredibly powerful influence; and it has proven to be far more controlling than any of my strongest human impulses, urges, thoughts, or motivations. That tether, by far, is the single-most dominant influence in my life. While never interfering with my right to free will, it has *always* ***attempted*** to keep me on the most correct *spiritual path* (even when I had not been willing to remain on that ***correct*** *path* and had committed *worldly sin*). Although I have no way of knowing if my Heavenly "room" is, in any way, as perfect as that ultimate Heavenly "room" described by Christ, I know that it is wonderful enough; thus, it is *my preference* to choose to return there; and the tether's strong influence suggests that my Heavenly "room" would like me to return there as well. My only prayer is that I have not sinned too much.

If what you are saying might be true, how can a person best safeguard his or her return to Heaven?

The answer to the question regarding how a person can safeguard his or her return to Heaven could take a lifetime to answer because it will take a full lifetime for any person to completely create his or her personal spiritual frequency and identity. The good news is that a person's salvation, in most instances, is not determined by one deed or a single period of time but, instead, will be the result of a lifetime of experiences. A good physical world analogy is to equate a human being to a sculptor's project. At birth, each of us could be compared to a giant block of hardened clay (Isaiah 64: 7: "O Lord…we are the clay"). Every single thought, impulse, emotion, urge, and deed causes a piece of our clay to be chiseled away. Any one chisel would have a very small impact upon our finished work of art. Obviously, it would take hundreds of billions of chisels for the project to be completed; thus, we are able to make many, incorrect, chisels without any one of them having a lasting effect on the finished product as long as there are a sufficient number of correct chisels. If, instead of a block of clay, we recognize that we are molding spiritual energy (provided to us by the Holy Spirit), each of us would realize that we are creating our own unique spiritual frequency and identity (in a similar fashion); and it is our spiritual frequency which determines (1) who we truly are and (2) where (and how) we will spend eternity (Romans 9: 21: "Hath not the potter power over the clay, of the same lump to make one vessel unto honour, and another unto dishonour?").

The bad news is that there is very little that God can do to help alter our final outcomes once our sculpting projects are nearly complete. In reality (despite Old Testament teachings), our God is not a vengeful God (because vengeance is a human trait); there is no vengeance in Heaven. God gives us, as He did Eve, the *free will* to determine our own destinies; however, once we have fully defined who we truly are (by way of a lifetime of thoughts, emotions, experiences, and life choices), we have created our *spiritual identities*. At that point, we will, *automatically*, be drawn to that Heavenly "room" where we belong (Heavenly ascension or descent is, essentially, an *automatic* process). At that point, also, it is not likely that God will be persuaded to grant salvation, at the last minute, to very many of His wayward children. This was explained at John 12:47 when Jesus said, "As for the person who hears My words but does not keep them, ***I do not judge him***; for I did not come to judge the world, ***but to save it***". Jesus makes clear that it is not His role to decide who may achieve salvation or to what level of deliverance a soul might either ascend or descend. Instead, Jesus explains that His purpose is to show humans what steps ***they*** should take in order to **guarantee, *for themselves***, the best imaginable life after death.

This concept is summarized by Paul in his Epistle to the Galatians at 6:7-10: "A man will reap only what he sows. If he sows in the field of the flesh, he will reap a harvest of corruption; but if his seed-ground is in the spirit, he will reap everlasting life. Let us not grow weary of doing good; if we do not relax our efforts, in due time we shall reap our harvest. While we have the opportunity, let us do good to all men--***but especially those of the household of the faith***"; thus, Paul's purpose is to encourage all humans to, continually, attempt to sculpt the very best spiritual frequencies possible.

With such insightful Christian guidance, it is easy, then, to recognize the purpose for human existence: life in the physical world is merely a second gestation period. The nine months that embryos spend in the *amniotic sac* (the first gestation period) enable humans to develop minds and bodies that have the abilities to function in the physical world; and the eighty or so years that humans spend on Earth (the second gestation period) afford them the opportunities to sculpt their spiritual identities in preparation for ascending or descending to their most appropriate eternal Heavenly "room". Earth's atmosphere, hence, should be recognized as (merely being) a second *amniotic sac (or membrane).* God's love provides the spark of consciousness but, by granting free will, allows His children to sculpt their own unique spiritual identities; thus, God's love, *intentionally*, limits His involvement in the creation process to a partnership role.

Christians believe that they are born with the Original Sin that stems from Adam's and Eve's disobedience to God when Adam and Eve chose to eat the forbidden fruit. This Original Sin has, according to Saint Augustine, molded all human nature by transmitting "hurtful desires" (which (1) cause a separation from God and (2) produce dissatisfaction and guilt) to all inheritors of that Original Sin. Do you believe in Original Sin; and, if so, what does Original Sin mean to you?

Although most sincere Christians claim that they believe in *Original Sin*, the concept is so abstract and irrational that few Christians are truly capable of understanding the reason for it. The Church has taught that *Original Sin* explains the reason there is so much evil in the world; however, most insightful Christians fail to understand why a good and just God would have chosen to create such a world.

My dream has taught me that God's loving intention was to create His children, *entirely*, in His own ***spiritual** image.* In order to do that, God had to allow each of His offspring to experience individual *free will.* God, certainly, could have produced *sinless* children (in fact, He did when He created Angels); however, if His human children were to, indeed, be created in His image, they had to possess self-determination. Adam and Eve utilized that self-determination, for example, when they, willfully, chose to be tempted by evil. One of the most significant reasons humans must be, steadfastly, aware of the distinctions between good and evil is because humans are spiritual beings who exist within primate bodies that are driven by animalistic instincts, urges, and desires (all, of which, are manifestations of Original Sin). God's purpose for creating such a reality is to help God determine which impulses dominate and, thus, define the identity of each soul. God's loving hope is that humans develop such *spiritual strength* that they are able to *utilize and control* their life essential animalistic talents rather than *be ruled* by them; as a result, when humans allow themselves to succumb to their bodies' impulses and cravings (and permit those sinful urges and hungers to sculpt their identities), they fall victim to their Original Sin and, thus, fail God's test.

Humans have been granted the *freedom to, willfully, choose to be either good or evil*; thus, my dream has taught me that being born with *Original Sin* simply means that God's human children have been created with the *spiritual freedom* to (1) sculpt their, unique, ***divine** identities* for the purpose of (2) determining their ***eternal** spiritual destinies.*

Many people who have had near-death experiences report that they were, initially, greeted by deceased family members and friends who were there to escort them to Heaven. Do you believe that this really does, sometimes, happen?

If I had the ability to place my spiritual-self inside a human body, any other Heavenly spirit should be able to utilize spiritual omnipotence in order to meet and escort a loved one at the time of death. It *is possible* that the deceased friend or family member would utilize that power in order to help ease the transition from life to death by recreating a, *temporary*, colorful environment which contains reassuring, physical-world, details. Regrettably, however, that omnipotent spirit would not be able to sustain the transitional environment for very long nor would that spirit have any control over the recently deceased's final destination because, once a departed soul has transcended to the Heavenly plane, that person will be drawn ***directly*** *to the most appropriate spiritual "room".* The **true** spiritual family of the decedent is composed of those souls who reside in the "room" which is most compatible with the spiritual frequency of the departed *soul*; thus, that person's individual ascension to Heaven would be *entirely distinct* from the ascension of any other earthly friend or family member.

Most Christian teachings infer that we will be spending eternity with our saved friends and family members. Are you suggesting that we are not ever going to see most of them again?

If friends or family members had been so close and they had created *similar enough* spiritual frequencies, those friends or family members could possibly ascend to the same spiritual "room". Examples would be (1) married couples who truly loved one another or (2) families whose members remained close, committed, and *morally* compatible throughout life. This is the reason that Buddhists honor their ancestors.

In the overwhelming number of instances, however, souls will not encounter their earthly acquaintances or family members in Heaven because most modern-era humans are far too individualistic. The **truth** is that no one knows what is actually occurring in the hearts and minds of others, yet we can be certain that it is something very different than what is occurring in our own hearts and minds. One of the primary objectives of the Catholic and Amish communities, for example, is to make every attempt to keep all of their members connected to the same ***good*** *spiritual frequencies* throughout their lives. Regrettably, however, those efforts are only modestly successful.

Does your dream provide you with any insight as to whether God listens to prayers and intervenes on behalf of all of those humans who pray to Him?

My dream has taught me that Christians should demonstrate heartfelt gratitude for God's wonderful gift of life by refraining from constantly asking, begging, and praying for God's help. It is doubtful that He listens to *every prayer* because (since existence in the physical world is not the ***true*** *reality*) God is not likely to be as concerned with worldly events as humans hope.

Some humans believe, nevertheless, that their prayers are, *at times*, answered by "guardian angels" who could possibly be either angels or, in some instances, very close, departed friends or family members--not God. If so, it is feasible that those "angels" are adequately omniscient to hear prayers and are sufficiently omnipotent to help *by intervening in limited and indirect ways* such as (1) conveying messages in dreams and (2) providing *spiritual* guidance by encouraging their loved ones to connect with the best tethers and frequencies.

My dream made me aware that our human souls have the potential to connect with and, possibly, even visit a spiritual existence while in a dream state; yet, the only way that spiritual beings (with the exception of God Himself) can enter or reenter the physical world is by way of natural birth--(that fact was, initially, even **true** for Jesus). The *obvious reason* is that humans are directly linked to Heaven because their souls are composed of spiritual energy. In contrast, since no physical world matter exists in Heaven, God has made certain that there is no, readily available, means (besides natural birth) that would enable spiritual beings (with the exception of God, Jesus, and the Holy Ghost) to *directly and actively interact with* (*or return to*) the *physical* world.

Is there any evidence that what you are saying about Heavenly ascension is actually true?

Since I, like Jesus, am talking about non-physical phenomena, there has, ***until recently***, been very little physical world (and/or scientific) proof. This is where, and why, faith must play such a significant role in religious belief. I am merely sharing what I have learned, ***and believe***, from my dream. There are, however, countless anecdotal instances where people who have nearly died report that they saw their entire lives pass before their eyes in what should have been the last moments of their lives. Those reports could, possibly, verify that a spiritual record of everyone's entire life truly does exist. It is merely another way of suggesting that we have spent our entire lives sculpting spiritual frequencies which, ultimately, become our spiritual identities.

There have been other religions, and spiritualist groups, that have made the same observations. The Theosophy movement, for example, is a spiritualist society which gained great popularity from the middle of the nineteenth century to the present and believes that an Akashic Record (spiritual record) of the universe does exist. The word "akashic" derives from the Sanskrit word which means "ether" (a record in the ether). It is described by Alice A. Bailey in her book *Light of the Soul on the Yoga Sutras of Pant Anjali-- Book 3*. She writes: "The Akashic Record is like an immense photographic film, registering all the desires and Earth experiences of our planet. Those who perceive it will see pictures thereon: The life experiences of every human being since time began, the reactions to experience of the entire animal kingdom, the aggregation of the thought forms...of every human unit throughout time". Theosophists believe that it is possible for humans to access and read the Akashic Record.

Although it is **true** that the Theosophy movement has held *many non-traditional beliefs*, that spiritualist organization has accumulated a considerable number of *anecdotal accounts* of the existence of a "spiritual record". Such observations could never amount to scientific proof; however, most religions, including Buddhism and Christianity, have maintained a belief that such a spiritual record *does exist*. Christians refer to that record as "The Book of Life" or "The Book of the Living" and references to "The Book of Life" appear, for example, at: Psalms 69:28-29; Philippians 4:3; and Revelations 3:5; 13:8; 17:8; 20:12; 20:15; and 21:27.

While most people (and religions) have, thus far, been preoccupied, merely, with the belief that such a Heavenly record does exist, my dream has made me perceive the Akashic Record in a different way. It has always been my belief that The Book of Life exists at that location where a human's ***spiritual** energy* interacts with ***physical-world** energy* for the purpose of sculpting that person's spiritual frequency. Upon death, that person's spiritual frequency releases from the tether which connects the soul (and the Holy Spirit) with the physical world and ascends or descends to that person's appropriate spiritual "room". An Akashic Record, which is composed merely of inert physical world ether, is all that remains in the physical world after that disconnection. As a result, although ghosts do not exist (and most who claim to have seen ghosts are merely being dishonest), it is *possible* that *some people* who have an innate ability to access and read the Akashic Record could misinterpret the meaning of the ethereal "after-images" that they are able to view and, mistakenly yet honestly, believe that they have witnessed the existence of ghosts.

Some people claim that they are able to recall having lived previous lives. Do you believe that such people could be telling the truth?

In most instances, people who claim to remember having lived previously are either being dishonest or delusional. Nevertheless, it is not entirely impossible (although it is very unlikely) that a small percentage of humans have not only been reincarnated but, also, are able to recall their previous lives. **If** such recollections are possible, it is likely that the percentage of such *honest claims* will increase, dramatically, in future millennia after the births of hundreds of trillions of additional humans; thus, there is no better reason for humans to do everything possible to prevent this world from being destroyed by satanic influences.

Despite the *possibility* that reincarnation *could* be real, my dream has guided me to realize that, in most instances, people who honestly believe they have witnessed their own *past life regressions* were actually connecting with (and viewing) ethers in the Akashic Record that were, originally, created by ***other**, deceased, humans* who lived in previous decades or centuries. These distinctly ***other** humans* had already been guided to their Heavenly "rooms" by sculpted spiritual frequencies which are remarkably similar to the frequencies of those persons who believe that they are viewing their own past lives. Upon death, it is very likely that both persons who had created such remarkably similar frequencies will ascend to (and meet) in the same Heavenly "room" and will recognize one another, at that time, as eternal family members (not the same person).

When you suggest that, at least, some humans are tethered to their spiritual selves, it almost appears as though you are claiming that your life has been controlled more by predestination than free will. Do you believe that the lives of other humans are being predetermined and manipulated by God?

That question has been debated by wise men and women and has been a recurring theme in literature and theological philosophy for centuries. Initially, during my formative learning years, I was very much certain that I possessed free will and that it was an absurd notion to think that some distant god would have given me life for no other reason than to torment me and control me like a puppet. I have lived in the United States, a country which emphasizes the importance of freedom; thus, it should not be surprising that I became very much influenced by the poem written in 1875 and published in 1888 by, atheist, William Ernest Henley entitled "Invictus" (which, in Latin, means "unconquered"):

Out of the night that covers me,
Black as the Pit from pole to pole,
I thank whatever gods may be
for my unconquerable soul.
In the fell clutch of circumstance
I have not winced nor cried aloud.
Under the bludgeonings of chance
My head is bloody, but unbowed.
Beyond this place of wrath and tears
Looms but the Horror of the shade,

And yet the menace of the years
Finds, and shall find, me unafraid.
It matters not how strait the gate,
How charged with punishments the scroll,
I am the master of my fate:
I am the captain of my soul.

Henley wrote this poem after he had contracted tuberculosis, had one leg amputated, and was facing the amputation of his second leg. Despite worldly setbacks, Henley made clear that, even in the face of hardship and potential death, his soul was not defeated and would remain unconquered--he was the captain of his soul.

His mention of the "strait gate" is a reference to Matthew 7:13-14 in the King James Version of the Bible which states: "Enter ye in at the strait gate: for wide is the gate, and broad is the way that leadeth to destruction, and many there be which go in thereat: Because strait is the gate, and narrow is the way, which leadeth unto life, and few there be that find it". Despite the fact that Christ preached that the entrance to any Heavenly "room" is very narrow (and that many will fail to successfully enter the Heavenly gate), Henley, *correctly*, *asserts* that he, *alone*, will control his ultimate spiritual destiny.

For most of my life, I, too, have believed that I have been guided only by self-determination. I have always accepted responsibility for my decisions and actions; thus, I could never imagine blaming God for any hardship which might have befallen me. I, also, have seldom prayed to God to request some benefit because I have always believed that the gift of life was a sufficiently wonderful reward. In summary, I could never conceive of a situation where my life would have been spelled out in advance and controlled by God's predestination or intervention.

The slight difference between Henley's world vision and mine is that Henley was opposed to the notion that God (or any other spiritual entity--particularly the Holy Ghost) might be manipulating and controlling his fate. While I do not disagree with that belief (because *I know* that God grants free will to all of his children), I am aware that *most of my life choices* have been ***guided*** by a spiritual tether *created by my spiritual self* (which is directly linked to God's Holy Spirit); thus, I have always been aware that human predestination is not structured and planned by some distant uncaring god but is, instead, ***guided*** (not controlled) by our own spiritual tethers. That being the case, I am aware that God has allowed me, and all others, to be the masters of our own fates and the captains of our own souls; thus, I *know* that the inspiration for the poem "Invictus" did not originate as much from Henley's **godless** *beliefs* as it did from Henley's ***estranged****, inner, Spiritual voice.* Despite his atheist convictions, it would appear as though Henley has written the *definitive Spiritual Anthem.*

Can you provide any insight as to how people living in this modern-era can create optimal spiritual frequencies for themselves?

I have always believed that achieving the optimal spiritual frequency requires a person to make every effort to live a life that is filled with goodness, love, **truth**, humility, and peace. Of the five, **truth** is the most important. Jesus explained the significance of **truth** at John 14:6 when Jesus answered, "I am the way and the **truth** and the life. No one comes to the Father except through Me". Christ made clear that the one spiritual frequency which leads, directly, to the optimal Heavenly "room" is the **truth** frequency. Knowing how to live a ***truthful*** life is the key. At John 8:31-32, Jesus instructs, "If you live according to My teaching, you are truly

My disciples; then you will know the **truth**, and the **truth** will set you free" (set you free from the chains of a worldly existence and lead the way to the optimal Heavenly "room").

What is the best way to live a truthful life?

The best way for all of us to follow Jesus' teachings is to choose to live our lives as though everyone were able to (1) read each other's thoughts and (2) sense each other's feelings; thus, good human beings should, through habit conditioning, train themselves to never think even a single thought that they could not utter aloud. Proverbs 23:7 in the King James Version teaches that sin starts in the mind because we are what we think: "For as he thinketh in his heart, so is he". In most cases, (1) the thoughts that we think when we are certain that no one is listening and (2) the choices we make when we are certain that no one else knows about those choices are the two strongest ***frequency*** influences. A person's inner-secrets ***mark*** that person forever; thus, it makes sense to have only the *purest types of secrets*. People who choose to be *spiritually awakened* should make every effort to develop the skill to totally control the kinds of thoughts, emotions, impulses, and urges that surge through their bodies and ensure that those are always the best possible emotions, impulses, and urges. If their thoughts and feelings are vibrating at the same "frequency" as the "Heavenly frequency", those persons will encounter no difficulty entering the "strait gate" of Heaven.

Remarkably, we are most clearly defined by those *very first impulses* we may think, or feel, in response to a person or an event (because they are our ***truthful*** *impulses*). Quite often, those thoughts and feelings are so very quiet and subtle that most of us easily utilize social skills which allow us to override and conceal our ***true*** *natures*. Unfortunately, those social skills have no influence upon our spiritual frequencies.

Our spiritual frequencies are, continually, being sculpted by *our* ***true*** *mental and emotional responses* rather than by our phony social facades; thus, it is the ***character*** *of our thoughts and feelings that* ***foremost*** *defines us--****not, necessarily***, the degree of emotional intensity which accompanies those thoughts and feelings. That is why it is so important to utilize habit conditioning to make certain that we achieve, and maintain, a "***singularity***" *with* ***truth*** *and goodness.* That is also why it is so important to teach and train the very young to, *innately, be as good and* ***truthful*** *as he or she can possibly be.* Allowing a child to "run wild" is perhaps the most harmful form of abuse that an adult could inflict upon a child.

Far too many people, nevertheless, choose to live in just the opposite fashion. They believe that, rather than cultivating the most spiritually evolved human qualities possible, it is in their best ***material*** *world interests* to develop skills that will, instead, enable them to conceal the more undesirable facets of their **true** natures. They seem most proud when they master the ability to be convincing liars. They revel in knowing that they might have successfully betrayed, duped, cheated, or harmed another trusting person; thus, they, *mindlessly*, go through life being totally oblivious to the fact that their type of behavior is the most, *spiritually*, self-destructive behavior imaginable.

Rather than spend an entire lifetime developing and utilizing evil talents, those types of persons should, instead, be attempting to achieve **"*singularity*"**, a state where a person's thoughts, feelings, impulses, urges, and animal instincts are vibrating as closely to that person's desired Heavenly spiritual frequency as possible. At Matthew 16:26, Jesus makes this point very clear when he asks," What good will it be for a man if he gains the whole world, yet forfeits his soul?"

Do you believe that all humans are being guided by good spiritual tethers?

For most of my life, I, naively, had been willing to believe that all humans were attached to some *good* form of spiritual tether (similar to the one that has guided me); thus, I had been willing to trust that most humans are upright. In recent decades, however, my belief has been challenged because I have interacted with far too many people who seem to be more, innately, defined by a malevolent frequency than by a good frequency. In too many instances, it appears as if savagery lurks just beneath a *very shallow veneer* in many seemingly "civilized" people. If that is the case, it would appear as though too many modern humans have made a ***willful*** *choice* to deny the teachings of Christ and have chosen, instead, to mimic that "foolish man who built his house on sand".

This has led me to, reluctantly, conclude that we do not all come from the same Heavenly "room" or have the same earthly objectives. My goal has always been to return to my place of origin; however, if other humans come from a far less desirable place of origin, their purpose should, most likely, be to add sufficient goodness to their spiritual frequencies to justify being upgraded to a better Heavenly "room".

If they are, nevertheless, being guided by a somewhat tainted (or evil) frequency, it would take an immense amount of ***truth*** *and goodness*, on their parts, to prove that they are worthy of those upgrades. Regrettably, it would appear as if, even when given a second chance, far too many souls allow themselves to be misguided and, thus, doom themselves again.

Your previous explanation suggests that some souls are being reincarnated. Christians do not believe in reincarnation. What is your basis for such a unique claim?

God has the power to do anything that God might choose; thus, if God wishes to reincarnate a human being, God can, and will, reincarnate a human being. Certainly, Christians believe in *Christ's* reincarnation; and Christians do anticipate Christ's return. Matthew 24:30 states: "They will see the Son of Man coming on the clouds of the sky, with power and great glory". With that being the Christian belief, why, then, would Christians not recognize that reincarnation *could* be possible in other situations as well?

The concern raised (about my choice to return to Earth) by my friend in my childhood dream, most likely, provides the best answer to that question: If a soul is already residing in a wonderful Heavenly "room", why would that soul choose to live as a human and be exposed to the possibilities of sin, pain, suffering, evil, and death? It is not that Christians do not believe in reincarnation; Christians merely realize that *most residents of Heaven* would not have any reason to choose to return to a human existence once those souls had been permitted to enter the "strait gate" of Heaven.

One question remains: if some souls are residing in less desirable "rooms" but demonstrate a *potential for greater goodness*, ***might*** God, mercifully, choose to utilize reincarnation to give them an additional chance to demonstrate, and prove, that those souls are worthy? Undoubtedly, the answer is, "Yes".

Do you believe that the Hindu Religion is correct when it teaches that humans can be reincarnated into the bodies of animals?

It *certainly* is within God's power to place a human soul within an animal's body. That soul, however, would be limited in the way it perceives and interacts with the world because of (1) that animal's innate instincts, (2) that animal's physical limitations, and (3) the size and the capabilities of that animal's brain. Such an existence would, undoubtedly, seem to be a form of imprisonment (somewhat equivalent to a human being confined to a strait jacket). It is not anything that most evolved souls would choose, but I would not doubt that it is something that God, sometimes, allows to happen (particularly in situations where spiritual lessons can be learned).

Returning to your response to the previous question, you stated that you have finally realized that it is possible that not all humans are tethered to good spiritual frequencies. Do you believe that there is any likelihood that a psychopath might be tethered to some type of good spiritual frequency?

The behavior of a psychopath makes it quite clear that not all humans are tethered to good spiritual frequencies; thus, I do, reluctantly, accept the **truth** that some humans *could be* tethered to very evil spiritual frequencies. The qualities that define psychopaths are anti-social behavior, diminished empathy or remorse, poor impulse and urge control, poor behavioral restraint, meanness, sadistic and exploitative intentions, and cruelty to gain empowerment. Quite often, there is an emotional and intellectual coldness and detachment; thus, it is not as much the emotional intensity which sculpts evil spiritual frequencies as it is the ***nature and character*** *of the thoughts and impulses*. Such people seem to be guided by "automatic pilots"; and since there is such a low level of goodness, it is possible that *evil tethers* are those "automatic pilots".

If, indeed, humans have the potential to be tethered to various types of spiritual frequencies, that fact would mean that Earth is a crossroad between Heaven and hell. If **true**, Christians who seek spiritual salvation must learn to be very aware of the types of humans they accept into their lives because it would be very difficult to live as Christians, otherwise. Psalm 1: 1 wisely reminds us to avoid those persons who, willfully, choose to do bad things by advising that, "Blessed is the man who follows not the counsel of the wicked, nor walks in the way of sinners, nor sits in the company of the insolent".

In what part of Heaven, then, do you now believe the majority of spiritual tethers originate?

It would seem that if there are a large number of Heavenly "rooms", there are also a large number of possible types of spiritual tethers. My inference is that the spiritual frequencies attached to the majority of humans are composed of a broad combination of both good and evil tethers, and each human is free to embrace and create a "*singularity*" with whichever tethers that human prefers. For example, any person who chooses to believe that there is neither a god nor an afterlife *might* decide that there is no reason to be a good human being. If that person has no expectation that he will ever be held accountable for his actions, why would that person choose to be good or to have any regard for **truth**, decency, society, or another person? Even if that person's frequency is, originally, rich with goodness, why would that person choose to be good or to put anything ahead of that person's own, physical-world, self-gratification? If, indeed, life on Earth is God's testing facility, what better way is there for assessing His children than by creating an environment where both good and evil interact?

Most Americans believe that God favors societies which are based on Democratic principles. Do you agree that such a belief is correct?

Such a belief is correct, but not for the purpose that most Americans would hope. The *sole reason* God would prefer Democracy is that it is a governmental system which allows humans to reveal their **true** spiritual natures. That is not always possible in other, more oppressive, societies.

Is it conceivable that a Muslim suicide bomber could, possibly, be tethered to a good spiritual frequency?

The belief that a person who has died as a result of a, significant, single *selfless act* will ascend to the most desirable Heavenly "room" is a belief that is shared by Muslims and Christians alike. Instead of being compared to the product of a sculptor (who requires a lifetime to sculpt a block of clay), a martyr should, more properly, be compared to the product of a diamond cutter who is sculpting a rough diamond. With only one proper impact, that diamond cutter could, possibly, create a flawlessly formed core diamond with brilliantly sparkling facets. The diamond is representative, of course, of a perfectly formed frequency and soul--one that would, immediately, be able to ascend to the most perfect "room" in Heaven. This should be the ultimate goal for everyone.

The suicide bomber's greatest obstacle to fulfilling this objective, however, is being able to convince God that the slaughter of innocent humans, *in God's name*, is really an example of a martyr's selfless act. That can ***only be true*** if the bomber's actions are pure and, continuously, altruistic and innocent (*as well as* ***correct***). If, however, the bomber's reasons are wrong and/or there is the slightest presence of sadistic pleasure or satanic evil intent (*at any moment* during the commission of such a destructive deed), that bomber, instantaneously, disconnects from a pure frequency and, immediately, reconnects with one of the most evil frequencies imaginable. At that point, the suicide bomber would condemn himself to eternal damnation. Even worse, most suicide bombers are being drugged so excessively that they are hardly able to comprehend what they are doing; thus, it is impossible for any of them to be either sufficiently altruistic or innocent in the eyes of God.

Sadly, God's position was made quite clear in the Book of Genesis. Such actions, even when made in God's name, are not proper. We know that after Eve was ***tempted*** to bite into the forbidden fruit, God was unforgiving. It did not matter if she failed to fully conceptualize that she had, *unwittingly*, done something which, in fact, was evil. God had no patience for her level of *foolishness*; thus, He allowed her to be cast out. In summary, if God perceives the actions of suicide bombers as being similar to those of Eve's, it is very unlikely that God will recognize, or accept, those actions as being representative of **true** martyrs (or even good human beings).

Your response, almost, seems sympathetic toward those bombers. The Fifth Catholic Commandment clearly states that humans should not kill, and the Sixth Protestant Commandment clearly states that humans should not murder. Why would you imply that there is even the slightest possibility that God could be forgiving toward a suicide bomber?

Spiritual salvation or damnation is influenced less by an actual physical world action than it is by the motivational intent which guides that deed. Ultimately, it is the *sculpted spiritual frequencies* which result from human thoughts and emotions (not the human deeds themselves) that concern God the most. *Well-meaning humans* have always tried to comprehend God's delineations between good and evil; thus, a review of the various forms of homicide can demonstrate, for example, how complicated such understanding can be.

It might seem as if taking another life would be the most serious human transgression possible; however, that is *not always* ***true***. If a homicide is committed by a person who has no other choice than to defend himself, his family, or his friends against a life-threatening violent attack (either at peace time or during war), such an act of self-defense is always recognized as being excusable and/or justifiable; thus, no *human penalty* will ever result from that form of homicide. If, during the event, that defender's spiritual impulses were ***purely*** *innocent*, it is not likely that his or her *spiritual frequency* would be damaged in any way either.

Murder, on the other hand, is one of the most serious human transgressions because "malice aforethought", a legal term which summarizes the conditions that amount to murder, is present. For express malice, there must be a real intent to kill someone (or there is an actual intent to kill someone but another person is, instead, killed).

Malice can also be *implied* in situations where there is no actual intent to kill, but a person's conduct is so reckless, and is so indicative of such an abandoned state of mind, that the resultant behavior amounts to the equivalent of an actual intent to kill. For example, a person cannot shoot a gun into a crowd and say that he hopes he doesn't kill anyone when there is an almost certain probability that some people will be killed. Actions of this magnitude, regardless of whether they are either the result of an intent to kill or an intent to engage in outrageously reckless behavior, will have a very negative impact on the formation of a person's spiritual frequency. This is one of the greatest obstacles that a suicide bomber has to overcome and justify.

The most diabolical form of homicide is often referred to as first-degree murder; it is the ultimate betrayal to both humanity and God. In this type of homicide, not only is there an intent to kill, but the death is also the result of planning, deliberation, and *premeditation*. Obviously, ***willful evil*** guides every aspect of this deed. There can be little doubt that this type of murderer has caused irreparable damage to his or her spiritual frequency.

The problem with classifying the actions of a suicide bomber results from the fact that even though premeditation and the intent to kill are present, that person, when motivated solely by *altruistic intentions*, perceives himself as engaging in a form of self-defense that is necessary to protect and defend his convictions. He, therefore, convinces himself that it is God's will which commands the commission of his act. Regrettably, since God did not allow such misconceptions to save Eve, it is unlikely that God pardons mass murderers (of any kind) because their ***reckless abandonment*** *harms too many* ***entirely innocent*** *human beings*. Despite the fact that God has allowed countless atrocities to occur throughout history, it is doubtful that very many of those souls who have committed barbaric acts of violence have ever entered the strait gate of Heaven.

CHAPTER THREE

SCIENCE

Do you, then, because of your dream, believe, with certainty, that human souls will survive the deaths of their bodies and, subsequently, either ascend to Heaven or descend to hell?

Since I have never spoken directly with God (and I am not a prophet), there is no way that my *dream knowledge* could have provided me ***absolute assurance*** that my soul will survive the death of my body. As a result, ***I cannot be certain*** *that God exists, that there is a Heaven, or that my soul will either ascend to Heaven or descend to hell.* It is the scarcity of physical world evidence which causes me, then, to rely upon my *Christian* ***faith*** for spiritual assurance.

Despite the absence of ***worldly*** *certainty*, my ability to *believe in God, Heaven, and eternal salvation* has, nevertheless, remained strong, primarily, because of the *uncanny way* that so many aspects of my dream have, continually, influenced me and remained with me for more than six decades (since the age of seven). I am, thus, able to sustain my Christian faith because, after having spent a lifetime searching for any physical world explanation which might invalidate my dream experience, I have, as yet, been unable to uncover any evidence that another human being (or physical world phenomena) could have, in any way, been responsible for my dream.

I have, for example, thoroughly investigated the concept of subliminal hypnosis--a skill that, allegedly, enables one person to telepathically (and/or sentiently) send ideas and/or feelings to the mind, glands, and nervous system of someone else; thus, I have wondered if *another person* ***might*** *have*, somehow, *embedded* my dream memories into my mind. Despite my best efforts, I have been unsuccessful at uncovering any believable facts which could substantiate that possibility (for multiple reasons).

The first reason is that, ordinarily, end-of-the-school-day hours would have been the least likely time period for anyone to send a subliminal message to a child's mind because it is that time of day when a child would, usually, be most wide-awake and active. In addition, no one, other than my mother, knew that I had stayed home from school that day; and, even, she did not know that I was sleeping because my sister had just returned home; and the two of them were engaged in conversation during the entire time of my dream. It is highly improbable, then, that my mother (or any other *human*) would have chosen those particular moments to have, subliminally, imprinted my mind with *so much* spiritual wisdom.

The second reason results because of the remarkable way that my dream has maintained constant influence (and even control) over me, every moment, for more than six decades. My glandular connection with the Holy Spirit has been so strong that my glands have constantly served as a second source of intelligence and have, continually, communicated with me by way of a highly influential and morally consistent, non-verbal, messaging system--a system that cannot be explained as being either animalistic instinct or innate intuition. Instead, I have always believed that I have been *guided by a series of pre-planned spiritual prompts from the Holy Spirit* (which have, at appropriate times, ***attempted*** to intercede and, even, countermand *some* of my human intentions) for the purpose of reminding me to stay on the proper spiritual path; thus, I recognize that I have always been a beneficiary of the spiritual gift that Jesus revealed at John 14: 26: "the Holy Spirit, whom the Father will send in my name, will instruct you in everything and remind you of all that I told you".

Finally, it took only a few minutes during that single childhood dream to fill my mind, glands, and nervous system with all of the spiritual knowledge that I have shared in this interview (and more). It is difficult for me to believe, then, that the substance and quantity of that spiritual wisdom could have, instantaneously, been embedded in my mind and body by *any* of the humble, and modestly educated, people who surrounded me during my childhood years because, despite the fact that so many of those perceptions differ from conventional religious teachings (my description of Heaven, for example), Christians can, nevertheless, readily recognize *the correctness* of my dream insights. It is, primarily, for these reasons that I, knowingly and willingly, maintain my belief in God, Jesus, and the Holy Ghost.

Thus far, no agnostic or atheist could have, possibly, been swayed by any of your explanations because their non-religious convictions rely upon scientific evidence (something that you have, scantily, provided). How can you, in the absence of specific scientific proof, intelligently refute (1) the agnostic doubt that a spiritual creator could exist or (2) the atheist belief that God does not exist?

To begin, it is necessary to understand that agnosticism and atheism are two distinctly different *speculation* systems. Agnostics believe in a philosophy which teaches that only *perceptual phenomena can be objects of exact knowledge*; thus, while agnostics do not deny the existence of God entirely, their philosophy requires them to question and doubt

God's existence because there is no way for humans to *perceive* Him, find Him, identify Him, and know Him (*with* ***exact*** *knowledge*) *in the physical world.* On the other hand, atheists do deny the existence of God (and even the possibility of the existence of God) entirely.

Both believe that it is their higher-level, analytical skills, and their understanding of scientific principles, which require them to question and/or deny God's existence; thus, they mutually conclude that, because of the absence of exact knowledge, only the most silly and unintelligent humans would choose to believe in God.

They prefer to rely solely upon scientific explanations even though the scientific community acknowledges, for example, that it still knows nothing definitive about the composition of ninety-five percent of the universe--other than that sixty-eight percent of the universe is composed of *unknown dark energy* and twenty-seven percent of the universe is composed of *unknown dark matter.* Additionally, ***theoretical*** physicists' best *mathematical conclusion regarding the force of gravity infers* the likelihood that multiple dimensions do exist. Since (1) there are so many ***scientific*** questions that have yet to be *conclusively* answered and (2) there is just as much ***worldly*** *uncertainty* within the scientific community as there is within the religious community, most humans who do, truly, possess higher-level, analytical thinking skills realize that no scientific explanation has, as yet, succeeded in (1) definitively disproving the Christian explanation for ***consciousness*** or (2) furnishing a ***provable*** alternative explanation for ***consciousness***.

Despite the fact that my dream did not provide me with ***absolute proof*** *that God does exist*, my dream did, nevertheless, endow me with sufficient intellectual skill to readily refute most atheist and agnostic *notions*. It does seem odd that so many atheists and agnostics willingly, yet blindly, believe in *every aspect* of the Darwin's *Theory* of Evolution despite the fact that all *scientific* ***theories*** (including Darwin's) are merely assumptions and guesses based upon limited information and inexact knowledge. If agnostics and atheists were as insightful as they presume, they would recognize (after all religious beliefs are removed from consideration) that there are only two possible conclusions concerning the *non-existence of God* (neither of which is a presently accepted agnostic or atheist belief).

In all instances where agnostics have developed mental abilities which enable them to utilize higher-level thinking skills and, thus, *fully understand* the most relevant and proven scientific findings, their analytical skepticism should have caused them to, first, recognize and, then, logically conclude, by a preponderance of all presently known scientific evidence (that means: ***more likely than not***--a greater than fifty percent probability), that (1) human souls *will survive* the deaths of their bodies and that (2) (***more likely than not***) a spiritual creator, of some kind, must *truly* exist.

Should the atheist belief that random happenstance (rather than a Spiritual Creator) is the correct explanation for human existence on Earth, those atheists who have developed higher- level reasoning skills should recognize that their convictions must be similar to the belief expressed in the Thirteenth Article of the Jewish faith which states that "The dead will be resurrected" because (***beyond all reasonable doubt and with absolute scientific certainty***) the ***only*** *logical conclusion* that could possibly be extrapolated from an atheist belief system is that every human being will be reborn, repeatedly and forever (***in some form***), ***somewhere*** *in this physical universe.* Although, initially, most humans ***might***, blissfully, regard such a prospect as a blessing, ***insightful humans*** will, instead, immediately recognize that reincarnation in a ***Godless world*** would (more likely than not) amount to a form of eternal damnation. Let us pray, then, (for the sake of all humanity) that atheists are wrong and that God does exist.

***

Despite the fact that the next portion of this interview begins with a (rather complex) scientific analysis, it is, nevertheless, necessary for Christians to understand all of these following scientific explanations (as completely as possible) because they provide PROOF, by a preponderance of evidence, that Jesus' messages regarding "life after death" and "the existence of Heaven" are not fairy tales and fiction (as claimed by so many scientists, agnostics, and atheists) but, instead, are correct scientific explanations which had been revealed by Jesus more than two thousand years before modern physicists, mathematicians, and cosmologists learned enough about the workings of the universe (and the multi-verse) to, finally, verify Jesus' accounts.

This ensuing scientific explanation provides the necessary tools for Christians to intelligently and effectively refute all pseudo-scientific, anti-Christian, and non-Christian attacks against Christianity's most fundamental beliefs. It is no longer necessary for Christians to be inspired, merely, by blind religious faith because, modern-era, scientific findings corroborate Jesus' teachings; thus, Christian beliefs can, no longer, easily be "dismissed" by non-believers.

***

What scientific knowledge could you possibly rely upon to support your unique observations?

As remarkable as it may seem, some of the most recently theorized, and even proven, scientific hypotheses (the Higgs boson particle and M Theory, for example)--when ***properly*** evaluated and understood--provide *tantalizing evidence* which supports (rather than disproves) the likelihood of (1) God's and Heaven's existence and (2) the continuation of spiritual life after the death of the human body.

How could the Higgs boson particle possibly provide any form of proof that God exists?

The best way to explain how Professor Higgs' ideas (***in conjunction with several other theories***) can, *by a preponderance of* ***theoretical*** *scientific evidence*, support the belief that a spiritual creator, *most likely*, does exist is to, ***first***, present the following (challenging, yet fairly-easy-to-understand,) summary of the Higgs Boson Theory:

To begin, the Higgs boson particle is a (difficult to detect) elemental bit of matter which, until recently, had remained an **unproven** aspect of *Quantum Mechanic's* ***Standard Model of Particle Physics***, a set of equations (rules) for how the group of *seventeen (presently known)* ***elemental*** *particles* should *interact* (rules which encapsulate scientific understanding of the forces, components, and reactions of the seventeen *presently known* fundamental building blocks of the universe). One of the primary objectives for the ***Standard Model*** is to explain (1) ***matter fields***: elements which are composed, for example, of electrons, leptons, and quarks and (2) ***force fields***: elements which are composed, for example, of ***bosons***, gluons, gravitons, and photons (particles which (1) are responsible for all physical force and function and (2) are believed to be the glue that holds matter together); thus, an additional purpose for the ***Standard Model*** is to explain *three of the four basic* ***forces*** *of nature*: *(1) electromagnetism, (2) the weak force, and (3)the strong* *force.* (Regrettably, *gravity*, the elusive fourth ***force*** of nature, has remained an enigma which the ***Standard Model*** cannot, as yet, fully explain *with certainty*).

An additional important purpose of the ***Standard*** Model, then, is to classify all *fundamental* ***matter*** *particles* and identify their *building block elements*. ***Matter field*** particles include **six fermions (**which have been identified and labeled as: *up quarks*, *down quarks, strange quarks, charm quarks, top quarks* and *bottom quarks*), and **six leptons** (which have been identified and labeled as: *electrons, muons, tau, electron neutrinos, muon neutrinos*, and *tau neutrinos*). It is these twelve elements that have the capability to join together and create all of the ***matter*** that humans perceive; and it is only because **large combinations of fermions and leptons do join together** that protons and neutrons come into existence and form every aspect of what the scientific community recognizes as the ***only real world*** (because most scientists have ***concluded***, [sic])--***in the absence of any provable evidence***--that, *without mass*, this universe would have, forever, remained ***cold, dark***, and ***LIFELESS***).

Since Physics teaches that **everything** in the *physical world* is composed of **matter field elements** such as atoms, electrons, protons, and neutrons which, in turn, are made up of quarks and other subatomic particles, scientists have long been puzzled as to how these, miniscule, fundamental ***building blocks*** of the universe acquire mass (because their elemental energy particles *cannot, alone*, glue themselves together for the purpose of creating mass and matter).

The Higgs boson Theory, postulated by physicists Peter Higgs, Francois Englert, and Robert Brout in 1964 (expanding upon the ideas of Phillip Anderson), initiated the hunt for this particle by hypothesizing that an (at that time) unknown, sub-atomic, particle *or force* had to be creating a "sticky" *field* that inhibits the movement of other particles and, resultantly, causes those particles to join together as one.

Higgs (and the others) believed that particle to be a ***boson*** (one of the fundamental ***force field** elements*) and proposed that their *theorized* Higgs boson particle is that element which provides the ***force*** which has enabled ***mass*** and all other ***matter field elements*** to combine and, resultantly, create the physical world; hence, the Higgs boson particle has been nicknamed, "**The God Particle**". Christians can readily infer, then, that the Higgs boson particle is that physical world tool which God uses to create everything in ***this*** universe.

The easiest way to comprehend the concept of ***mass*** is to realize that (1) ***mass*** is another way that ***energy*** is able to exist and (2) ***mass*** is the part of matter field elements which fights against movement in any direction. With that understanding, Higgs bolstered his hypothesis by explaining that his theorized Higgs boson particle adheres to the requirements of the ***Conservation of Energy Law***, which states that energy is neither created or destroyed but, instead, is transferred. His hypothesis speculated that, initially, a gauge boson energy particle merely vibrates as a form of ***massless kinetic energy*** (which is in continuous motion) within the Higgs' *force field* (an energy field that had been theorized by physicists to exist as an energy membrane everywhere in the universe; and, within which, all particles intermingle) until such time as *that gauge boson begins* to *directly interact* with the *Higgs energy membrane* itself. By interacting with the forces within the *Higgs energy membrane*, the movement of the gauge boson slows and becomes heavier; and the amount of ***kinetic (moving)** energy* in the gauge boson is *reduced, but not destroyed*. The ***kinetic** energy* is, instead, *converted* to ***mass** energy*; and the ***mass*** (a form of energy which fights against movement in any direction) that, resultantly, emerges is the **Higgs boson *particle***.

The **Higgs boson *mass*** that is created can be verified by Einstein's $E=mc^2$ equation (which has proven that (1) mass and (2) a large amount of energy are equivalents and that there is a symmetry between energy and matter); hence, ***energy and matter have been proven to be two aspects of the same thing***. Einstein not only understood that mass was merely an alternative form of energy that fights against movement in any direction, but Einstein was also the first person to recognize that the vast amount of energy in mass could be measured by multiplying that mass by the square of the speed of light.

Higgs, as a result, was able to conclude that the various *elemental* **matter** *field particles* (which are also moving within the *Higgs energy membrane*) attract *Higgs boson particles* (in varying degrees) and, by so doing, generate additional mass through their (glue-like) interactions with other particles; thus, the larger the number of *Higgs boson particles* that the *elemental* **matter** *field particles* attracts, the larger the resultant ***mass*** will be.

As tantalizing as Higgs' *theory* seemed, it remained an unverifiable hypothesis for, approximately, fifty years until such time as the Large Hadron Collider at CERN (European Organization for Nuclear Research), the world's most powerful particle accelerator and atom smashing machine (located 328 feet underground), was constructed, mainly, to provide massive amounts of electrical energy (in a 16.8 mile loop of super-powered electromagnets) to two sets of protons that, first, had their electrons separated from them and, then, were accelerated (at fractions of the speed of light, in opposite directions) for the purpose of setting them on a collision course with each other. The intention of the particle collisions is to allow protons to smash together at such great force that the Collider can (1) recreate conditions similar to those which occurred during the earliest moments of the universe, (2) break the particles into fundamental constituents, and (3) deform space around the impact points. Some scientists theorized (and this is a very important observation to remember) that the energy state is so super-charged that it *could*, possibly, provide a peek into an alternate dimension.

Since most attempts do **not** result in **direct** hits, they fail. Nonetheless, each collision *does* produce trillions of, even more, elemental particles which are detected by sensors that surround the point where the protons collide; and the massive amount of data which results is, then, evaluated by a super computer. It has been calculated that the odds for capturing sufficient trace evidence to prove the existence of the Higgs Boson particle are only one in ten billion because it is believed that the Higgs boson particle either immediately (1) decays into other more stable particles or (2) escapes into other dimensions).

Despite the high potentiality for failure, success was, nevertheless, finally achieved March 14, 2013, when the Large Hadron Collider at CERN was able to detect, observe, and confirm decaying remnants which provided sufficient circumstantial evidence that *seemed to, indirectly, verify* that the theorized Higgs boson particle does exist.

Once CERN was able to ***experimentally confirm*** the existence of the Higgs boson particle, that discovery should have raised more scientific questions because (since the most fundamental **discernable** *particles of matter and force* in the physical world are so elegantly complex) their behaviors suggest that they, ***more likely than not***, have to be composed of even smaller *components of energy*; thus, the most intriguing question that should have been asked (but was not--**at that time**) is: in the event that even smaller, ***meaningful*** *energy components* of the physical world's tiniest known *particles of force and matter* do exist, does that not mean that those smaller components would, most likely, be composed of non-physical-world energy? Since the most rational inference suggests, then, that *non-physical-world energy* (the type of energy which exists in Heaven) ***could*** exist, does it not seem odd that the scientific community has (*until very recently*) neglected to even consider that possibility?

The primary reason for ignoring *non-physical-world energy* is because there is no way of verifying its existence; and the scientific community believes that if a theory cannot be proven by laboratory testing, it is not science--it, instead, is philosophy. Accordingly, too many scientists elect to embrace the agnostic belief which teaches that only *perceptual phenomena* can be objects of *exact knowledge; and the* ***persuasive soundness*** *of that scientific explanation* is the, regrettable, reason that so many people no longer choose to believe in God.

Strangely, many of those same scientists are, nevertheless, willing to ***blindly believe*** that, if the Higgs boson particle did not exist, the physical world would have remained ***cold, dark***, and ***LIFELESS*** (even though that is a conclusion (1) which, also, can never be factually proven in a laboratory and (2) which ignores the ***proven fact*** that energy and mass are merely two aspects of the same thing. That conclusion is nothing other than a modern-era example of the type of narrow-minded, empty-headed, and prideful assumptions which, centuries ago, insisted that (1) the world was flat and (2) the Earth was the center of the universe. Nevertheless, it should be noted that when scientists (pick and choose and) *foolishly misrepresent* ***unprovable silliness*** *as being sound scientific reasoning*, they, too often, succeed in persuading (and, sometimes, forcing) others to repudiate and abandon religious beliefs. That type of irresponsible scientific foolishness needs to stop.

You just (1) stated that one of the reasons the Higgs boson particle is so difficult to identify is because it may "escape into other dimensions", and you (2) implied that

life can exist even in the absence of mass and matter. Those science fiction-like claims seem, also, to be "unprovable silliness". What is the scientific basis for YOUR "silly" observations?

Initially, I explained that the answer to this question would seem clear after the Higgs boson Particle Theory was analyzed ***in conjunction with*** *several other physical, mathematical, and cosmological* **theories** because the most *advanced mathematical theoretical conclusions* do more to support (rather than disprove) the likelihood that (1) parallel universes do exist and that (2) other parallel universes could, conceivably, contain intelligent life and civilizations whose existences emerged from entirely different laws of nature and physics. Understanding those complex physical, mathematical, and cosmological theories is, nevertheless, quite difficult because physics has depended upon two, totally different, sets of rules to explain most aspects of the physical universe (*even though* ***neither*** *set of rules fully explains* ***all*** *aspects of the physical universe*).

The first set of rules results from the study of gravity. In 1665, Isaac Newton theorized that the force that pulled an apple from a tree to the Earth is the same force which holds the moon in orbit and controls tides. He called that force "gravity" and created a mathematical formula which *correctly predicts* physical world phenomena. His formula is able to identify the strength of gravity with great accuracy; however, he was not able to determine how gravity works or what causes gravity. That answer was provided several hundred years later by Albert Einstein in the early Twentieth Century.

Einstein's picture of gravity, which he named *The Theory of* ***General*** *Relativity*, both defines gravity and determines how fast gravity travels. Einstein correctly theorized that space is, essentially, a fabric or an ***energy*** *membrane* composed of four dimensions which he called space-time (the three spatial dimensions—left/right (width), back/forth (depth), and up/down (height)--***and*** time). Einstein believed that (1) the space-time membrane can be warped (or curved) by heavy objects such as planets and stars in the same way that the fabric of a trampoline yields to the weight of a jumping person and that (2) smaller objects travelling in that space-time membrane feel the pull of the resultant gravitational force that is created; thus, Einstein, correctly, concluded that gravity is the curvature of the energy membrane of space-time.

Einstein's theory explains that the reason Earth stays in the same orbit as it revolves around the sun is because Earth continues to follow the channel that its size and weight had created within the sun's-influenced, space-time membrane. Since Einstein's theory has since been independently verified, his *accurate calculations* have, subsequently, been used to *reliably predict and track* the movements and behaviors of all large objects in the universe because, when scientists include the effect of gravitational forces upon the movements of large objects, Einstein's Theory of General Relativity provides the most accurate means of predicting the behavior of planets, moons, solar systems, and galaxies.

The second set of rules, Quantum Mechanics, was first postulated as the "*Heisenberg Uncertainty Principle*" in the 1920's by German theoretical physicist Karl Heisenberg (with the assistance of Max Born and Pascual Jordan). Heisenberg reported that the uncertain behavior of particles on the sub-atomic (quantum) level is entirely different from the predictable behavior of large objects. Heisenberg revealed that it is almost impossible to measure the speed and position of sub-atomic particles because the act of merely observing sub-atomic particles dramatically affects their behaviors. (The Quantum Mechanics Theory explains that empty space is not really empty because it is filled with "virtual" particles which constantly flash in and out of existence). As a result, Heisenberg concluded that sub-atomic calculations can, at best, only be based upon probabilities (not certainties) because it is impossible to make precise predictions about the movements of sub-atomic particles which (1) have no single location and (2) can be in more than one place at the same time (including alternate dimensions)--thus, uncertainty rules. Since Heisenberg's observations dramatically conflict with Einstein's *Theory of General Relativity,* which concludes that *the behavior of all natural phenomena* ***can be*** *accurately predicted*, an enormous schism developed in the field of *theoretical* physics.

It is remarkable, then, that despite the fact that Einstein's "General Relativity" and Heisenberg's "Quantum (Sub-atomic) Mechanics" are two entirely different sets of rules which explain how the universe operates, both are, nevertheless, correct. They, thus, remain the *two pillars* of Modern Physics. Einstein's mathematical formulas continue to, accurately, predict and explain the laws which govern the behaviors of planets, galaxies, and solar systems; and Quantum Mechanics correctly describe the behaviors of the fundamental building blocks of the physical world (even though those behaviors can only be described in terms of probabilities).

Like most other agnostics and atheists, Einstein's good friend, Danish quantum physicist, Niels Bohr, concluded, then, that the world could be no more predictable than the toss of dice. In response, Einstein (a man who maintained an *unconventional* faith in the existence of God) explained his religious belief as being an "unbounded admiration for the structure of the world" which caused him to recognize that "God's presence was evident in the order and rationality of nature and the universe in all of its aspects and expressions". Since Einstein never abandoned his belief that the world behaves in ***certain*** ways, he refuted Bohr's observation by stating that "God does not play with dice"; and, in an effort to prove his ***religious*** *belief*, Einstein devoted the last two decades of his life attempting to verify that *all natural phenomena* (*as well as all other aspects of the universe*) were, indeed, predictable.

Einstein believed that he would be able to formulate a grand unification theory that combines the principles of (1) gravity and (2) Quantum Mechanic's electro-magnetism into *The Theory that Explains Everything*, one master mathematical equation which would correctly (1) explain away the improbability of Quantum Mechanics, (2) describe all of the workings of the universe, and, thus, (3) become the Holy Grail of Modern Mathematical Physics in the same way that James Maxwell, in 1873, formulated the "Second Great Unification of Physics" when (with only four easy-to-understand equations) Maxwell correctly theorized that electricity, magnetism, and light are all manifestations of the same phenomenon. Einstein was certain that ***mathematics*** would provide an understanding of God's design for the universe.

Despite the fact that both forces travel at the speed of light, Einstein was never able to account for the dramatic differences between the strength of electro-magnetism's force and the strength of gravity's force because (*on the sub-atomic level*) electro-magnetism is one thousand, billion, billion, billion times more powerful than gravity. The differences in the strength of the two forces far outweigh their similarities. It does seem odd (since Earth's gravity holds the moon in orbit and controls the movement of waves) that gravity is so much weaker than electro-magnetism; yet, the act of picking up a metal coin from a floor with a small magnet demonstrates how easy it is for even a *weak* magnet to overcome the gravitational force that holds a coin to a floor.

Einstein's two decades attempt to formulate *The Theory That Explains Everything* proved fruitless because the only way Einstein could have possibly unified electro-magnetism and gravity into one theory was by verifying that the strengths of both forces were equivalent (and that was one obstacle--among several others--that Einstein was never able to overcome); however, his pursuit was not a complete failure because it was the genius of Einstein's unsuccessful effort which motivated, and mobilized, the next two generations of theoretical mathematicians and physicists to, finally, succeed in formulating what, *most likely*, is *The Theory That Explains Everything*.

Inspired by Einstein's failure, thousands of theoretical physicists, cosmologists, and mathematicians (with the intention of formulating a *quantum theory of gravity*--a theory that could correctly describe the Quantum Mechanics of space-time) subjected mathematical formulas to more and more extreme situations by extrapolating experimental data in every imaginable way. By the nineteen-eighties, *theoretical physicists* John Schwartz and Michael Green (along with Juan Maldacena) introduced a ***radically different concept*** (***based entirely upon mathematical computations rather than scientific experimentation***) named ***String Theory*** (an encapsulation of what Schwartz's, Green's, Maldacena's--and other physicists'--mathematical equations revealed); thus, a unified, *yet still theoretical*, description and explanation of the interaction of ***gravity*** *and all* ***elemental*** *particles* was on the verge of being realized.

Until the 1980's, physicists had believed that matter was composed of particles. String Theory (an alternative unifying principle of nature), instead, postulates that (1) everything is composed of ***infinitesimally small***, one dimensional, *vibrating* ***strings*** *of energy* which twist and turn in complicated ways and that (2) the ***unique*** *shape and* ***vibration*** of each string explains the reason why so many different particles exist in the universe: each string generates its own ***distinct*** *energy frequency* (or music-like note) which, in turn, causes its own particular form of matter to emanate into existence (the **distinctive** vibrating string pattern which results, thus, determines the mass and electrical charge of every individual particle that emerges into the physical world).

Initially, string theorists, incorrectly, concluded that *ten* dimensions exist in this universe (nine spatial dimensions plus time) instead of the four space-time dimensions theorized by Einstein--left/right (width), back/forth (depth), up/down (height), and time. The additional spatial dimensions, *although infinitesimally small*, accounted for all of the possible vibrating movements of each individual string (within a field of strings). The problem that immediately arose from the acceptance of a ten dimensional universe solution is that the resultant mathematical data, *mistakenly*, led to the conclusion that ***five*** (***not just one***) *distinctly different string theory explanations* could be equally correct.

At the same time, Michael Duff of the University of Michigan (as well as Ashoke Sen, Chris Hull, and Paul Townsend) was championing a concept similar to String Theory known as Eleven-Dimensional Super Gravity Theory which postulates that the universe is composed of *eleven* dimensions (ten spatial dimensions and time). The addition of an eleventh dimension enabled theoretical physicists to, finally, recognize that the five "string theories" are, merely, five different manifestations of a single, more fundamental, theory. This new mathematical concept (first conjectured by Edward Witten in 1995) named M Theory--or (perhaps) Membrane Theory--has determined that the massive amount of energy which was generated by the original Big Bang of the universe stretched the fabric of space-time and caused all of the strings in the universe to interact and create a three dimensional *energy membrane or surface* (the eleventh dimension) which, although microscopically thin (less than one trillionth of a millimeter wide), extends for the entire length of the universe.

What is most remarkable is that Membrane Theory ***also postulates*** that this universe is only one membrane among (anywhere between ***eleven*** and an *infinite number* of) parallel membranes (or universes)--all existing, side-by-side (less than a trillionth of a millimeter apart), within one, much larger, unified multi-verse. The easiest way to comprehend this *extreme* ***theoretical*** *concept* (of the existence of additional hidden worlds just beyond human senses) is to compare the multi-verse with a very large loaf of bread. This universe is only one slice among a (possible) infinite number of additional slices (parallel universes or dimensions) that have also been cut from the multi-verse's loaf. M Theory's calculations recognize, also, that (1) the shape and size of each parallel universe's membrane could be dramatically different, that (2) many membranes could have no stable mass or matter, and that (3) other membranes could, conceivably, contain intelligent life and civilizations whose existences emerged from entirely different laws of nature and physics.

You explained that one reason Einstein was unable to successfully theorize a unification theory was because he could not account for the dramatic disparity in the strength of gravity's and electro-magnetism's forces. How does M Theory account for that difference?

The work of Harvard University's Lisa Randall (among others) focused on the weakness of gravity; and the data that results from M-Theory calculations *suggests* that the force of gravity is, in fact, equal to the force of electro-magnetism; however, the reason why the force of gravity ***seems*** *to be so much weaker in this universe* is because (1) gravity is the glue-like energy force which links all parallel universes together, (2) most of gravity's force is, therefore, spread-out among an infinite number of parallel universes, (3) gravity is not leaking away from this universe but, instead, is leaking into this universe from all of the other universes, and (4) gravity's force is so diluted by the time it reaches this universe that gravity ***only appears*** *to be weaker* than electromagnetism. Once the multi-verse concept was recognized (and included) as an essential element of M Theory, the resultant *mathematical computations* finally (1) fitted exactly and (2) explained the reason for gravity's weakness in this universe. As a result, many *theoretical mathematicians and physicists* have, confidently, concluded that M Theory is, ***more likely than not***, "*The* ***Theory*** *That* ***(really does)*** *Explain Everything*".

Even if that explanation were true, how is it be possible that gravity can enter and escape this dimension when other forms of energy cannot enter and escape?

M Theory postulates that (1) most strings (such as the strings of matter and light) are shaped like open-ended hooks and (2) those hooked shapes cause *most strings* to remain tied down, confined, and attached to this universe's three-dimensional membrane (in a manner that is similar to the way the Higgs boson particle interacts and remains attached to--what was, then, called--the Higgs force field *membrane*). Other strings such as *Gravitons* (gravity's most fundamental sub-atomic strings), however, are believed to be closed-looped strings whose movements (because of their shapes) are not confined by, or restricted to, the membrane of a single universe but, instead, are free to travel to and from other universes.

How does the shape of a string explain why gravity can exist in all of the parallel universes, yet virtually all other mass and matter remains confined only to this universe?

Two very easy to understand illustrations explain how gravitons (and, possibly, other similarly shaped strings--***including the strings that compose human souls***) are able to escape this universe's membrane and travel freely between universes. First, imagine this universe as being one gigantic pool table and all of the strings of this universe as being pool balls. Observe how the balls are confined to the surface of the table. None drop through the table surface to the floor or fly into the air. Notice, too, that when the balls collide with one another, they create sound vibrations that do leave the table and reach our ears. Humans are able to hear the *sound* of the colliding balls because the movement of the sound waves is not restricted by the table surface in the same way that the surface restricts the movement of the balls. Similarly, gravity and, perhaps, *the human soul* are not confined to, or restricted by, this universe's membrane in the same way that most other physical matter is confined and restricted.

For a second illustration, envision this universe as a slice of bread lying flat on a surface. Next, imagine that slice being thickly covered with peanut butter. Notice that when the slice is turned upright, all of the peanut butter remains stuck to the bread; and none of the peanut butter is free to leave the surface of the bread. If, however, that slice of bread is, instead, covered with celery seeds while lying flat on a surface and, then, turned upright, ***virtually all*** of the celery seeds do slide off of the surface of the slice (and only a very small number of irregularly shaped seeds remain). These two visual illustrations, thus, explain the new reality that M Theory's ***mathematical*** *computations* have revealed.

M (Membrane) Theory is a mathematical theory which includes multiple aspects (particularly parallel universes) that could never be proven by scientific research; thus, most experimental scientists must regard M Theory as merely being a philosophy (and not real science). How could you refute the scientific community's justification for being unwilling to recognize the validity of M Theory?

Even though Einstein died in 1955, four decades had passed before Edward Witten, in 1995, conjectured the underlying principles of M Theory; thus, after forty years of non-stop failure, theoretical physicists and mathematicians, finally, believed that (by using the same mathematical approaches that enabled Newton to identify the strength of gravity and Maxwell to recognize that electricity, magnetism, and light were the same) they had, correctly, conceptualized *The Theory That Explains Everything*. Thereafter, the major distinction was that Newton's and Maxwell's theories were able to be confirmed by independent experimentation; but M Theory was not--that is, until March 14, 2013 when the Large Hadron Collider at CERN finally (1) detected, observed, and verified the existence of Higgs boson particle remnants and, resultantly, (2) indirectly ***confirmed*** Higgs' explanation of how the Higgs boson particle came into existence. Higgs had theorized that the massless *kinetic energy* of the gauge boson energy particle was slowed and converted into a *mass* particle because of its interaction with, what was then called, the Higgs' force field membrane (but is now acknowledged by M Theory as being this universe's membrane); thus, proof of the existence of the Higgs boson particle also, more likely than not, *proves the existence of this universe's membrane*; and although it is unlikely that humans will ever be able to confirm, *with certainty* (by way of scientific experimentation), that additional parallel membranes do exist, *the most rational* ***scientific inference*** that can be extrapolated from those portions of the M Theory mathematical computations that have been verified is that, ***more likely than not***, parallel universes, indeed, exist.

You do understand how most scientists will, nevertheless, justifiably continue (1) to refuse to accept all of M Theory's, unprovable, mathematical conclusions and (2) to doubt and/or deny the existence of God. What is your response to such continued skepticism?

What is most disheartening for Christians is the harm which results from the continuous attacks directed against Christian beliefs by the scientific community (even though most scientists acknowledge that, despite their higher-level scientific understandings, few have developed ***all** of the required intellectual abilities* which would, sufficiently, prepare them to be the ultimate determiners of God's existence). Most scientists readily concede that their scientific studies are so, narrowly, subject-specific that few of them have acquired sufficient skills, knowledge, and wisdom to qualify them to know any more about God's existence--or non-existence--than anyone else. It is regrettable, then, that far too many scientists choose to ***misrepresent*** their limited (subject specific) scientific understandings for no other purpose than to promote their, already preexisting, agnostic and/or atheist beliefs.

Some people might interpret this statement as being an insult to the entire scientific community. Can you clarify what you mean?

My intention is not to insult the scientific community but, instead, to challenge its long-standing, unwarranted, attack on Christian beliefs (which has succeeded in convincing millions of humans to abandon their faith) because much of the scientific community's prejudice against Christianity is based upon incomplete and/or mistaken, yet unchallenged, *assumptions*.

Are you suggesting that scientists apply one criterion when evaluating theories which support the possible existence of God and Heaven, yet apply a different standard when evaluating other scientific theories?

That does seem to be the case. For example, most scientists --*in the absence of any provable evidence*--have, successfully, convinced most educated humans to believe that the ***only real world*** is the ***physical*** *world* because, *without mass*, the universe would have, forever, remained ***cold, dark***, and ***LIFELESS*** (while, conveniently, ignoring the proven fact that energy and mass are merely two aspects of the same thing). The scientific community has, irrationally, concluded, then, that when the human body dies, the spirit, soul, and human consciousness ***must*** *also die* (since human consciousness and spiritual uniqueness can ***only*** *exist* within the confines of a living human body which is composed of mass).

From the scientific community's perspective, that does seem to be the only rational conclusion. How else can human consciousness be explained?

The explanation for human consciousness provided by Jesus in conjunction with (1) M Theory, (2) String Theory, (3) the discovery of the Higgs boson particle and, even, (4) *my dream* provides a far more believable explanation than any other, presently accepted, neuro-scientific theory. For example, one of the most respected (and widely recognized--**yet unproven**) *human consciousness* ***hypotheses*** was ***postulated*** in 1990 by Francis Crick, the brilliant molecular biologist, biophysicist, and neuroscientist who was the co-discoverer of the structure of DNA. Crick ***theorized*** that when electrical signals in the brain oscillate, they cause a ***sense*** *of self-awareness*. He ***suggested*** that consciousness ***might***, therefore, result from the electrical activity of many neurons oscillating together as they share and integrate *all incoming sensory* information *throughout the entire brain network*; thus, by acquiescing to *Crick's neural-process* ***theory***, a large percentage of the neuro-scientific community has *willingly* ***inferred*** *that consciousness is* ***merely*** *an incidental by-product* which results because of the arrangement, oscillation, and interaction of *all* of the atoms that compose the cells, synapses, and neural networks within the brain.

Far too many neuro-scientists have, since, accepted this ***unfounded (and unprovable) philosophy*** even as they continue to acknowledge that no one understands, or can even explain, ***the reasons why humans are self-aware beings***. Crick's theory ***conjectures*** that consciousness and self-awareness require mass in order to exist and, thus ***infers***, that when the electrical activity of those many neurons and synapses ends, human consciousness ceases to exist as well.

The neuro-scientific community has chosen, then, to discount and/or ignore (*what is,* ***most likely,***) ***the best explanation*** as to why humans are self-aware (for no other reason than that explanation has been formulated from the conclusions of (1) M Theory, (2) String Theory, (3) Higgs Boson Theory, and (4) Jesus Christ). Those scientists have chosen, particularly, to ignore the fact that the Higgs boson particle is the glue-like particle which enables ***vibrating forms of energy to, TEMPORARILY, resist movement*** (1) by, ***briefly***, converting energy into mass and (2) by creating unique aspects of the physical world--such as bodies and brains--***for short periods of time***. Neuro-scientists should, instead, recognize that ***mass*** (1) is nothing other than an alternative way that vibrating electromagnetic energy is, ***briefly***, *able to exist* and (2) is that part of matter field elements which, ***temporarily (not permanently)***, fights against movement in any direction; thus, neuro-scientists should realize that the mere presence (or absence) of physical world mass (neural networks and electrical currents, for example,) ***could not possibly be the complete explanation*** as to why life, human consciousness, spiritual uniqueness, and self-awareness exist.

M Theory postulates, and Jesus Christ taught, that the ***true*** *source of consciousness, spiritual uniqueness, and self-awareness* is not dependent upon the presence of mass at all. Instead, human life (and *spiritual* awareness) actually derives from ***infinitesimally small, vibrating, STRINGS of SPIRITUAL energy***. It is worth repeating, then, that the ***unique*** *shape and* ***vibration*** of each string explains the reason so many different particles exist in the universe. Each string generates its ***distinct energy frequency*** (or music-like note) which, in turn, causes its own particular form of matter (and *consciousness*) to emanate into existence. The distinctive vibrating string energy pattern that results, thus, determines the mass and electrical charge of every individual particle which emerges (*for brief periods of time*) into the physical world.

While it is **true** that strings *do* create neural networks (and *do* cause electrical oscillations), ***consciousness*** is *not likely* to be, entirely, dependent upon those neural networks and electromagnetic oscillations in order to exist. Human consciousness and spiritual uniqueness must, primarily, be the product of ***infinitesimally small, vibrating, STRINGS of SPIRITUAL ENERGY*** (which according to Biblical teachings) is a form of energy that is *not confined only to this universe* but (like gravitons) can free themselves from the physical body (and the physical world) in order to rise to Heaven or descend to hell. M Theory supports Christ's two thousand year old explanation that human souls do survive the deaths of their bodies by concurring that (1) alternative spiritual universes (which Jesus called Heaven and hell) do exist and that (2) because of the closed-looped shapes of the strings (***which--based upon Jesus' teachings--are the types of strings that, most likely, are responsible for the creation of human souls***), there is a way (that can be scientifically explained) for *consciousness* to escape the confines of the physical world and travel to alternate dimensions (Heaven and hell) when the human body dies.

Since Jesus had revealed ***HIS SCIENTIFIC* insights** more than two thousand years before (1) M Theory was conceived and (2) the existence of the Higgs boson particle and this universe's membrane were confirmed, the scientific community's steadfast refusal to even consider ***JESUS' SCIENTIFIC* teachings** does seem to be based upon an arbitrary, disingenuous, and atypical criterion. Why would any sufficiently educated scientist conclude that the only real world is the physical world when this *impermanent world* is composed of mass (a form of matter which can only resist movement for brief periods of time before that mass disintegrates and returns, once again, to *vibrating forms of energy*) rather than recognize that ***infinitesimally small, vibrating, STRINGS of SPIRITUAL energy*** are the ***true reasons*** that self-awareness and human consciousness exist?

*****

PLEASE NOTE: In late 2020 (two years after the 2018 copyright of *The Boy's Dream* (*and all of these scientific explanations*), Professor Johnjoe McFadden, a Professor of Molecular Genetics from the University of Surrey, United Kingdom, published his (*unproven*) ***theory*** in the Oxford University Press Journal's *Neuroscience of Consciousness* that ***electromagnetic*** energy in the brain enables brain matter to create our consciousness--that consciousness is the brain's energy field. He wrote that he believes there is a distinction between matter and energy (*rather than matter and the soul*); thus, he has concluded (with far less evidence than was provided by Jesus two thousand years ago) that when neurons fire, they not only send signals throughout the wires of the nervous system, they also send electromagnetic energy into surrounding tissue as a *wave of energy* rather than a flow of atoms. He has concluded that the mystery of consciousness (how brain matter becomes aware and manages to think) is, *thanks to him*, no longer a mystery; it is the experience of nerves plugging into the brain's self-generated electromagnetic field to drive what we call "free will" and our voluntary actions.

*****

In response, it is worth repeating for a third time, then, that the ***unique*** *shape and* ***vibration*** of each energy string explains the reason so many different particles exist in the universe; thus, human life actually derives from ***infinitesimally small, vibrating, strings of SPIRITUAL energy***. Each string generates its ***distinct energy frequency*** (or music-like note) which, in turn, causes its own particular form of matter (and *consciousness*) to emanate into existence. The distinctive vibrating string (energy pattern) which results determines the mass and electrical charge of every individual particle that emerges (*for brief periods of time*) into the physical world and, thus, is *the* ***only, conceivable, explanation for the existence of human consciousness and self-awareness*** that makes sense. M Theory's *mathematical* conclusions, by providing a complete understanding of God's design for the universe, has, thus, succeeded in strongly supporting Einstein's belief that "God", indeed, "does not play dice with the universe".

What is the scientific basis for your claim that Crick's theory is an incomplete explanation for human consciousness?

Consciousness could not possibly exist, *solely*, because of the electrical and/or electromagnetic activity of many neurons oscillating together as they share and integrate ***all*** incoming sensory information throughout the ***entire brain network*** because consciousness and self-awareness are not, in any way, diminished (even in instances when virtually all neural networks have been damaged and/or have stopped functioning). While it is clear that *consciousness* does interact with, and does exercise control over, all neural functions, there is scant evidence that consciousness (1) resides within *any,* ***particular,*** *neural spaces* or (2) is dependent upon the continued existence of ***any*** *neural activity* in order to survive the death of (any or all) neural networks. Human bodies do die, but consciousness and self-awareness can survive (in the manner taught by Jesus) as long as consciousness is composed of ***closed-looped strings***.

For example, when humans lose the ability to see and hear (and all associated neural networks shut down), the loss of sight and hearing has no effect upon the self-awareness and consciousness of those persons. That is also **true** for people who lose both arms and legs and for individuals who receive any one of many different organ transplants. Years ago, Polio caused some victims to lose the ability to breathe on their own. In order to remain alive, they were confined to breathing machines called Iron Lungs; nevertheless, even when the neural networks that facilitated breathing failed, the consciousness and self-awareness of those victims did not diminish in any way.

Since it is clear that the death of so many different neural networks has little or no effect upon the continued existence of self-awareness and consciousness, Crick's postulation (that consciousness ***might****, merely,* be the product of oscillating electrical signals throughout the ***entire*** *brain network*) ***cannot*** *possibly be*, ***totally****, correct.* If consciousness were, indeed, fully integrated with all of the brain's various neural networks, (1) consciousness should either be diminished or cease to exist whenever ***any*** of those neural networks stops functioning (but is not diminished and does not cease to exist in any way) and (2) the location of consciousness should be easy to isolate and identify (but is not); thus, in the event that any brain mass might, even partially, contribute to the existence of consciousness and self-awareness, that mass would have to occupy a much smaller (and/or more elusive) area of the brain than Crick had, originally, theorized.

The neuro-scientific community should have, by now, recognized that (1) brain cells and (2) the oval-shaped strings that are responsible for consciousness are composed of two, distinctly different, forms of *energy.* M Theory (and Quantum Mechanics) *suggest* that (1) consciousness exists, primarily, on the sub-atomic level, (2) consciousness occupies the same, infinitesimally, small space as all other strings, and (3) consciousness's behavior is similar to all quantum forces (by being able to occur in more than one place at the same time and by being able to freely slip in and out of this universe). Calculations regarding human consciousness must, then, (at best) only be based upon probability (not certainty) because, according to Heisenberg, it is impossible to make precise predictions about the movements of sub-atomic particles which have no single location (and can be in more than one place at the same time--including alternative dimensions). Since Heisenberg's Uncertainty Principle has proven that the mere act of observing sub-atomic particles, dramatically, affects their behaviors, neuro-scientists should recognize that, more likely than not, it would be nearly impossible to, *concurrently*, measure both (1) the speed and (2) the position of those sub-atomic forces which are responsible for human consciousness and self-awareness.

During the late Medieval Era, Christian philosophers were perceived as being silly for questioning, debating, and speculating upon the number of angels that could dance on the head of a pin. Thomas Aquinas, in 1270, asked, philosophically, if several angels could be in the same place at the same time. As ridiculous as those metaphysical questions may have once seemed, they, nevertheless, do demonstrate that, even then, *inspired Christians* possessed profound understandings of the **true** nature of human consciousness; thus, two provocative, yet equivalent, Modern-Era, M Theory-based questions are: (1) "How many closed-looped strings are required to cause a human soul to come into existence?" and (2) "Might the total number of those closed-looped strings be so, *infinitesimally*, small that they, also, are able to fit upon the head of a pin?"

While, initially, your explanation seems insightful, most neuro-scientists would, immediately, point out that the symptoms of Alzheimer's disease disprove your theoretical conclusions. How could you possibly disregard the fact that (because of brain damage) Alzheimer patients lose both mental function AND consciousness?

My conclusion is that (1) mental function and consciousness are entirely different and that (2) consciousness in not dependent upon a properly functioning brain in order to exist ***somewhere***. I learned this **truth,** at the age of four, as a result of having no memory of any events that occurred throughout the first ***four*** years of my life. I, nevertheless, do recall my first living memories as vividly as if they occurred yesterday.

I awakened from a nap on my family's dining room couch, crying, because I had no idea where I was. A strange woman (my mother), instantly, came to me and, lovingly and attentively, embraced me and reassured me. Almost immediately, I began holding my crotch (although I did not understand why). My mother, however, did and, kindly, showed me how to urinate (as if she were teaching me for the first time). Once she fully calmed me, she took me to one of the Colonial-style living room windows (which were less than two feet from the floor) and encouraged me to wait for my father who, she explained, would be arriving home from work, shortly.

As I knelt there, I wondered what a father was and who it was that I was waiting for. What is most remarkable about those first memories is that my mind was able to reason in the same manner that my mind reasons today; thus, I was able to fully analyze that situation with the identical, unwavering, spark of consciousness which defines me at this moment. What, also, is extraordinary was the fact that, despite my limited vocabulary, I, from that very first moment of my *conscious* existence, nevertheless, had a full understanding of the English language and the organizational structure of the language.

So many people passed by that window (because, in1950, most neighbors either walked or rode public transportation home from work). I remember, repeatedly, asking myself, "Is that the person I'm supposed to be waiting for?" I had no idea. I, also, remember pondering what existed just beyond my sight (at the end of that street) as I wondered where those people were coming from. I was fascinated. Needless to say, my father passed the window and entered the house without me recognizing him. My mother greeted him at the door and informed him that I had been waiting for him (but must not have seen him). At that moment, she made me aware that he was, also, someone whom I should value and love; and I believed and trusted that very nice woman's words.

Shortly after, I was sitting in an elevated chair and eating with my entire family (even though I had no idea how to eat or why we were eating). Again, my mother (patiently and kindly) partially fed me, taught me to eat independently, and explained why humans eat and drink (as if she were helping me for the very first time). I learned that my brother and sisters attended school, and my father went to work (although I had no idea what any of that meant). Thereafter, I, repeatedly, asked my father, "Daddy, do you go to work tomorrow, and the next day, and the next day, and the next day?" The following weeks, months, and years of my life were consumed with my non-stop quest to acquire the answers to all of my curiosities. I possessed an insatiable inquisitiveness to learn about everything and everyone.

What is most puzzling about experiencing my first moments of human consciousness at the age of four is the reason for my total inability to ***ever*** recall, even, a single memory from the first four years of my life. I had, obviously, known my mother on the previous day; so (1) why was I unable to recognize her (or anything and anyone else) and (2) why was I, nevertheless, able to fully understand and speak the English language? It is conceivable that I had sustained a concussion, experienced another form of permanent memory loss, or, possibly, suffered from a congenital birth defect or a developmental brain disorder. It is even feasible (1) that I *might* have spent most of the first four years of my life traveling back and forth between my spiritual and earthly existences and (2) that the time had finally arrived for me to, prudently, extinguish all *spiritual* memories (for the duration of the time that I chose to continue existing within a human body). The four questions that have remained unanswered for my entire life are: (1) "How could my consciousness have emerged, *instantaneously*, ***so totally intact***?" (2) "If portions of my brain had been damaged, why hadn't ***any portion*** *of my consciousness* been damaged as well?" (3) "Is it possible that my consciousness had been dead for the first four years of my life?" *and* (4) "If not, where had my consciousness been residing during the entire time?" Because of that childhood experience, I realize that spiritual consciousness and the human mind *must be* entirely different entities and that, even when damage occurs to the brain, self-awareness, nevertheless, remains intact ***somewhere*** (even in those instances when consciousness--either temporarily or permanently--fully disconnects from all brain functions).

Since Alzheimer's symptoms are remarkably similar to those which I experienced during my early childhood, I am confident that even though the disease causes consciousness to disconnect from an Alzheimer sufferer's brain and body, it is unlikely that the sufferer's spiritual uniqueness is damaged and ceases to exist (any more than my early childhood spiritual uniqueness had been damaged or had *permanently* ceased to exist *before* I reached the age of four).

Agnostics, atheists, and the scientific community conclude that Alzheimer's disease causes consciousness to die forever. In contrast, *Christians* (who fully understand M Theory's theoretical conclusions) *prefer to believe Jesus' explanation* (that souls do survive the deaths of bodies) is, ***more likely than not***, the correct explanation.

Francis Crick (in an effort to explain (1) how molecules transition from the non-living to the living, (2) how genetic information might be stored in molecular form, and (3) how brains create conscious minds) was responsible for one of the most significant scientific breakthroughs in history when, in 1953 (with James Watson), he identified (1) the double helix structure of the DNA molecule and (2) the manner by which that molecule is able to hold genetic

information in cells. Because of his discovery, and his genius-level insight, Crick (along with seventy-two other Nobel laureates and seventeen states' academies of science) chose to publicly oppose the theory of Creationism when they advised, in the Supreme Court case, Edwards v. Aguillard, 482 U.S. 578 (1987), that "Creation-science simply has no place in the public-school classroom" (at a time when the existence of the Higgs Boson Theory--and this universe's membrane--had not, as yet, been confirmed). Are you suggesting that your level of genius exceeds Crick's and the other seventy-two Nobel laureates?

Although I believe that (after having lived more than six decades) I have developed ***some*** higher-level, analytical thinking skills, I recognize that I am, nevertheless, an ordinary man with *limited* scientific training; thus, I acknowledge that I do not possess Crick's scientific background or *proven* genius. There is the possibility, then, that the scientific community will contest at least some aspects of my, ***Jesus-inspired,*** scientific analyses.

In the event that the scientific community ***might,*** *effectively, refute and/or discredit any of my observations* (which, to some extent, (1) cannot be verified by scientific experimentation and (2) *originated in the dream memories of a seven year old child*), I am certain that, soon thereafter, God will inspire and motivate other, more talented and insightful, Christians to unearth the necessary scientific evidence which bolsters my dream observations in the same way that Einstein's brilliant and *inspired* (yet unrealized) *visions* motivated his successors to search, non-stop, until, finally, they succeeded in formulating (and partially verifying) a *credible* Theory That Explains Everything.

It is because of their genius-level scientific insights that Crick and seventy-two other Nobel laureates claim that

"Creation-science simply has no place in the public-school classroom". How could you possibly refute such an intelligent conclusion?

Their successful effort to convince the United States' Supreme Court to ***outlaw*** Christian beliefs in public-school classrooms was not a demonstration of the Nobel laureates' genius but, instead, was, merely, an example of the narrow-minded bigotry of a small group of *non-Christian* and/or *anti-Christian* dogmatists who chose to *misuse* their Nobel-award status for the purpose of forwarding their, pre-existing, *anti-Christian prejudices*. While Louisiana included the teaching of Evolution Science in its law for the purpose of providing a ***well-rounded understanding*** of the *various* (*origins of human existence*) *theories*, it was the Nobel laureates who insisted upon the exclusion of all but one, *propagandized*, explanation. *Edwards v. Aguillard* did strike down the Louisiana law (which, according to the Supreme Court, violated the Establishment Clause of the First Amendment (1) for advancing a particular religion (2) by requiring that Creation Science be taught whenever Evolutionary Science is taught); nevertheless, that Court's decision correctly (and quite obviously) concluded that, **"*teaching a VARIETY of scientific theories about the origins of humankind* to school children *might* be validly done with the clear secular intent of *enhancing the effectiveness of science instruction*"**. The Court, thus, determined that *the complete exclusion of Creationist-**scientific*** concepts from the science classroom was, **also**, an unconstitutional action.

Because the explanation for ***human consciousness*** provided by Jesus in conjunction with (1) M Theory, (2) String Theory, and (3) the discovery of the Higgs boson "God Particle" provides a far more complete, ***and believable***, explanation than Darwin's ***theory*** for *both* (1) the origin of the species and (2) (more importantly) the *emergence of human self-awareness*, there should, no longer, be any justifiable, court-mandated, reason for not teaching "*a* ***VARIETY*** *of scientific theories about the origins of humankind* to school children" (if the legitimate purpose of the "origin of the species science program" is, ***truly***, *to* ***properly educate*** *and develop young minds*).

Public education's core objective has always been to stimulate students' intellectual growth (to the best of their abilities) by teaching them how to develop higher-level, analytical thinking skills (not to either (1) appease anti-Christian bigots or (2) brainwash impressionable young minds with *imperfect and quasi-factual* **theories**, solely, for the purpose of undermining the majority population's value and belief system by indoctrinating Christian children to turn against their traditional culture and religion). *Edwards v. Aguillard*, *indifferently*, failed to consider (or even anticipate) the harm that Evolutionary Science was, likely, to cause if utilized, primarily, as an *un-Democratic and anti-Christian* ***propaganda weapon*** to, corruptly, convince young and impressionable Christian minds (living in--what is supposed to be--a majority-ruled, Democratic society) to abandon and scorn their *majority culture's Christian beliefs* despite the fact that, in 1985, *Grand Rapids School Dist. V. Ball*, 473 U.S. 383 ***instructed*** *that the classroom will* **not, purposely**, be used to advance religious views that may conflict with the private beliefs of students and their families; (yet that is precisely what *Edwards v. Aguillard* and other subsequent, concurring, Federal Court decisions have done).

Perhaps because of the undue influence of so many Nobel Prize winners, *Edwards v. Aguillard* chose to ignore the fact that evolutionary science is, itself, the fundamental ***religious belief*** **of** ***intolerant*** agnostics, atheists, all Communists, and most ***secular*** Jews and Christians; thus, the Supreme Court, inexplicably, elected to discriminate against (and ban) the majority culture's Christian convictions (while ratifying the ***bigoted*** *minority culture's dangerous and anti-religious dogmas*) by determining that Evolutionary Science is fact-based while "Creation Science is simply a religious belief that has no place in the public-school classroom".

Since The Theory That Explains Everything (and the amalgamation of M Theory, String Theory, and Higgs Boson "God Particle" Theory--with Jesus' and Biblical teachings) presents the most *compelling "theoretical s**cientific** explanation"* for the ***emergence of consciousness*** **and *self-awareness***, the only way (moving forward) that public schools can comply with *Edwards v. Aguillard*'s and *Grand Rapids School Dist. v. Ball*'s decrees (and, finally, **end *all violations*** of the Supreme Court's Establishment Clause mandate) is: (1) to recognize that **there is no justifiable or legal reason to *promote* the *religion of Evolution by pretending*** *that Evolution is not the pillar of a particular anti-Christian, atheist, religious belief system* which also violates the Establishment Clause of the First Amendment; (2) to correctly concede that Darwin's *Theory* of Evolution (one of ***several*** *origin of the human species* ***theories***) is an *incomplete and quasi-factual explanation*; (3) to recognize that the Justices who decided the *Edwards v. Aguillard* case, by neglecting to understand that *Darwin's theory* ***does not provide a factual explanation for the existence of consciousness and self-awareness***, were too ill-prepared to, correctly, conclude that Evolutionary Science is the sole, *factually complete*, explanation for the origin of human existence because other, subsequent, theories such as the combination of M Theory, String Theory, Higgs Boson "God Particle" Theory, and Christian Mammalian Differentiation Theory (which will be introduced and fully explained in the next Chapter of this interview) were never even considered by *Edwards v. Aguillard*'s judges; (4) to acknowledge that Jesus' explanation (the remarkable, abstract, scientific theory which foreshadowed, by two thousand years, the conclusions of several, recent, breakthrough scientific theories) does enhance scientific instruction; and (5) to, thus, reinstate the teaching of "*...**a variety of scientific theories*** **about the origins of humankind to school children...with the clear secular intent of *enhancing the effectiveness of science instruction*"** and, correctly, acknowledge that the teaching of a combination of insights contributes to a superior scientific understanding of the universe. This approach would, finally, satisfy the Establishment Clause's three-pronged test which requires that (1) legislatures must adopt laws with secular purposes, (2) a statute's primary purpose must be one that neither advances **nor *inhibits religion***, and (3) a statute must not result in an ***EXCESSIVE*** *entanglement* of government with religion, *Lemon v. Kurtzman*, 403 U.S. 602, 612-613 (1971).

The primary purpose for a scientific education is (1) to teach students how to develop those higher-level thinking skills which will lead minds beyond information that is known and (2) to help students foster the skill to, successfully, explore and discover all that is yet to be known. The educational benefit which results from utilizing a comprehensive approach when teaching Evolution Science is that a comprehensive approach, more effectively, facilitates intellectual development (than does an inaccurate, and incomplete, single-theory explanation). It should be clear that the bigoted belief expressed by Francis Crick, and seventy-two other Nobel laureates, that *"Creation-science simply has no place in the public-school classroom"* (1) does not facilitate analytical learning and (2) is not a good example of higher-level, Nobel Prize-worthy, thought processes.

Although, as an adult, Einstein chose not to be associated with any organized religion (or to embrace any *established* religious beliefs), he had, nevertheless, been reared in (and influenced by) a *highly moral Jewish family and community.* It was because of Einstein's Hebrew religious instructions (which had introduced him to--and, thus, helped him to develop--*abstract, spiritual, thinking* processes) that an adult Albert Einstein was able to envision those (as yet to be known) theories which transformed the scientific world; thus, it was only because Einstein had fully developed the mental ability to, *first, imagine* (1) his Special Theory of Relativity, (2) $E=mc^2$, (3) his General Theory of Relativity, and (4) his Unified Theory Which Explains Everything that those physicists who followed in his footsteps were able to, factually, duplicate and/or prove the correctness of Einstein's ***spiritual*** *inspirations.*

In an October 26, 1929, interview with *The Saturday Evening Post*, Einstein explained that the **true** sign of intelligence is not knowledge, but the ability to imagine (since Einstein conceptualized his most brilliant and correct theories by, first, imagining--or perhaps dreaming-- them). He explained: "I believe in intuitions and inspirations.... I am enough of an artist to draw freely upon my imagination. Knowledge is limited to all we now know and understand. Imagination" (however) "encircles the world."

Einstein restated this belief in his 1931 book, *Cosmic Religion and Other Opinions and Aphorisms*, by explaining: "At times, I feel certain I am right while not knowing the reason.... Imagination is more important than knowledge; for knowledge is limited, whereas imagination embraces the entire world, stimulating progress, and giving birth to evolution. It is, strictly speaking, *a real factor in scientific research*". If this is what Einstein believed, why, then, would any scientist (particularly a Nobel laureate) insist upon stifling the development of such abilities in the science classroom?

It is most likely that Crick and the Nobel laureates were not attempting to stifle the development of higher-level

abilities but, instead, merely believed that fairy tale-like Biblical allegories have no place in the science classroom.

Earlier in this interview, you stated that Jesus often identified many Old Testament stories as parables (stories which illuminate a moral attitude or a religious principle); and it is for that reason you have always concentrated on the message conveyed in the Garden of Eden story, for example, rather than the FACTUAL truthfulness of the story. You also declared that whenever a person questions the FACTUAL truthfulness of some facet of a Biblical story (a snake talking to Eve, for example), that person might sometimes be advised to not question any aspect of the Holy Scriptures but, instead, blindly accept that which cannot be explained. You added that (1) such an edict creates problems for the Christian religion because few people are willing to, blindly, believe anything and (2) parables must be recognized as being instructive stories--not FACTUAL accounts; thus, the primary objectives for all Christians should be (1) to fully understand and internalize Christ's teachings for the purpose of making them an automatic part of one's nature as completely as possible and (2) to, so completely, understand the lessons taught elsewhere in the Bible that it is easy to make that wisdom an instinctive part of one's nature as well. Your conclusion was that some Christians may claim they have faith that a snake spoke to Eve, but few really believe that it did. What is most important to understand is that the Garden of Eden parable teaches a significant lesson.

It would seem that Crick and the Nobel laureates were correct to remind the Court that these types of lessons are best taught outside of a science classroom. How could you possibly disagree?

It would be *difficult* to successfully assert that literal, Fundamentalist interpretations of the Book of Genesis (the world being created in six ***Earth*** days; Eve speaking with a serpent; the great flood; and Biblical chronology, for example,) are verifiable ***scientific*** explanations; however, the, lower-court, Federal ***District*** case of *Kitzmiller v. Dover Area School District*, 400 F.Supp. 2nd 707 (2005) determined that, even, a discussion of the concept of Intelligent Design (a *scientific approach* which, without identifying any particular designer, explains that the physical properties of living organisms are so complex that the *wisest* conclusion which can be drawn is that life, consciousness, and self-awareness had to have been "***designed***" *by some form of intelligent entity*) must be excluded from the science classroom because, in that Court's view, intelligent design is not a testable theory and, therefore, could not be science because it "cannot uncouple itself from its Creationist, thus religious, antecedents". When that ***single***, *lower-court*, Federal District judge concluded that Intelligent Design cannot be taught as a complement to evolution in the public school, *Kitzmiller* created a, nearly, impossible legal hurdle for Christians to overcome.

Since (fortunately) that decision was not appealed to the Federal Circuit Court and, then, to the Supreme Court because (1) the (newly-elected) school board responsible for making that appeal did not support Creationism and because (2) the justices who sat on the 2005 Supreme Court were certain to have affirmed the Lower Court's anti-Christian decision (regardless of the evidence), science students are, no longer, being exposed to those abstract scientific concepts which would facilitate them to properly develop, insightful, analytical minds.

Tragically, it is only the *majority culture's belief system* (in, what is supposed to be, a Democratic society) that has been excluded from the science classroom. For example, when science teachers conclude (*in the absence of any provable--or testable--scientific evidence*) that, *without mass,* the universe would have, forever, remained ***cold, dark***, and ***LIFELESS*** (despite the proven fact that energy and mass are merely two aspects of the same thing), students who do not embrace that, *entirely unproven*, ***atheist*** *religious belief* fail to earn passing grades. Such an approach is not education but, instead, anti-Christian indoctrination (which has succeeded in causing irreparable damage to this country's moral integrity). What could possibly be wrong with introducing students to rational (and analytically sound) theoretical explanations in a science classroom (if the intention of the learning program is, truly, to develop intelligent minds)?

It would seem that the *Kitzmiller v. Dover Area School District* case has determined, then, that M Theory, String Theory, the Higgs Boson Theory, and The Theory That Explains Everything cannot be taught in the science classroom, as well, because: since the original theorist of those scientific concepts was Jesus Christ, all of those theoretical mathematical conclusions (regardless of whether they are testable or untestable), also, derive from Creationist roots. If the *Kitzmiller v. Dover Area School District* (or any concurring decision) were to be affirmed by higher Appellate courts, hundreds of other scientific *theories* would, most likely, also have to be excluded from high school classrooms because (by merely being *untestable theories* which might, possibly, have origins in *some* religious contexts) they could not be recognized as science since they, too, would not be able to "uncouple themselves from their … religious antecedents". This would include, for example, Crick's ***theorized*** *explanation* (that when electrical signals in the brain oscillate, they cause a *sense of self-awareness*; and consciousness ***might***, therefore, result from the electrical activity of many neurons oscillating together as they share and integrate *all* incoming sensory information *throughout the entire brain network*) because his ***theory***, also, (1) is not a testable theory and (2) is, merely, another affirmation of *anti-Christian, **atheist**, points of view* which violate the tenants of (1) *Lemon v. Kurtzman* by ***inhibiting religion*** and (2) *Edwards v. Aguillard* by refusing to allow inclusion of "*...a **variety of scientific theories** about the origins of humankind to school children...with the clear secular intent of **enhancing the effectiveness** of science instruction*".

You just claimed that (in part) the reason Kitzmiller v. Dover Area School District was not appealed to a higher Federal court was because the justices who sat on the 2005 Supreme Court were certain to have affirmed the Lower Court's anti-Christian decision--regardless of the evidence. Why would you say such a thing?

Toward the end of his life, retired Supreme Court justice, Harry Blackmun, (a Justice who provided one of the anti-Christian votes in both the abortion case of *Roe v. Wade* and the Creationist case of *Edwards v. Aguillard*) admitted that some of his decisions were not based upon the law, Democratic principles, or the United States' Constitution but, instead, upon his own personal philosophies. In other words (just prior to his death), this *never-married* Justice felt compelled to reveal his *deviant intentions* by gloating about how he had *exploited* his position of ultimate power to, ***tyrannically***, ***force*** unwarranted transformations upon an, unsuspecting, Christian country. His confession caused the, *overwhelming, majority* **Christian** *population* to finally realize that it must, thereafter, scrutinize ***all*** subsequent judicial appointments.

America's founding fathers did not favor a religious test for judicial appointments (Article Six of the United States' Constitution) because they wished to avert the antagonism, and frequent wars, that continually erupted between Catholics and Protestants; however, when they made that determination, the founding fathers had never envisioned the possibility that Muslims, Jews, Satanists, atheists, and Communists would ever be in the position to *censure and eliminate Christian beliefs* (in this Christian country). Nevertheless, as recently as 2017, California Senator Dianne Feinstein and Minnesota Senator Al Franken (members of one of this country's smallest, non-Christian, minorities) felt compelled to subject Christian judicial candidate, Amy Coney Barret, to religious tests when the senators confronted and expressed their disapproval because the judicial nominee had, at a previous time in her life, identified herself as being an *Orthodox* Catholic. For some odd reason, Senator Feinstein was not held accountable by media (or her colleagues) for her anti-Christian prejudices when she made biased statements to the nominee such as "the dogma lives loudly within you" despite the fact that no Christian is ever permitted to even question the affiliations and beliefs of other non-Christian and anti-Christian judicial nominations. Irrespective of the founding fathers' original intention, the two senators' bigoted, anti-Christian, beliefs and attitudes have "opened the door" for Christians to behave similarly (because the senators' anti-Christian prejudices illustrate why, ***in modern times***, the absence of ***Christian beliefs*** should be the ***primary reason*** for this, *still, Democratic--and majority Christian* country--to disqualify judicial nominees). Too many non-Christian, anti-Christian, and make-believe Christian Justices (without any forms of scrutiny and accountability) have *continually* failed to maintain proper judicial objectivity. ***Where***, in the United States' Constitution, could such savages have possibly found, for example, the ***right*** to murder unborn children?

The failure of Congress to scrutinize judicial candidates' underlying non-Christian and anti-Christian values and beliefs was, finally, recognized to be the most serious threat to the survival of America's democracy when President

Clinton appointed Ruth Bader Ginsburg in 1993 and Stephen Breyer in 1994--and President Obama placed Elena Kagan on the Supreme Court in 2010. Justice Kagan's bewildering appointment caused thirty-three percent of the Supreme Court to be comprised of Jewish Justices even though Jews (a minority, *with a very troubled history*, whose beliefs are guided by a very different value system than Christians) constituted no more than 2.6 percent of the United States' total population at that time--(the majority, of whom, were recent immigrants); thus, by making such a nomination, President Obama (like Justice Harry Blackmun) revealed his willingness to completely disregard all ***Democratic*** principles. Even worse, had President Obama's nomination of Merrick Garland (to fill the vacancy created by the death of Anthony Scalia in 2016) been approved by Congress, Garland would have become the fourth Jewish Justice to serve on the Supreme Court (at the same time).

Despite the fact that those appointments are some of the most troubling developments in America's governmental history (because seizing control of the judiciary is the primary way, in a Democratic form of government, to effectively unleash tyranny upon a free citizenry), America's fake media (which, ***presently***, *is, also, controlled by non-Christians, anti-Christians, and make-believe Christians*) ignored and/or concealed the un-Democratic nature of those nominations and confirmations. Why?

Since the media (as well as the legal and political communities) so convincingly categorize *each and every Justice* as being "honorable" and "above reproach" professionals, all present Supreme Court Justices (as well as future judicial nominations) will, ***no doubt*** [*sic*], hereafter, quite willingly, ***contractually*** *consent* to (corruption-proof) polygraph testing (1) for the purpose of verifying their "above reproach" integrity and (2) for the purpose assuaging the majority culture's concerns regarding potential impropriety. Since it is so, obviously, clear that regular polygraph testing is an absolute necessity for employees of governmental agencies such as the F.B.I., the border patrol, and the C.I.A., Justice Blackmun's confession has revealed why ***frequent*** polygraph testing is an even greater necessity for *all* judicial appointments.

This same type of **bias** was, once again, *inadvertently, revealed* by Justice Ginsburg's niece when she reported, just days prior to Justice Ginsburg's death on September 18, 2020, that the Justice dictated the following statement: "My most fervent wish is that I not be replaced until a new President is installed".

Judge Ginsburg was aware the President Trump would appoint a Christian justice who will interpret the Constitution as it is intended to be interpreted. Even on her deathbed, such an appointment was unpalatable to Justice Ginsburg. It is not a coincidence, then, that President Trump's nomination to replace Justice Ginsburg was, indeed, Amy Coney Barret (who, on October 26, 2020, became the one hundred and third Justice of the United States Supreme Court).

Fake media's *chilling explanation* for championing the many non-Christian, anti-Christian, and make-believe Christian societal transformations (that have deceptively, yet tyrannically, been forced upon the majority Christian population of the United States since the early 1960's) is that the United States has been transitioned into a "Participatory Democracy". What that term *actually means* ***to them*** is: Democracy no longer exists in the United States; instead, the United States is ruled by a coalition of minorities (even though (1) that *entire* coalition amounts to less than twenty percent of the population and even though (2) no vote has ever been taken (and no civil war has ever been fought) for the purpose of converting this United States' governmental system into a "*Participatory Democracy*" (a *tyrannical* governmental concept that is devoid of *all* democratic principles).

Recently, a Jewish comedian and political commentator (referring to the Christian majority) quipped, "When are ***you people*** going to realize that this isn't your country anymore?" The appointment of three (plus one) Jewish judges to the Supreme Court and hundreds of Jewish and anti-Christian judges to lower Federal judgeship does seem to verify *that* anti-Christian insult (because far too many of Justice Ginsburg's, Justice Breyer's, and Justice Kagan's decisions--like Justice Blackmun's and many others--have, ominously, demonstrated an intention to, ***tyrannically***, transform and/or replace America's, Christian-based, Democratic principles). For these reasons, it is fortunate that the *Kitzmiller v. Dover Area School District* decision was not appealed to an Appellate Federal Court in 2005.

Any suggestions by Christians that it is time for the United States to return, once again, to a ***Democratic, majority-ruled society***, after more than one-half century of patient acquiescence to the non-stop societal atrocities perpetrated by members of America's non-Christian, and/or anti-Christian minorities (led by the likes of Myer Lansky, Irv Kovens, Demetrius Flenory and hundreds of thousands of their progeny), Christians are now scorned as merely being bigoted (and racist), white, European supremacists.

With media's propagandizing support, proponents of "Participatory Democracy" believe (and are able to effectively assert) that (1) the ***majority Christian population*** should no longer have any rights to determine the course of the United States' future and that (2) all opinions which reflect Christian advocacy must be regarded as hate speech; therefore, the majority culture should not be allowed to even challenge, for example, the continuous influx of non-Christians into the United States until such time as Christians of European descent no longer compose the majority of this country's population (or, even, compose a large enough percentage of the population to enact new Constitutional amendments). Christians should realize, then, that (1) their decades of tolerance, generosity, decency, (and sacrifice of Christian lives) will never be appreciated, and that (2) if that coalition of non-Christian and anti-Christian minorities were to ever prevail, Christians would, most likely, be doomed to the same genocidal fate that was suffered by (the majority) Ukrainian Christian population in the early 1930's.

At the same time, remarkably, those duplicitous advocates for "participatory Democracy" in the United States believe, for example, (1) that Israel should continually deny all rights to its minority, (2) that Israel should never become a "participatory Democracy" and (3) that Israel should prevent Palestinians from ever composing even a small portion of Israel's judiciary. What type of malevolent value system could possibly be inspiring such unprincipled dissemblers?

The time has arrived for Christians to expose such ingratitude, hatred, and savagery by, finally, confronting those ***evil-hearted hypocrites*** in a way that is comparable to Jesus' confrontation of the moneylenders in the temple. This can best be done by ***demanding that a TRUTHFUL history of America's minorities*** be taught to all American public school children. That curriculum ***must*** *include*: a ***truthful*** European, Middle-Eastern, and American Jewish history; a ***truthful*** Native American history; a ***truthful*** account of Africa-American behavior in the South since 1865 and, particularly, African-American behavior in the North since 1940; and a ***truthful*** history of atheism, Satanism, and Communism. Once those ***truthful histories*** are revealed, no *rational* human would conclude (1) that "Participatory Democracy" in the United States could possibly be a good idea or (2) that anti-Christian, non-Christian, and/or make-believe Christian justices should ever, again, be permitted to dominate Federal and state judgeships in this Democratic, ***Christian***, society.

Until such time as all of the anti-Christian bigots have been remove from Federal judgeships and Christian can, once again, be assured of fair judicial decisions, how do you believe that the scientific concepts of Evolution and Jesus' lessons might be allowed to, legally, co-exist in the public science classroom?

Although the intention of the *Grand Rapids School Dist. V. Ball*, 473 U.S. 383 (1985) decision was to exclude Christian beliefs from the public classroom, it, nevertheless, has ruled that the classroom will not, purposely, be used to advance religious views which may conflict with the private beliefs of students and their families. That protection should extend to Christian students and families as well but, thus far, does not. Because *Edwards v. Aguillard* concluded that, **"*teaching a variety of scientific theories about the origins of humankind* to school children *might* be validly done with the clear secular intent of *enhancing the effectiveness of science instruction*"**, there is no justifiable Constitutional reason to exclude ***any Christian scientific*** theory that (1) has advanced scientific understanding and/or (2) can be shown to help facilitate the development of higher-level thinking skills.

The easy-to-understand scientific explanations which I have, thus far, summarized in this interview demonstrate how wrong Crick and the other seventy-two Nobel laureates were to conclude that "Creation-science simply has no place in the public-school classroom". For example, in all instances when science teachers explain that the simplest way to comprehend the concept of ***mass*** is to realize that (1) ***mass*** is another way *energy* is able to exist, (2) ***mass*** is the part of matter field elements which fights against movement in any direction (for brief periods of time), and (3) the Higgs boson particle is that element which provides the ***force*** which enables ***mass***, and all other ***matter field elements***, to combine and, resultantly, create the physical world (for brief periods of time), it would be highly inappropriate to exclude the fact that the primary reason that the (non-religious) scientific community named the Higgs Boson Particle the "God Particle" is because it was Jesus, millennia ago, who championed the concept that ***spiritual ENERGY is the basis for all life (and human existence) in the physical world***; thus, verification that the Higgs boson particle exists corroborates Jesus' ***scientific*** explanation.

When science teachers explain that the existence of the Higgs boson particle (as well as this universe's membrane) has been scientifically confirmed (and, further, reveal that M Theory's mathematical equations provide convincing verification of the ***likelihood*** that multiple dimensions *may* co-exist alongside one another within a larger multi-verse), it would be remiss (and discriminatory) for science teachers to fail, also, to, at least, discuss the fact that M Theory's multi-dimensional conclusion authenticates the ***scientific insights*** forwarded by Christ, more than two thousand years ago, when He identified the existence of alternate dimensions (which He *labeled* Heaven and hell). At that point, science teachers should be sufficiently free to, at least, include the fact that this ***scientific explanation*** (first introduced by Christ--which provides one of the foundations upon which the Christian belief system is based) affords theoretical scientific evidence that supports Christian teachings.

In addition, when the theoretical manner by which close-looped gravitons are able to escape the boundaries of this universe (and travel to parallel universes) is explained to science students, it would be remiss (and discriminatory) to ignore the fact that Jesus, over two thousand years ago, was one of the first persons in recorded history to explain that human souls can survive the death of their physical bodies and travel to other dimensions as well, (*most likely*, because of the existence of closed-looped strings).

Although atheists have continually (and successfully) ***demanded*** that they be allowed to ***brainwash*** *children to believe that it is impossible for human souls to survive the death of human bodies*, the theoretical scientific community's recognition that closed-looped gravitons can escape this universe (and travel to parallel universes) does, finally, provide the convincing, *theoretical, scientific explanation* which illuminates how human souls are able to survive the death of human bodies. It, then, would be quite incorrect for science teachers to ignore, or intentionally exclude, Jesus' contribution to this groundbreaking scientific theory by omitting (or disregarding) the fact that there is a, **highly believable**, ***scientific explanation*** *which clarifies how it is possible for souls to survive the death of their bodies*.

In those instances when science instructors teach M Theory's explanation for the weakness of gravity by explaining that M-Theory's calculations *conclude* that the force of gravity is, in fact, equal to the force of electro-magnetism; however, the reason why the force of gravity ***seems*** *to be so much weaker in this universe* is because (1) gravity is the glue-like energy force which links all parallel universes together, (2) most of gravity's force is, therefore, spread out among a massive number of parallel universes, (3) gravity isn't leaking away from this universe but, instead, is leaking into this universe from all of the other universes, and (4) gravity's force is so diluted by the time it reaches this universe that gravity *only* ***appears*** *to be weaker* than electromagnetism, science teachers should include Harvard University's Lisa Randall's theory and, thereby, also acknowledge the high probability that most of the string energy that is responsible for the creation of life travels along that gravitational path which leaks from those other dimensions into this dimension in the manner that was

explained, first, by Jesus *over two thousand years ago.* Again, the failure to present a *complete and* ***truthful,*** *theorized,* ***scientific explanation*** (by omitting Jesus' contribution to these scientific breakthroughs) would be nothing other than dishonest, tyrannical, propaganda.

If the scientific community (and the world in general) recognizes Einstein as a genius, (1) how is it possible that the scientific community could not recognize (and, thus, be awed by) Jesus' genius and scientific insights as well, and (2) how is it possible that ***only*** Jesus' brilliant, ***scientific***, teachings are banned from the science classroom *in this, allegedly,* ***free Christian democracy***?

Now that you have connected-the-dots by providing valid scientific explanations which clarify why some Christian concepts should not (and cannot) be excluded from the public science classroom, do you believe that Christians will, ever, prevail when future Federal Court challenges occurs?

As long as **anti-Christian bigots** (who have *not* ***proven their integrity*** by successfully--and regularly--passing polygraph examinations) remain in control of the United States' judicial system, Christians will continue to be defeated--regardless of the soundness of their evidence; thus, ***now***, regrettably, is not the appropriate time for Christians to initiate new legal challenges. Since it had taken decades for anti-Christian, non-Christian, and make-believe Christian conspiracies to gain such disproportionate control of the United States' judiciaries, educational systems, and fake media, a comparable amount of time *might*, possibly, be required for Christians to re-assume their control of those areas. Any Democratic governmental system which, willingly, chooses to cede command of its Federal Court system, educational systems, and media to its **malevolent**

minorities for the sole purpose of ***appeasing*** those who would prefer to live in a "*Participatory (Communist) Democracy*" (rather than a ***true*** *Democracy*) is a Democratic governmental system that has a death wish. The time has arrived, finally, for the majority Christian citizenry of these United States to begin the process of escaping the grip of that death wish.

The greatest, modern-era, American tragedy is that every sentient person in the United States is aware that recent, anti-Christian, judicial decisions (handed down by too many Harry Blackmun-like justices) do not truly reflect the intentions of this country's founding fathers. The Federal Courts' callous assertions that Creationist concepts are best taught in philosophy classes is comparable to Marie Antoinette's cruel "Let them eat cake" response when she learned that the French poor, without even bread to eat, were starving to death. Those Federal justices were aware (1) that philosophy is not an educational program that is taught on any public school grade level and (2) that it is because philosophy education does not exist anywhere in any public school curricula that philosophical ideas must be (and, in every other instance, ***are*** being) integrated within the context of each particular course's subject matter. Because of these "chilling" Federal court decisions, it is, primarily, Christian philosophies which are, thus, being excluded from all public school classrooms. The Federal judiciary is also aware that its "chilling" decisions to exclude the teaching of all Christian beliefs (and righteous principles) has transformed these United States into such an immoral, corrupt, unprincipled, drug-dependent, and Godless society (equivalent to that which existed under, tyrannical, Communist rule in the Soviet Union) that, by comparison, this country, now, makes Sodom and Gomorrah seem virtuous.

Do you believe that the theoretical mathematicians and physicists who are responsible for String Theory, M Theory, Higgs Boson Theory, and the Theory That Explains Everything would agree with your Christian interpretation of their scientific theories?

Some will, and some will not. It is my hope that the majority of theoretical mathematicians and physicists will champion these Christian interpretations of their theoretical mathematical and scientific conclusions; however, there are, at least, two reasons why many may not. The first reason arises because no scientist will ever be content with any discovery that cannot be confirmed by scientific experimentation; thus, insightful, inquiring scientific minds will continue to search, non-stop, for even better, scientifically verifiable, formulas and theories.

The second reason, however, is more *diabolical*. All anti-Christian and non-Christian bigots, by preferring to *embrace* (and champion) agnostic and/or atheist beliefs, will, instead, continue to behave like Francis Crick and those seventy-two other Nobel laureates (even if their anti-Christian agendas requires them to contradict their own scientific conclusions). Some members of the scientific community have demonstrated themselves to be so anti-Christian that they, predictably, can be expected to, willingly, "cut off their own noses to spite their faces" by, steadfastly (yet falsely), insisting that there could not possibly be any connection between The Theory That Explains Everything and Christian beliefs.

Most atheist and agnostic scientists are likely to insist, for example, that there is no, scientifically proven, evidence that human souls are composed of oval-shaped strings which have the ability to survive the death of the human body and travel to others dimensions. Why, then, are you so

certain that there is a valid connection between (1) The Theory That Explains Everything, (2) the verification of the existence of the Higgs boson particle and this universe's membrane, and (3) Christian beliefs?

Despite the absence of ***worldly certainty***, my ability to ***believe*** in God, Heaven, and eternal salvation has remained strong. The fact that I experienced a remarkable dream at the age of seven (which (1) provided me with the foundation for all of the insights that I have shared in this interview and (2) has maintained a continuous, uncanny, spiritual influence over me for more than six decades) convinces me to believe that other spiritual dimensions do exist and that human souls are able to survive the deaths of their human bodies in ***precisely*** the way that Jesus taught. Nevertheless, even though the Holy Spirit within me (1) did bless me with sufficient intellectual ability and (2) did, *continually*, make me aware that I would (at an appropriate time--prior to my death) utilize those intellectual skills to share (with the entire world) all of the spiritual insight that I acquired from my childhood dream, that same Holy Spirit (for more than six decades), continually, restrained me from *even speaking about my dream*--until such time as confirmation of the existence of the Higgs boson particle, in 2013, brought humans as close as they are ever liable to come to (1) scientifically substantiating the likelihood of God's existence and to (2) proving, ***more probably than not***, that Heaven does exist. It is for this reason that I am confident there is a valid connection between (1) The Theory That Explains Everything, (2) the verification of the existence of the Higgs boson particle and this universe's membrane, and (3) Christian beliefs?

The Holy Spirit has *inspired* me to be concerned for the long-term viability of the Christian faith and, thus, taught me how to explain (1) why Christians should not abandon their beliefs and traditions--regardless of the intensity of the modern-day, non-stop, anti-Christian propaganda that is, successfully, causing so many to lose faith and (2) why it makes sense for all Christians to, once again, be guided by the teachings of Christ. It is my hope, by sharing my dream experience, that I can help those humans regain some recollection of (1) their own dream experiences and/or of (2) their connections with the Holy Spirit. It would seem, then, that the Holy Spirit's primary reason for, continually, reminding me of my childhood dream has been to ensure that I, ***at the appropriate time***, inform all humans that ***verification of the existence*** *of the Higgs boson particle, and this universe' membrane, has, finally, provided the* ***scientific evidence*** *which corroborates Christ's teachings.*

Notwithstanding the fact that my dream's description of Heaven varies, somewhat, from those beliefs embraced by many Christians, my dream has, nevertheless, enabled me to recognize that (1) the scientific conclusions of M Theory and (2) the Christian belief that a *spiritual* afterlife exists are, remarkably, similar. For example, my dream revealed a vivid description of a spiritual realm where life and consciousness thrive despite the absence of all forms of this universe's mass and matter. Since the sole purpose for human bodies is to facilitate survival in the physical world, the most obvious inference is that (1) human souls, (2) consciousness, and (3) degrees of goodness, love, peace, humility, and **truthfulness** (not physical bodies) are those aspects of God's image which will define and distinguish individual identities after death. It can, therefore, be concluded that those human characteristics which have the potential to survive death and ascend to an alternate dimension (Heaven) must be those spiritual qualities that are **true** reflections of God's image and goodness.

My dream also guided me to understand that "time" is not linear but, instead, is merely an illusory measuring construct that enables humans to observe and define the speed by which the forces of gravity cause mass and matter to come apart (and, thus, return to their original states of vibrating energy). This insight explains why time passes more slowly in outer space (where mass and matter experiences a much weaker gravitational pull). Since the concept of "time" can *only* be relevant in dimensions where there is mass and matter, "time" could not possibly exist in dimensions (such as Heaven) that are devoid of mass and matter.

Because M Theory and the Theory That Explains Everything support (rather than disprove) the likelihood that (1) parallel universes exist and that (2) many of those universes must contain intelligent life and civilizations whose existences emerged from entirely different laws of nature and physics, the blending of Christ's teachings with M Theory's conclusions can be summarized with the following ***SCIENTIFIC*** explanation: *Christ taught that despite the fact that all physical-world mass, particularly the human body, can only resist movement (and, thus, survive in the physical world) for brief periods of time, consciousness (by being composed of closed-looped, sub-atomic strings--rather than mass) does not decompose and, resultantly, cease to exist when the human body dies. Instead (like gravity), the human soul has the ability to travel through various dimensions until such time as the strings which constitute that soul's shape and frequency are caught by, and become attached to, the membrane of that* **single dimension (or room)** *whose shape and frequency is identical to the shape and frequency of the strings of that particular human soul.*

It is probable that Jesus, thoroughly and repeatedly, explained these very same ***scientific*** *principles* that have recently been rediscovered, and encapsulated, in the Theory That Explains Everything; yet, the most-likely reason Jesus' explanations (along with the majority of His other words) were excluded from the New Testament (and, thus, lost) is because ***most*** *of His explanations were* ***too, scientifically,***

advanced for His followers to, *completely*, comprehend. A good example of such misunderstanding appears at John 14:2-4: "In my Father's house are many "rooms"…. I am going there to prepare a place for you". I am certain that Jesus explained much more about those "rooms" to his followers during his ministry, but this passage is His only Biblical reference. My dream taught me that not only is the eternal world divided between Heaven and hell; but Heaven is, also, partitioned into many (distinct) "rooms". Resultantly, those persons who are fortunate enough to ascend to Heaven will find themselves in that "room" where they ***spiritually*** belong; and that "room" will *only* be occupied by other ethereal beings whose souls vibrate on that identical spiritual "frequency".

At Mark 13: 24-25, Jesus shared an equally misunderstood Biblical passage: "During that period, after trials of every sort, the sun will be darkened, the moon will not shed its light, stars will fall out of the skies, and the Heavenly hosts will be shaken". Even though Mark seems to have misinterpreted these words as being, ***solely***, *a foreboding warning*, Jesus, in fact, explained that, at the end of times, an alternate dimension (one which is devoid of mass and matter--most-likely Heaven) would, nevertheless, continue to exist.

It would seem as though the number of dimensions (or rooms) existing in Heaven is incalculable; however, the difference between the strength of gravity and electro-magnetism (in this universe) does provide some insight regarding the size of Heaven (the multi-verse). On the sub-atomic level, the strength of electro-magnetism is one thousand, billion, billion, billion (or, possibly, "*ten to the five-hundredths*") times more powerful than gravity. It is rational to infer, then, that ***if*** gravity's force is spread *equally* among all parallel universes, it is possible that as many as "*ten to the five-hundredths*" parallel universes (rooms) *might* exist. Since that figure far exceeds the total number of humans who have ever lived (in ***this*** universe), it should be clear that (1) Heaven and hell exist, side-by-side (less than one trillionth of a millimeter apart), in vast expanses of multi-verse space; yet, (2) Heaven, most likely, occupies only a small portion of that space. This reality reinforces the lesson taught at Matthew 7: 13-14: "The gate that leads to damnation is wide, the road is clear, and many choose to travel it. But how narrow is the gate that leads to life, how rough the road, and how few there are that find it!" That description of the "narrow gate of Heaven" implies, then, that Heaven occupies only a small portion of the multi-verse.

It is difficult to imagine the type of existence a soul might encounter in one of those, countless, other dimensions (or rooms) in the event a soul might become attached to the membrane of one of those alternative dimensions rather than one of Heaven's membranes (rooms); however, Jesus provided sufficient insight (***and warning***) by making humans aware that *a vast hell does exist in the afterlife.*

It is worth repeating, then, that despite the likelihood that each individual soul is created from a ***particular combination*** *of closed-looped, vibrating strings*, all ***human souls***, nevertheless, exist within mammalian bodies which are driven by, animalistic, survival urges and instincts. God's love provides the spark of consciousness; but, by granting individual freewill, God allows His children to complete His creation by sculpting their own unique spiritual identities. Life in the physical world, then, should be understood to merely be a second gestation period which God has created for the purpose of enabling humans to utilize their free-will to determine whether their spiritual identities are sculpted by the *spiritual tethers* with which they were born or, instead, by the *animalistic thoughts, feelings, instincts, urges, values, actions and desires* generated by their physical bodies (the source of Original Sin).

It should be clear, then, that the reason God created the physical world was to provide God a means to, *correctly*, identify which impulses dominate and, consequently, reveal the *identity of each soul* so that God can, appropriately, ***segregate*** *good souls from bad souls in the afterlife*; thus, humans have been granted freewill so that they may control both (1) the sculpting of the frequencies of their closed-looped strings and (2) the defining of their, unique, spiritual identities that will determine the dimension (or room) to which they will, ultimately, be drawn (immediately after their physical bodies die). It is fortunate, then, that (1) oval-shaped, vibrating strings are not, significantly, affected by a single deed or period of time and that (2) it takes a lifetime of thoughts and deeds to fully create each, unique, spiritual frequency and identity. This **truth** is best summarized by Paul in his Epistle to the Galatians at 6:7: "A man will only reap what he sows. If he sows in the field of flesh, he will reap a harvest of corruption; but if his seed-ground is in the spirit, he will reap everlasting life".

Even though you have already provided a brief description of Heaven, would you, please, summarize what, you believe, humans will experience should they be fortunate enough to ascend to Heaven?

My dream revealed that *existence* for those souls fortunate enough to reach the alternate dimension of Heaven is determined, entirely, by different Laws of Nature. Ethereal souls are omniscient and omnipotent, able to hear without human ears, perceive without human eyes, communicate with other beings by way of telepathy rather than vocal chords, sustain their existences indefinitely (in the absence of physical death), and (most importantly) experience innumerable spiritual abilities that are beyond human comprehension (and my knowledge).

One of the most fascinating means by which Heavenly omnipotence is realized results from the fact that spiritual being are able to (1) observe what is occurring in alternate dimensions (including this physical world), (2) *spiritually* communicate with humans, and (3) (should they desire) even travel to this world by ascending (and traveling upon) the oval-shaped gravitational strings which link all of the dimensions. Despite the fact that few spiritual beings would ever choose to return to this physical world, some, such as myself (*according to my dream*), do; and since only God has the ability to bypass the birthing process and *spontaneously* emerge as a human form, ***the single way*** other ethereal beings (including Christ) could possibly transition to this dimension is by utilizing (1) the Higgs boson particle (the God Particle) and (2) the natural birthing process because the Higgs boson particle and natural childbirth provide the *sole means by which* **spiritual** *string energy* can be converted to mass in ***this*** dimension.

This omnipotent spiritual ability does, then, *possibly*, explain how the Virgin Mary's Immaculate Conception was able to occur. After all, since spiritual beings have the ability to control the function of the Higgs boson particle, choose particular mothers, genders, and physical and mental abilities, why, then, wouldn't spiritual beings be able to also utilize (and, thus, manipulate) the Higgs boson particle to create those essential chromosomes which initiate the conception process (even in the absence of sexual activity)? Such a power could not possibly be beyond the omnipotent capabilities of Heavenly souls.

Earlier, you declared that God had endowed you with sufficient intellectual skill to, readily, refute most agnostic and atheist notions; and, thus, you would demonstrate, to even the most intelligent agnostics, that their analytical skepticism should cause them to, first, recognize and, then,

logically conclude (1) by a preponderance of all presently known scientific evidence (which means: more likely than not--a greater than fifty percent probability) that human souls will survive the deaths of their bodies and (2) (more likely than not), a spiritual creator, of some kind, must, truly, exist. You have provided sufficient scientific evidence to succeed in that effort.

You have not, as yet, however, addressed the beliefs of atheists who deny the existence of God (and even the likelihood of the existence of God) entirely. You claimed that the only logical conclusion that could possibly be extrapolated from an atheist belief system is that every human being will be reborn, repeatedly and forever, in some form, somewhere in the physical universe; yet, you warned that (1) reincarnation in a Godless world would, instead (more likely than not), amount to a form of eternal damnation and that (2) (for the sake of all humanity) atheists should pray that their beliefs are wrong and that God, truly, does exist. Atheist beliefs are far more dogmatic than agnostic beliefs. How can you possibly convince atheists that they are misguided?

Atheists embrace Francis Crick's theory which ***hypothesizes*** that when electrical signals in the brain oscillate, they cause a *sense of self-awareness*. Crick ***speculated*** that consciousness ***might***, therefore, result from the electrical activity of many neurons oscillating together as they share and integrate *all* incoming sensory information *throughout the entire brain network*. Crick's theory ***conjectures*** that consciousness and self-awareness require mass in order to exist and, thus, ***infers*** that, when the electrical activity of those many neurons and synapses ends, human consciousness ceases to exist as well. According to this ***atheist theory***, there is only a finite number of ways (perhaps trillions of combinations) by which atoms and other sub-atomic particles can arrange themselves within a brain before an identical replication of that sub-atomic arrangement must re-occur and, resultantly, cause the reincarnation a human being's consciousness.

What might seem encouraging about ***this belief*** is the probability that, at most, *only a small section (not the* ***entire*** *brain)* is responsible for the existence of human consciousness. If this, indeed, were so, reincarnation would occur frequently because only a few hundred-billion distinct combinations of atoms and sub-atomic particles would account for all human consciousness. What *seems* to be the most encouraging and enticing aspect of *this* ***atheist theory*** is the fact that *random chance* determines the time when any subsequent reincarnation occurs. Rebirths (according to this theory), then, can occur at any time--including *immediately* after death or, even, during the same time period in which a person is still living.

There are, however, troubling aspects of this theory which atheists have not considered. Because of the vastness of this universe, the atheist belief-scenario that human consciousness is merely composed of a particular arrangement of atoms and sub-atomic particles (not a spiritual soul) leads to the, obvious, conclusion that consciousness will emerge, repeatedly and frequently, ***anywhere*** *in this dimension--not just within the confines of the brain of a human being*. That means that ***most*** human reincarnations will not result in a return to a human existence but, instead, to an entirely alien, (and, perhaps, even) harsh, hostile, frightening, and painful existence in an extreme environment ***elsewhere*** *in this universe*. It is nearly certain, then, that those types of reincarnations will not be accompanied by any other human body parts (because human bodies are not able to survive in outer space); thus, human abilities such as sight, hearing, speech and mobility are not likely to be available to those reincarnated souls--instead, merely a conscious sense of isolation, fear, and (perhaps) extreme torment. It is possible, then, that many of the **Bible's *physical* descriptions of hell** are, *in fact*, descriptions of what human souls (who are confined to this dimension after death--since they are not able to ascend and travel to an alternate, Heavenly, dimension) will experience because all distinct combinations of atoms and sub-atomic particles that survive in this universe (just outside of Earth's immediate atmosphere) would exist in environments that are the equivalents to Biblical descriptions of hell?

Could this, then, perhaps, be what Jesus meant when He warned at Matthew 19:24; Mark 10:25; and Luke 18:25 that: "It is easier for a camel to pass through a needle's eye than for a rich man to enter the Kingdom of God"? Is it possible that the first of the many gates "that leads to damnation" begins within this dimension? Do humans who devote their lives to being overly occupied with material things (such as wealth, revenge, dishonesty, hedonism, cruelty, sadism, and power) modify the shapes of their closed-looped strings so dramatically that the strings which define their souls are (1) no longer closed-looped but, instead, (2) reshaped to become strings which are restricted by this dimension's membrane in the same manner that pool balls are confined to the surface of a pool table. Do those *regrettable sinners*, thus, condemn themselves to endure the harshness of this tumultuous universe forever? In other words, was Jesus explaining that *souls of the worst humans* (who allow themselves to be controlled and, thus, overwhelmed by their animalistic impulses of Original Sin) are doomed to remain confined to *this dimension's hell* for eternity? If so, it should seem obvious that the possibility of experiencing repeated reincarnations in a Godless universe must be one of the most horrible of all fates that could possibly await humans. Even if atheists continue to choose to deny the existence of God, it would, nevertheless, be prudent for all atheists (1) to reflect upon all of their behavioral choices throughout their lives and (2) to *pray* that God, truly, does exist.

Most atheists and agnostics (as well as many Jews) will, most likely, continue to, confidently, anticipate a fate that is expressed by the Thirteenth Article of the Jewish Faith which assures humans that the dead will be resurrected; and most atheists and agnostics will continue, then, to believe that the reincarnation of consciousness within human bodies will occur, repeatedly, without any need for God's assistance. Could they possibly be correct?

Regardless of whether God, Heaven, and spiritual souls do exist, atheists and agnostics are correct to conclude that the particular arrangement of atoms and other sub-atomic particles which compose their brains will, *eventually*, reemerge within the brains of other future human beings. What atheists and agnostics fail to realize, however, is, without ***spiritual*** souls, there cannot be any more connection between those two humans who share the identical brain cells as there is between two identical twins. If that future clone has no recollection of a previous life, how could that re-creation of a human brain, possibly, matter?

On July 5, 1996, Ian Wilmut and Keith Campbell at the Roslin Institute (which is a part of the University of Edinburgh in Scotland) succeeded in cloning a mammal (Dolly the sheep) by utilizing a cell that was taken from another adult mammal. By so doing, they discovered the process by which ***identical copies*** *of mammals* can be created. While it ***may*** *be more difficult* to clone some mammals (such as primates) than others, the assertion that humans cannot be cloned is a dishonest claim (especially since China--a country whose cloning research is years behind Western countries--reported that, even, China's scientists have been able to, successfully, clone monkeys).

Although cloning humans ***may*** *be more difficult* than cloning other primates (and, perhaps, requires more failed attempts), it can be certain that many, *very wealthy, humans (perhaps, Steve Jobs) have, already, succeeded in cloning themselves.* If so, the scientific community should have determined, by now, whether cloned brains result in (1) the reproduction of *indistinguishably identical* human beings or, merely, (2) identical twins. The likelihood is that cloning creates twins--not the same person. If so, that result would verify Jesus' teaching that minds and souls are, distinctly, different entities. This realization, then, provides encouraging evidence that a spiritual after-life does, indeed, exist. The basis for such a conclusion results from the fact that the world's first cloned cat (cloned by Dr. Duane Kraemer at Texas A&M University in 2002) did not have the identical fur coat as its genome donor despite the fact that both shared the ***identical*** nuclear DNA. Dr. Kraemer discovered that the cloned cat was not an identical replication because s*ome inactive genes* located on the donor's X chromosome triggered alterations to the resultant cells in the cloned offspring; hence, the offspring proved to be a fraternal twin rather than an identical duplicate.

What if, ultimately, cloning demonstrates that identical humans can be reborn? Would this fact, then, prove that human souls and Heaven do not exist?

If scientific cloning were to, indeed, result in *human rebirths*, that breakthrough would only mean that humans have been allowed, ***by God***, to discover the process by which God creates life in this dimension. The most likely reason would be that God has chosen, once again, to extend the period of time that He allows humans to remain on Earth. Such a scientific advancement does not, however, disprove the existence of God and Heaven any more than other previous scientific advancements (which extended lifespans) have disproven God's existence. Such a scientific breakthrough would not alter the fact that (as wonderful a gift as human life has proven to be) God's *most marvelous blessing* is the granting of ***spiritual*** *consciousness* which (Christians are correct to believe) continues to exist after the death of the human body. Regardless of the length of time that humans are allowed to spend on Earth, the fates of humans, in the afterlife, will, nevertheless, ***still*** *be determined* by the frequencies and shapes of the spiritual souls they sculpt throughout their second gestation periods. The greatest risk which results from extended lifespans is: the longer any human remains on Earth, the greater the likelihood that the spiritual frequency of that human's soul will be corrupted. This, then, is the basis for, Greek philosopher, Herodotus' proverb: "the good die young" (because the shorter the length of human existence, the fewer the number of sins). To paraphrase Herodotus: "whom the gods love dies young; best go first).

At the beginning of this interview, you were asked if you believed you were a Modern-day prophet. You replied that a prophet is a person who is under divine influence and is directed by God to teach God's will to others. You explained that (1) you had been guided only by your spiritual self (which you have always interpreted as being a miniscule spark generated by the Holy Spirit) to follow a certain path in an effort to ensure a successful return to the place of your origin, that (2) you are aware you have been provided a very incomplete picture of spiritual existence during your dream, and that (3) you were allowed to retain just enough insight to effectively guide you through life.

Now, however, you explain that (1) the Holy Spirit (for more than six decades) continually restrained you from even speaking about your dream--until such time as the

existence of the Higgs boson particle was confirmed, in 2013, (2) the Holy Spirit inspired you to be concerned for the long-term viability of the Christian faith and, thus, taught you how to explain why Christians should not abandon their beliefs and traditions, and (3) that it would seem, then, that the Holy Spirit's primary reason for, continually, reminding you of your childhood dream has been to ensure that, at the appropriate time, you would inform all humans that verification of the existence of the Higgs boson particle, and this universe's membrane, has finally provided the scientific evidence which corroborates Christ's teachings. How does this not make you God's prophet?

Although I expressed hope (and belief) that the Holy Spirit has been inspiring and guiding me, I have, nevertheless, also, *suspected* that my, most likely, guardian angels *might be* those spiritual friends I visited during my childhood dream. It is possible that my spiritual friends are those ethereal beings who have guided me, protected me, and urged me (throughout my life) to refrain from sharing any information about my dream with others. It should be obvious that (for more than six decades) I have *not* lived the life of a prophet or been directed by God to teach God's will. Instead, I had been instructed to live the imperfect life of an *ordinary man*, experience (and cherish) a *simple existence*, and ***struggle*** (like all other mortals) to stay on that path which will return me to the place of my origin. Essentially, I was guided to avoid a life "full of sound of fury" (the type of life lamented by Macbeth in Act V, scene v, of William Shakespeare's *Macbeth* because, on the spiritual plane, all such human folly, actually, "signifies nothing". It is *only now*, as the end of my life rapidly approaches, that I have, ***finally***, *been inspired* (by either my guardian angels, the Holy

Spirit, or, perhaps, all) to explain the details of my childhood dream. It would seem, then, that *my only spiritual assignment* is to help all humans recognize that science has (more likely than not), ***finally***, substantiated the Christian belief (taught by Jesus) that God, Heaven, and hell do exist.

CHAPTER FOUR

THE MODERN ERA

When, earlier, you explained the various forms of homicide, you demonstrated how difficult it is for humans to identify the differences between good and evil. Would you be willing to share, additional, insights that your dream has taught you so that others can better identify with goodness and, therefore, avoid evil?

I am agreeable to revealing how my dream knowledge has helped to mold *my* ***real life*** *beliefs* as long as it is understood that I am sharing the ***personal*** *viewpoints of* a ***living human being***. My insights should ***never*** be perceived as the teachings of a modern-day prophet. I will do this because I believe that the greatest obstacle facing the long-term viability of the Christian Church is the absence of modern-day relevance. While Christ's parables were filled with allusions which afforded clear meaning to His contemporaries (most of whom lived in an agrarian and oppressed society), the importance and the meanings of Christ's allegories do not always have the same, real world, impact because they seem less germane to modern situations. I am, thus, willing to examine ***some*** of the more complex, modern, issues in a manner that ***I believe*** would concern Jesus if He were alive today; and I am agreeable to utilizing my dream knowledge ***to speculate*** *how Christ* would have, most likely, responded to those issues. What is the first concern?

Earlier, you explained that your original intention was to live as a human for a very short time and, then, return to your spiritual existence; the inference is that you intended to allow your young human body to die. In another previous response, you also pointed out that God has, frequently, allowed some of the most decent people to endure horrible deaths. It would appear that neither God nor you have a very high regard for human life. Can you explain?

First, since I have lived as a human for so long, it is difficult for me to recall what my earliest intentions actually were. Just a few months before my dream, I had had my tonsils removed; and it is possible my objective had been to leave my human body during that surgery. By inference, then, I suspect that I had planned to separate my spiritual-self from my human-self before the age of eight; however, I changed my decision because I did not want my very kind mother to be tortured by such a cruel action. Just the year before, she had lost her youngest brother (who had been serving in the United States' Army during the Korean Conflict); and she had been ***extremely*** *traumatized* by his death. I did not believe that she deserved to have that happen to her again; thus, my uncle's death is, most likely, the reason why I chose to remain.

Second, it is **true** that, throughout history, God has allowed millions of decent human beings to suffer and endure untimely and horrible deaths. It would seem that a just God would not allow such bad things to happen to good people. I have always believed, however, that God allows holocausts to occur because human existence is not the **true** and eternal reality. Human life, instead, is merely a testing facility (God's version of a video game, perhaps). The temporary horror of any bad event which happens to anyone in this life is fleeting, yet such events provide His children with opportunities to intensify their best spiritual qualities at that moment when they are being returned to their spiritual homes. It is easy to conclude that God's interest focuses more on the spiritual evolution (and spiritual stability) of his children (and less on their human misadventures and complications). As a result, it is very likely that God is not as concerned about worldly activities as most humans might hope.

If you believed you had planned to allow a young boy to die so that you could return to your spiritual home, please explain how your intention is different from the intention of any woman who chooses to abort an unborn, viable, child from her womb.

To begin, I have no idea when, during the gestation period, my spiritual-self would have attached to that child (and become viable) in my mother's womb. If my permanent connection between Heaven and Earth required a great amount of time to make a *spiritual* transition, I might have been inside my mother's body for an entire nine-month period (that may be the reason why a womb environment is closer to a Heavenly environment than any other environment on Earth). If, on the other hand, I had the unlimited ability to travel back and forth between Heaven and Earth during the gestation period, I would have chosen the very last possible instant to make that transition from the spirit world to the physical world; thus, I have no greater insight as to when spiritual life may actually become viable in the womb than any other human.

My best presumption would be that God is less concerned with the killing of an unborn child than God is concerned with the spiritual frequencies which were connected to (and influencing) that woman (and the others involved) when she aborted that child. Was she motivated by fear, anxiety, regret, hopelessness, confusion, and goodness; or was she driven by cruelty, sadism, selfishness, indifference, diminished empathy or remorse, poor behavioral restraint, deficient urge and impulse control, coldness and detachment, a total disregard for another's life, and evil? The urges (or impulses) which controlled her "*choice*" would have had a significant effect on the molding of her personal spiritual frequency. If God's loving purpose is to give his children an opportunity to create that spiritual frequency which is most appropriate for them, the decision to abort an unborn child would, certainly, be one of those *most determinative* "*choices*" in a woman's life. It is **true** that (*in most cases*) one event, action, or "*choice*" in a person's life could not, significantly, shape any person's spiritual frequency; however, if the decision to abort were driven by evil impulses and urges which are similar to the urges and impulses of a psychopath, such a decision could not possibly please God; thus, the goal of an anti-abortionist is not, only, to attempt to save the life of an unborn child. The goal, also, is to attempt to help prevent that mother from causing, irreparable, damage to her soul.

Although I am sure that the Catholic Church would strongly disagree, it is fortunate that a morning-after pill now exists because it certainly spares a woman from having to make a life or death decision. There, however, is still the issue of those behaviors, decisions, and urges that, initially, put that woman in the situation which led to her unwanted pregnancy and her decision to abort that pregnancy. Those types of, regrettable, behaviors would sculpt her spiritual frequency as well; thus, if she were the type of human who could readily (and callously) abort a child, her willingness to resort to that type of evil could possibly continue to define her as she lives the remainder of her life.

It is difficult to comprehend how and why *any* woman would be ***so*** hedonistic and irresponsible that she wouldn't have insisted upon engaging in safe, protected sex. Had safe sex been impossible [*sic*], then, it is difficult to understand why she would not have purchased a morning-after pill in order to prevent all possibility of a resulting pregnancy. It is also problematic to grasp how *any* woman could allow more than one month to pass without noticing the physiological changes occurring within her body which indicated that she might be pregnant.

What is most disheartening is the fact that such a woman demands that others pay all expenses for her "choice" to abort a viable life. "Choice" is, by definition, an "election"; yet elective surgery has *never* been covered by insurance or governmental subsidies for any other elective medical procedures. For example, some unattractive people would make "choices" to undergo plastic surgery in order to improve their appearances; however, they realize that *they* must assume full financial responsibility for *their* ***personal*** "choices". Why, then, should anyone else (particularly a Christian) ever be forced to pay another person's medical debt that results from the ***murder*** of an unborn child?

What is most remarkable about abortion immorality is the fact that although Christians and pro-lifers believe that a child's *soul* will survive an abortion, they, nevertheless, are the humans who choose to save the physical-life of that child. In contrast, atheists, and others who do not believe in a spiritual existence, are those who are most willing to terminate a child's life (even though their conviction is certain that the child *will never have any other opportunity to experience human existence*). *The innate, sadistic, cruelty which drives such a belief system cannot easily be ignored.* That level of evil will, *significantly*, influence a person's spiritual stability and the development of that person's frequency.

You seem to be suggesting that all of the responsibility rests with the pregnant women. Do you not believe that the aborting doctors, the counseling staffs, and the parents (if the women are underage) should also share some responsibilities?

The greatest tragedy regarding abortion is that, despite continuous denials, far too many abortions have occurred at a point in time when the unborn child could have, in fact, survived outside the womb. In those instances, therefore, counselors, parents, and the women themselves are all aware that the decisions to abort are, incontestably, decisions to murder; nevertheless, even then, there is scant hesitation to abort.

The most evil behaviors, of course, belong to the abortionists themselves. When performing *clandestine, late-term abortions*, those "*doctors*" ***know*** that they are ending the lives of innocent human beings. The thoughts, feelings, and spiritual frequencies that drive those abortionists (as they perform late-term abortions) are closer to those of psychopaths and mass murderers than to doctors who heal the sick. I cannot conceive of the type of "room" where such humans will spend their eternities. Despite such monstrous evil, only a few abortionists have ever been criminally prosecuted for their *atrocities* because, virtually, no proper investigative efforts (such as sting operations) are being conducted *to prevent such* **murders**. This makes no sense in a moral society.

Is there anything else that makes no sense concerning abortions?

Not long ago, one of the largest, and best-known, breast cancer charities was exposed for, *clandestinely*, diverting a considerable sum of *breast cancer research contributions* to abortion agencies. The breast cancer charity did this even though its officers were aware that a substantial portion of those charitable gifts were being made by Christians who were opposed to abortions. To make matters worse, the *primary* mainstream television and radio news explanation for the subsequent decrease in donations (after the **truth** concerning this deception had been uncovered) was that contributors were upset that their gifts were no longer being allowed to subsidize abortion clinics' *services*. This mainstream media misrepresentation of the **truth** was, repeatedly, broadcast despite the fact that ***all** of the donors* had been led to believe that their contributions were being spent ***only*** on breast cancer research; and ***none** of the donors* were aware that their contributions were helping to pay (either directly or indirectly) for abortions. It would have been difficult to have found even a single mainstream media voice that honestly represented Christian values and interests despite that fact that there was extensive Christian outrage in response to the ruse.

The cancer charity's deception is a microcosmic illustration of how difficult it is for good human beings to locate, identify, and associate with other good human beings in a modern *free* society. All of the "family planners", abortionists, staff members, charity workers, and reporters ***appear*** to be just as normal and decent as any other good people. *Superficially*, they seem moral and upright; yet, internally, too many have allowed themselves to be tethered to *tainted* spiritual frequencies. I am certain that, from God's Heavenly perspective, none of those sinful behaviors make any sense. They certainly make no sense to me.

Earlier you said, "It is easy to conclude that God's interest focuses more on the spiritual evolution and spiritual stability of his children and less on their human

misadventures and complications". We are members of a modern society which has become excessively dependent upon drug and alcohol use. Do you believe that these types of human misadventures might have some form of negative influence on our "spiritual stability" and the molding of our spiritual frequencies?

Obviously, the use of chemical substances which have a direct influence on thoughts, feelings, and impulses must also have a significant effect on the way a person is able to sculpt (or even maintain contact with) one's spiritual frequency. My belief has always been that *no one should mess with* ***the gift*** (***the gift***, of course, is the gift of life, consciousness, and self-awareness). I have never understood why anyone would risk, permanently, damaging those parts of the mind and the nervous system which define who a person truly is; and I have always been saddened when I have witnessed the results of such damage.

Drugs make it difficult (if not impossible) for anyone to *properly align* one's best thoughts, feelings, and impulses with that person's spiritual frequency for the purpose of creating a "singularity". Drug use, usually, accentuates the ***basest*** *types of behavior*; thus, two questions must be asked: (1) "How could any drug user sculpt the best possible spiritual frequency when he or she is too often under the influence of drugs?" and (2) "What could a user's spiritual frequency possibly be like after a lifetime of drug use?" It would be prudent for drug users to sober themselves, long enough, to realize that God is, most likely, far more disappointed with their activities than He had been with the activities of citizens from Sodom and Gomorrah.

Of course, not all chemical substances have equal negative effects. Throughout history, alcohol had been regarded as one of the first wonder drugs. It cured infections, eased pain, and reduced (or eliminated) the sicknesses that would have resulted from having eaten tainted food or having drunk polluted water. It was imbibed at most meals, including The Last Supper. Countless monasteries produced alcoholic beverages; and wine has always been used, symbolically, to represent Christ's blood in the Communion Ceremony. My suspicion is that, throughout history, Communicants were frequently allowed generous portions of wine for *practical reasons* such as easing muscle pain, killing bacteria that would be in the mouths and stomachs of the parishioners, and *enticing* reluctant parishioners to attend church and to willingly participate in confession and Communion. It is easy to infer that the quality and quantity of wine, positively, influenced the number of Christians attending a Sunday service; a good burgundy *could have, quite possibly*, helped make some sinners more devout. All of these uses would have been in moderation and would have caused limited adverse effects.

The key word regarding alcohol use is "moderation". Although it is wisest to avoid alcohol use, entirely, a modest amount of alcohol in neither sinful nor harmful. An excessive amount, however, can be damaging to a person's *spiritual stability*. While one night (or even one week) of excessive drinking (1) does impair (and possibly damage) brain cells and neurons and (2) can, temporarily, disconnect anyone from his or her spiritual frequency, the negative effects of these activities are not permanent. Long-term instances of excessive drinking, however, are certain to destroy the liver, the glands, the nervous system, and the brain; thus, it is very likely that an individual's ability to connect with (and to sculpt) a spiritual frequency would be severely damaged as well.

The primary spiritual risk associated with the use of any chemical substance results from the fact that the substance can strengthen connections to evil spiritual tethers which may be present in a person's spiritual frequency yet remain dormant and inaccessible until alcohol or drug use activates that person's connection to those evil tethers. One such example occurs when a person exhibits violent behavior ***only*** while under the influence of alcohol even though, when sober, that person would never resort to any form of physical brutality. The mere activation of that frequency does define a person's spiritual identity; thus, it would be *most wise* for all persons to avoid excessive alcohol use.

Is narcotic use any more damaging than alcohol use?

Despite claims to the contrary, narcotic use has the potential to be far more damaging than alcohol use. Although negative effects vary according to the drug being abused, virtually all drugs damage the mind and nervous system, virtually all drugs are addicting, and virtually all drugs interfere with a person's ability to connect with, and properly sculpt, the best spiritual frequency. Narcotics can only be beneficial if they are used *temporarily* in a medical treatment program supervised by a qualified and ***ethical*** *physician.*

You explained that one of the primary, acceptable, purposes for alcohol use is to ease pain. Why would you think that opioids would be any more damaging than alcohol?

According to the Center for Disease Control, two hundred and fifty-nine million *legal* prescriptions for pain-killing opioids such as Vicodin, OxyContin, and Percocet were written in 2012 (and one hundred and ninety-one million *legal* prescriptions were still being dispensed as recently as 2017), "enough for every American adult to have a bottle of pills". Unfortunately, these figures do not include (1) the illegal use of opioids such as those which have been stolen *and*, of course, (2) heroin use, which the Mental Health Services Administration *estimates* had climbed to at least six hundred and seventy thousand Americans by 2012 (and according to the National Survey on Drug Use and Health--NSDUH--that number had increased to approximately nine hundred and forty-eight thousand Americans by 2016). Sadly, that total has only *increased* since then.

While legally prescribed opioids can be beneficial when used, *briefly*, to relieve pain; opioids are far more likely to be addictive than alcohol (and are a threshold to heroin use). Opioids are prescribed several times a day, every day, for extended periods of time (abusers take these drugs more often). Opioids cause drowsiness and mental confusion and, dramatically, reduce a person's ability (1) to control his or her own behavior (by hijacking all decision-making processes) and (2) to properly connect with and sculpt that person's spiritual frequency. These drugs change the personality of a user as the addiction worsens. The only thing that matters, then, is an additional dose; and a desperate addict will do *anything* for the next one. By that time, the addict has lost most of his or her humanity. The addict's spiritual frequency is so damaged that the addiction *just might turn that person into a lost soul*. If so, drug abuse is, far more, a spiritual issue than most humans realize. It is bad enough when an addict destroys his or her mind and body; it is quite another matter when an addict destroys his or her soul and the pathway to spiritual salvation.

What is most fascinating about the excessive use of opioids is that virtually all users *claim* they require these drugs because they are experiencing *unbearable body pain.* Such claims are being made in an era when men and women perform a reduced amount of physical labor (and experience far less physical damage) than the men and women of any other historical time period. This is quite an unbelievable paradox. Throughout history, men and women have been able to endure life without narcotics. Today, despite comfortable lifestyles and the absence of hard labor, most Americans, and their ***unethical*** *doctors*, *claim* that their pain is so great that they cannot live without narcotics.

The problem which results when an *overwhelmingly large percentage* of modern-day adults are, at the very least, allowing themselves to be addicted to these painkillers is that such drug abuse turns them into creatures whose senses are so deadened that nothing ever matters. To them, "anything goes". They separate themselves from love, **truth**, goodness, empathy, order, balance, and all other, meaningful, values and principles. The only human talent they struggle to preserve is that skill which enables them to maintain an ***untruthful*** façade. Needless to say, even though they may effectively fool other humans, they are never able to deceive their spiritual frequencies; thus, their drug-use habits have the potential to result in nothing other than a form of *spiritual suicide*.

If a large percentage of opioid prescriptions are refillable prescriptions, the only logical inference is that far too many adult Americans are drug dependent. The most frightening aspect of this data is the fact that opioids represent only a small percentage of the total number of narcotics that Americans consume. What effect might other narcotics have on the sculpting of a person's spiritual frequency?

The above-cited Center for Disease Control's data does not include prescriptions written for stimulant medication such as Adderall and Ritalin, nor does it include the number of people who, illegally, abuse stimulants such as cocaine, and methamphetamines (speed). Although these types of drugs affect the mind, body, and soul differently than opioids, they are, equally, as addictive and damaging. Stimulant addiction destroys the brain and causes hostility, paranoia, exhaustion, and apathy. When, for example, an abuser shows extreme hostile and paranoid mood swings, that person is clearly not the same human being (and is clearly not connected to that same spiritual frequency which guided that person at birth).

In addition, depressants such as barbiturates, marijuana, Librium, valium, inhalants and solvents are examples of yet another class of drugs which most drug-use proponents *claim* has similar effects as (and are no more damaging than) alcohol. The differences, of course, are (1) the greater likelihood for addiction and (2) the greater probability of permanent damage in a much shorter period of time. Barbiturates slow the normal function of the central nervous system, suppress neural brain activity, and alter all senses. Almost immediately, these changes can be permanent. In reality, such drugs also kill segments of a person's identity and, thus, weaken that person's connection with his or her spiritual frequency. Explained figuratively, barbiturate use converts that sharp chisel which was provided at birth (in order to sculpt the best spiritual frequency) into a very dull, worn-out tool that can have little or no ability to sculpt a frequency which connects to the best Heavenly "rooms". This is an incredibly high price to pay for such a "brief dose" of physical-world pleasure. Drug use is not worth the spiritual consequences.

In summary, it is clear that a very large number of Americans have allowed themselves to become drug dependent. The "elephant in the room" is the fact that a significant portion of those Americans also perceives themselves as being good Christians; and that, too, is an improbable incongruity.

The only way I can comprehend this paradox is to understand that it has never been God's intention to allow Heaven to exist on Earth. Since God has permitted modern-life to be longer and more comfortable than life had been in previous centuries, God has, also, allowed newer forms of turmoil and temptation to replace the types of turmoil and temptation that accompanied the hardships of previous eras. God tolerates drug proliferation for the same reason that He allowed Eve to bite into the forbidden fruit: God's love has granted all humans the opportunity to possess the freewill to do whatever they desire. Ultimately, of course, humans will have to assume responsibility, and accept the consequences, for their "**choices**".

Earlier, you stated that the "thoughts, feelings and spiritual frequencies" of late term abortion doctors "are closer to those of psychopaths and mass murderers than to doctors who heal the sick". Do you have a similar negative opinion of drug dealers?

The term "drug dealer" is a misnomer. The proper title for such a villain is either "drug predator" or "drug terrorist". Those predators who choose to earn easy money by selling illegal drugs at exorbitant prices, *rather than to contribute something positive to society*, are aware that they are destroying the lives of their victims but do not care; the resultant harm far exceeds the damage caused by late-term abortionists. These "drug predators and terrorists" pretend that they are friends with their customers despite the fact that they know their enticements will cause permanent damage. Their business plan requires them to turn their "trusting friends" into addicts because addicts account for the greatest amount of repeat business; and addicts will find the money to pay for illegal drugs by whatever legal or illegal means necessary. Is it that difficult to grasp the types of spiritual "rooms" that are awaiting such reprobates?

Your condemnation of "drug predators (terrorists)" is quite harsh. You had been less critical even when you were discussing suicide bombers. What you have just explained is, obviously, true; however, mainstream media seldom (if ever) honestly focuses upon the amount of evil a "drug predator (terrorist)" unleashes. Why?

I have always been puzzled as to why too many of those influential personalities in films, the music industry, and news reporting (who are most responsible for shaping public opinion) have (since the 1960's) , more often, chosen to glamorize drug use, and/or ignore the damaging effects of drug use, rather than properly condemn it. Notice how initial drug experiences are referred to as "drug experimentations". For example, "The parents caught their child *experimenting* with drugs". Our *media influences, too often, **foster*** the, ill-advised, belief that all intelligent and enlightened teenagers must sample every available drug because drug use and addiction are essential steps along the pathway to adulthood. Such ***corrupt propaganda*** could not be farther from the **truth**. The rash young persons who allow themselves to be conned (by media inducers and drug predators) into sampling drugs have always been the most easily manipulated, foolish, and valueless of all, weak-minded, human beings. For their own good, those gullible youths must be ***shamed for their stupidity*** because they need to be *protected* from drug predators--not *encouraged by media to "**experiment**" with drugs*.

When I first became aware of the dramatic increase in the use of opioids soon after the beginning of this century, I contacted the appropriate editor of one of America's major newspapers to alert him of the looming problem. Initially, I was puzzled as to why he was not interested in spotlighting this impending dilemma, and I was even more puzzled when he presented one phony justification after another as to why he did not think such a story was newsworthy. It was at that point that I suspected I had, most likely, been talking with a "druggie". As a follow-up, I shared the same data and concern with that newspaper's next-most appropriate editor. His response and excuses were *too* similar. Once again, I feared that I, most likely, was talking with another "druggie". Sadly, that newspaper ***never*** *made* ***any*** *meaningful attempt to warn society of the* ***impending*** *opioid abuse crisis.* That experience caused me to realize that a frighteningly large number of the wrong-types of people are, presently, in positions of responsibility and trust. Despite superficial appearances, it is obvious that far too many of those people do not live as Christians (or are, even, concerned for their own spiritual salvation).

If the ***proper type*** *of media and governmental influences* were implemented to convince **all** *citizens (particularly children)* to avoid using drugs and (more importantly) if the ***proper type*** *of adequate punishment* (including murder charges and executions) were ***universally*** imposed on all drug predators (including physicians), America would not have to waste billions of dollars fighting a drug war that is *intentionally* designed to fail. All that Americans have to do is choose, once again, to totally avoid drugs. That choice would immediately end all drug-related problems.

The conundrum is that, even, the *United States' government* will not allow decent American Christians to isolate and protect themselves and their children from the most evil humans in society. Through federal housing and school programs (for one example--***prior*** *to President Trump's executive override order*), *the United States' government* has been paying above-market rental rates in virtually every suburb, small town, and community in this country in order to move and house families who are in the business of distributing drugs; thus, it has been ***our own government*** that has facilitated and financed the establishment of the most extensive drug distribution network in the history of the world. Drug predators would have never found most of the communities that are now plagued by drug abuse problems if ***our government*** had not made all of the arrangements and paid all of the expenses for those drug predators.

Liberal governmental officials will, indignantly, object to your accusation and, instead, claim that it is Mexican drug cartels which have introduced illegal drugs into every small community in this country (not those citizens who are on public assistance). What is your response to such an explanation?

Curiously, the *United States' government* has been responsible for far too many *factual dishonesties* concerning illegal drug distribution. Mexican cartels have merely been supplying drugs to their American distributors (those miscreants our *government* relocates to other communities in suburbs and small towns). What is most ironic is the fact that America's *governmental agencies* refer to drug-dealing families as "needy" while those *agencies* ignore the fact that "needy" families have earned billions of illegal dollars by selling drugs and committing other more heinous crimes. Our *governmental agencies*, also, count fully-involved illegal drug predators as being unemployed and living below the poverty level even when those criminals are making tens of thousands of dollars a week selling drugs and committing other serious crimes.

Should *anyone* dare speak in opposition to such evil, that person is immediately branded by America's *mainstream fake media* as being intolerant, insensitive, a hater, or worse. No *moral and intelligent opposition*, or preventative action of any kind, has been allowed. *Mainstream media's mantras* have, repeatedly, been asserting (1) that "intolerance is the greatest sin", and (2) there is no place for Christian values, or beliefs, in what *media* proclaims to be America's new "multi-cultural" society. *Mainstream Media and* ***corrupt*** *governmental officials* have succeeded in obliterating the *basic principles of the* **Christian Democracy** that has always prevailed in ***our United (Christian) States***. This, too, must immediately be confronted and stopped.

Throughout history, these types of evil have only been allowed to prevail in countries where tyranny has reigned. Such criminality is never tolerated and, thus, never continues to exist in *truly* ***free*** *countries* that are guided by moral principles. The monstrous level of rampant law-breaking which has been allowed to persist, unchecked, in this country for over sixty years continues, *only*, because those institutions responsible for confronting and eliminating criminal behavior have chosen, instead, to either (1) profit from such evil, (2) condemn those who defend **truth**, justice, and decency, and/or (3) (even worse) chosen to remain silent in the face of this non-stop, terroristic, savagery. Drug-dealing criminals are ***urban terrorists*** who are far more dangerous than radical Muslim terrorists; thus, there is no sane, moral, or justifiable reason to continue to extend citizenship to such monsters and their accomplices. In a nutshell, *America's mainstream media and government* have chosen either to facilitate (and/or to virtually ignore) the mayhem and harm that "drug predators" and their ilk have unleashed against *defenseless citizens* of this, overwhelmingly, Christian country. Why?

Your explanation seems very hostile and, on the surface, appears to be inconsistent with Christian beliefs. From His Sermon on the Mount (Matthew 7:1-2), Jesus teaches, "If you want to avoid judgment, stop passing judgment. Your verdict on others will be the verdict passed on you". Surely, you realize that helping the poor is the Christian way.

Obviously, it is the Christian way to help those who are ***truly** needy and deserving*. However, soon thereafter, at Matthew 7: 6, Jesus clarifies His meaning by warning: "Do not give what is holy to dogs or toss your pearls before swine. They will trample them underfoot, at best, and perhaps even tear you to shreds". Paul elaborates this principle at 1 Corinthians 2: 15-16 when he explains that "the spiritual man…can appraise everything…;" thus, the spiritual man has the ability to *identify* the "dogs" and "swine" through a *discernment* which results from knowing the mind of Christ. ("*Discernment*" means keenness of insight and the ability to perceive. It stresses the power to distinguish and select what is **true** and appropriate from that which is not). Christ clearly instructs that there is a difference between *discernment* and *judgment*, and Christians are obligated to utilize their ***Christian discernment*** to help all Christians identify and protect themselves from the "*dogs*" and the "*swine*". It is my *Christian discernment* which guides me (and other Christians like me) to recognize (1) the evil that drives America's drug problem and (2) the roles that both mainstream media and governmental agencies play as facilitators for that evil.

Regrettably, too many powerful non-Christians, anti-Christians, and make-believe Christians control and manipulate America's media and educational system, so completely, that, despite their obvious contempt for Christian beliefs, the Christian way of life, and Christian children, they have assumed the role of indoctrinating and teaching Christians what Christians should tolerate and believe. At Matthew 7:15-16, Jesus warns: "Be on your guard against false prophets, who come to you in sheep's clothing but underneath are wolves on the prowl. You will know them by their deeds".

Are you suggesting that even our mainstream news media is in the business of brainwashing and corrupting Christians?

I was fortunate enough to learn (in the 1960's) of the frightening successes that commercial media and advertising strategies are achieving by (1) utilizing consumer motivational research to ***subliminally*** *influence* ***unwitting*** *consumers* to buy products they don't want or need and by (2) employing psychologically manipulative techniques in order to convince unenlightened and unsuspecting people to tolerate and accept beliefs that are not in their best interests. These diabolical tactics were revealed and chronicled in two wonderfully researched sociological treatises written in the late 1950's by Vance Packard entitled *The Hidden Persuaders* and *The Statue Seekers*. (I would recommend that all Christians read both (somewhat outmoded) books in order to learn more about the *inception* of the subliminal media techniques that have (1) so successfully corrupted our Christian society from then until now and (2) so effectively swayed the Presidential election results in 2020. What is most frightening is the fact that those media propaganda tools were primitive in the 1950's in comparison to how they (and more sophisticated subliminal techniques) are, ever more effectively, being utilized (not only in commercials but, also,) in programming, news-reporting, entertainment, and, now, even educational curricula.

Although any statement which claims that mainstream media is in the business of brainwashing and corrupting Christians is obviously extreme, brainwashing and propaganda techniques have been employed, for example, in order to persuade this predominantly Christian country to transform into a country which has legalized gambling, drug use, and homosexual marriages. (I suppose Euthanasia is next). In each instance, brainwashing and propaganda techniques have enabled mainstream media to transform public opinion (**and the laws of this country**) in less than a decade.

Although the brainwashing processes are far more complex (and diabolical) than the following summary reveals, the same ***basic*** *propaganda strategy* which had been used, each time, is easy to identify, explain, and *briefly* encapsulate: At first, there was an almost daily, *propagandized*, news story which restated and drilled the reasons why change was necessary and correct. That type of constant *bombardment*, which continued for years, so familiarized, yet *numbed,* the *trusting* viewing audience that most people merely wanted the non-stop *brow-beating* to come to an end (at any cost).

Simultaneously, **the obligation to accept and accommodate those propagandized ideologies was incorporated**, as mandated educational objectives, in all school curricula (*by educational accreditation agencies*--starting at the elementary level). During that time, there was seldom, if ever, an instance when ***correct*** *opposing facts* (and, majority, Christian beliefs and values) were ***properly and honestly*** *represented and taught.*

Usually, after an extended period of propagandizing, public opinion surveys became a part of each story. **Initially**, the, *allegedly*, *valid polling results* reported that, approximately, forty percent of this country's population approved of the change (Isn't that an *improbable* coincidence?); however, over the succeeding time period (in some instances, as brief as two years), each poll tracked a, ***purported***, gradual increase in the percentage of those in agreement until, finally, each poll revealed that well-over sixty-percent of all citizens, *allegedly*, expressed approval for a change in the law. (Isn't that still another, *doubtful*, coincidence)? Left-wing reporters and news commentators *always*, then, repeatedly discussed and praised the remarkable conversion in public opinion. At that point, *coincidentally* [*sic*], legislation was passed to legalize each of those changes.

During that time period, no one ever investigated or questioned the integrity of the news stories and the validity of the polls by examining the wording of the questions in those polls, the correctness of the samplings, the trustworthiness of the pollsters, the consistency and thoroughness of polling practices, and the reason that only one particular poll had been utilized (among many other polls which had revealed, *contradictory, results*). Keep in mind, *at most*, each of the polls was a sampling of just a few hundred or a few thousand opinions despite the fact that there are, well-over, two hundred and forty million Christians in the United States.

Those polls proved to be persuasive in the same way that, as a child, I had been persuaded to keep my religious insights to myself. I wanted to be able to fit in and to be accepted. Similarly, if a Christian is, repeatedly, informed that everyone else believes in something, it makes sense for *any **tolerant Christian** to go along with the majority opinion*. That is how easy it has been for non-Christians, anti-Christians, and make-believe Christians to manipulate and silence ***the beliefs of true American Christians***. Although *dishonest sampling* is just one of the many propaganda tools employed by mainstream media, *fraudulent polling* has been utilized so corruptly, for so long, that it is a tactic that must be identified as a ***primary propaganda tool*** and, thus, permanently banned from all media reporting.

Of course, there are other contributing factors which make the brainwashing of the general population so easy. First, rather than teach children (1) to reason and analyze properly and (2) to develop higher-level thinking skills that will enable them to discern for themselves, schoolchildren, for more than the past forty-five years, have been ***programmed*** to accept whatever they are told to believe ***without question***. The proof would be easily demonstrated, for example, by the mediocre (or worse) scores ***all*** modern-day, advanced-placement, high school juniors would earn on a mid-1960's S.A.T. (Scholastic Aptitude Test) because those tests were created for the purpose of ***validly*** *identifying* those young minds which had developed higher-level, analytical, thinking abilities. Second, unchallenged commercial advertisers have been so totally effective at incorporating subliminal suggestions, as a way of influencing consumers to buy their products, that those subtle influences have, successfully (yet unscrupulously), ***conditioned*** the general population to be susceptible to (and to be easily controlled by) ***all other*** *subliminal message cues* as well. Finally, far too many adults are, frequently, under the influence of some form of chemical substance. Sadly, *impaired humans* are far more easily manipulated and, as a result, are far less likely to be guided and influenced by moral principles (especially religious values and beliefs) than they would be if they were to remain sober.

This illustration of mainstream media's anti-Christian manipulation is *merely one demonstration* of how a media that is controlled by non-Christians, anti-Christians, and make-believe Christians has, ***intentionally***, chosen to damage America's core culture. Countless additional instances exist. Just recently, for example, two different evening network television series (in the same week) *vividly* provided detailed instructions on how to locate the carotid artery for the purpose of successfully slitting a person's throat. How is that entertainment for a *civilized* society? What could those networks' objectives possibly be? Media has earned billions of dollars (1) by representing "murder", "torture", "sadism", "drug use", "perversion", and "organized criminal behaviors" as *acceptable forms of entertainment* and (2) by, satanically, ***promoting*** *all forms of human* ***dysfunction*** for the purpose of *demanding societal* ***acceptance and normalization*** *of* *aberrant and evil behaviors* (despite the fact that dysfunctional humans have always been known to be (3) the most evil, eager, and prolific murderers and (4) the primary destroyers of stable societies). No Christian is, any longer, being fooled; it is clear that those monsters who demand such transformations, in fact, are attempting to subvert societal stability (and, in the process, seize all Christian wealth and power) by provoking, ever-escalating, civil conflicts until those struggles culminate in civil war; hence, these mainstream media efforts to ***instigate societal corruptions*** must, immediately and effectively, be confronted by ***all*** **Christians** ***and stopped***.

In another illustration, Christians who publicly explain or defend Christian beliefs are not only being portrayed, by mainstream media, as bigots and haters, they are, now, also being labeled as "extremists" and "radicals" (even though *those Christians* are expressing the beliefs of the *majority* population in the United States). It is clear that these non-Christian propagandists have been fighting and, thus far, winning an ***undeclared war*** *against an unsuspecting Christian majority* in a manner that is best explained by the words expressed in the motto of Mossad (the National Israeli Intelligence Agency): "By deception, we will do war"; in other words, "as we smile in your faces, we will stab you in your backs". The last time such an undeclared war against the Christian majority (by a non-Christian minority) was successful (beginning in the 1930's in the Ukraine), more than seven million innocent Eastern European Christians were, within less than a decade, ultimately *murdered.* This is the worst Holocaust in the history of the world (Christians were victimized because they were Christians); yet, this horrible event has been totally concealed from the American public by a totally treacherous American media that, presently, is controlled by non-Christians, anti-Christians, and make-believe Christians. Why?

The non-stop assault on America's Christian culture (and democratic way of life) is frightening; yet this onslaught can easily be thwarted by any *intelligent and **unified*** Christian response which ***honestly and correctly*** *identifies and exposes* all non-Christian, anti-Christian, and make-believe Christian miscreants for the types of ***evil*** *human beings they **truly** are*. The obvious conclusion is that America's Christians are not the Americans who are censoring, brainwashing, and condemning other Christians. This insight makes it, transparently, obvious that those minorities who are responsible for the shanghaiing of America's democracy represent a small number of very dangerous (non-Christian, anti-Christian, and make-believe Christian) bigots who are, clearly, the *wrong people* to be controlling this country's access to free speech. American Christians (1) must stop trusting and utilizing those types of evil-spirited people to be providers of information, entertainment, morality, and educational ***content***; (2) must organize for the purpose of effectively boycotting ***all advertisers*** who finance the activities of these anti-Christian bigots; and (3) American Christians must be wise enough to, instead, establish web-sites, social media platforms, search engines, newspapers, wire services, book publishing companies, movie studios, **educational accreditation agencies**, and (at least three) national media networks that will (4) report the news honestly, (5) correct the presently accepted (yet dishonest) versions of American and World History, (6) provide wholesome entertainment, (7) guarantee that Christian children are educated properly, (8) ensure that all children are exposed only to nurturing ideas and values, and (9) represent America's Christian Democracy fairly. Christians should, ***never again***, be foolish enough to, voluntarily, relinquish control of their country to non-Christians, anti-Christians, and make-believe Christians. As a first step, Christians would be wise to *permanently boycott **all*** Hollywood movies (and ***all other*** entertainment and media programming sites) which contain ***any** form* of anti-Christian, non-Christian, and/or make-believe Christian propaganda.

There is the likelihood that (if the Christian community were to ***unite*** and, then, choose to pursue legal remedies) Christians should have sufficient *factual justification* to cause the revocation and reassignment of the broadcasting licenses of a substantial number of television and radio stations throughout this country. The people operating those outlets merely possess governmental licenses to broadcast; their rights to continue to control those licenses are *conditional rights*. All that Christians need to do, in order to confront and correct media misconduct, is to (1) document *all* of those transgressions and, then, (2) formulate an intelligent, moral, and correct action plan; hence, large Christian groups (and wealthy, true-Christians) must unite and ***immediately*** (3) establish reliable media sources and (4) expose and confront *every instance* of un-American and anti-Christian propaganda.

One of the most appalling examples of un-American and anti-Christian bias (*at the time of this interview*) is mainstream media's non-stop effort (allegedly, because of recent school shootings) to remove the Second Amendment from the United States' Constitution and seize all self-defense weapons from law-abiding citizens. They have chosen to blame (1) guns and (2) the totally innocent majority populations for horrid societal events that ***have, in fact, been instigated, entirely, by mainstream media***.

For example, on November 24, 1971, an airplane was hijacked by a still unidentified man whom media misidentified as D.B Cooper. Had media reported ***that*** skyjacking event responsibly and professionally, there would have been very few additional hijackings. It was only because national media (1) sensationalized the crime by continually showcasing it as entertainment and, thus, (2) turned D. B. Cooper into a legend that ***national media*** *succeeded in* ***provoking*** hundreds of evil and/or disturbed individuals to become copycat skyjackers.

A car theft and murder (in Detroit in 1991) was the first instance where *media taught criminals* how easy it was for felons to violently steal cars. Until that date, "carjackings" seldom occurred; however, the National Crime Victimization Survey conducted by the United States' Department of Justice, quite predictably, reported that, between 1993 and 2002, approximately 39,000 carjackings per year occurred in the United States (immediately following media's irresponsible and sensationalized methods of showcasing those crimes, nationally, to the general public).

President Trump, in a speech to the NRA on May 4, 2018, stated that if national media's *rationale* for seizing guns were widely accepted and, likewise, applied to situations where automobiles were involved in violent crimes, cars would also, then, have to be taken away from car owners because if people were forced to stop driving, cars (1) could not be used as weapons to murder people; (also, (2) cars, then, would no longer be hijacked).

While mainstream media has been very quick to blame law-abiding, gun-owning citizens for high school massacres, they have consistently refused to *honestly* report (and, thus, teach) the **truth** about what happened to defenseless Christians in countries (such as the Ukraine in the early 1930's) after all of their weapons had been seized. Media has also failed to **truthfully** relate the most significant details regarding the ***first*** (modern era) high school *massacre* (that was *sensationalized* by national mainstream media) at Columbine High School in Littleton, Colorado on April 20, 1999. In their attack, Eric Harris and Dylan Klebold murdered twelve students, one teacher, and wounded twenty-one others. The most important detail (which national media believed was too insignificant to mention) is that Harris was

Jewish; and both assailants hated Christians so much that their intent was to murder as many ***Christians*** as possible (by identifying those children who professed belief in Jesus for the *specific purpose* of slaughtering them). Had (1) Harris and Klebold not committed their atrocities and (2) had national media not dishonestly and ***improperly*** concealed the underlying basis for their evil, no subsequent school mass murders would have occurred. If media had ***truthfully*** reported (1) that Harris was Jewish and (2) that Harris committed his atrocities because of his deep hatred for Christians--(***Who put those evil thoughts in his head...and why?***), media *would have* ***never***, ***thereafter***, ***DARED*** to insist upon the confiscation of guns from law-abiding, ***Christian citizens***. By using ***national media's*** *same method of reasoning*, it would seem that media should, instead, be (1) demanding the removal of all anti-Christian citizens from this country and be (2), *voluntarily*, surrendering ***all of their*** broadcasting licenses (rather than Christian-owned guns) to the government since America's biased and dishonest media is the single greatest threat to this country's freedom and ***safety***. After all, if media *must* assign fault, media should place blame where that culpability actually exists.

The primary reason this modern society has become so corrupt is that the massive sums of money earned from illegal activities (starting with Prohibition, gambling, and prostitution and continuing with illegal drugs and Wall Street and Governmental corruption) are presently the financial engines that are controlling American society (the bad guys now control everything); nevertheless, Christians can easily overcome this evil by uniting (because there are so many Christians yet so few bad guys).

Imagine the good that could result if seventy million Christians were to donate only five dollars each (at the same time). They would, immediately, have built a three hundred and fifty million dollars war chest for the purpose of starting the process of, once again, retaking control of America's media. Imagine if Christians contributed five dollars every week (or month). Before long, Christians would, once again, reassume control over their own culture and society. The difficulty, of course, would be to find a team of truly trustworthy and incorruptible Christians to manage those large sums of money. That, regrettably, will not be so easy--yet, is not impossible.

Returning to the drug abuse discussion--in truth, doesn't the willingness to share illegal drugs help less attractive males to be more alluring to attractive females; and isn't this the primary reason that so many young people choose to use drugs? If so, do you believe that such behavior is spiritually damaging?

The surest means by which an unmarried man is able to achieve sexual intimacy with an attractive woman (in this modern era) is by, first, sharing drugs and/or alcohol with her. This approach (a far cry from the flowers and candy gifts provided by suitors of previous generations) does enhance a less attractive male's prospects for having intercourse with a more attractive, drug-craving female. Because alcohol and illegal drug use has become such an integral part of the mating ritual, the possibility that a man and woman (in an alcohol and/or drug-sharing relationship) might **truthfully** fall in love with one another is highly unlikely. Both sexes become so habitually addicted to experiencing orgasms while high on illegal drugs (or alcohol) that the identities of their sexual partners no longer matter to them. Even when married, druggies will choose to have sex with anyone (at every opportunity) rather than honor their marital vows. Such behavior ***is*** *spiritually damaging* because the pursuit of *extreme pleasure* causes irreparable harm to spiritual frequencies by creating imbalances which result in the *disconnection* from too many of the "good" tethers which might have existed within those frequencies prior to drug use. Commitment and integrity are two concepts that do not exist in the minds of drug users; thus, it follows that God, most likely, is disappointed with those of His offspring who will not allow themselves to be sufficiently satisfied with the joy of drug-free sexual intercourse (and **true** affection).

It is obvious that modern society has become highly promiscuous, and the institution of marriage seems threatened. Do you believe that these types of human misadventures (even when the husbands and wives are not drug users) might, also, have some form of negative influence on "spiritual stability" and the molding of spiritual frequencies?

Even when husbands and wives are not drug users, the absence of commitment and integrity (as well as the betrayal of vows and trust in a marriage) are significant causes for spiritual frequency problems; however, the complete answer to this question concerning marital betrayal and sexual promiscuity is far more complicated because most of the Old Testament's prohibitions guiding sexual interaction were, most-likely, practical rules created by humans (to enable barbarians to live peacefully, safely, and healthfully together in civilized communities) rather than mandates ordered by God.

Originally, God created all mammals to have an overwhelming urge to procreate. It is clear that, at a time when the world was dangerously underpopulated, nothing was more important to God than the survival of as many members of the human species as possible. Rape (an act by which a stronger male sexually forces himself upon an indefensible female) had always been primitive primates' preferred way to achieve that survival goal. An excellent depiction of the violent lives of primitive and (frequently) half-naked humans was recreated in the 1982 R-rated film, "Quest for Fire", which is based on the 1911 Belgian novel by J. H. Rosny, *La Guerre du Feu*. Males would often fight one another for the opportunity to plant their genetic seeds; and females were always, sufficiently, compliant because they innately knew that the strongest males would ensure the greatest likelihood of robust children (and protectors). Since these inborn urges and traits were conceived by God for the purpose of insuring the survival of the human species, it is difficult to understand why God would condemn any of his children for behaving in the way that God, *intentionally*, created humans to behave. Despite those animalistic behaviors, it could not have taken very long, however, for any male offspring, who had been raised *and influenced* solely by a mother, to realize that a father's presence and support was essential; thus, those prehistoric rapists were, also, the architects of the world's earliest family units.

As humans transitioned from being hunters and gatherers into people who lived in communities, it became clear that laws were necessary in order to maintain stability and peace within those communities; thus, two of the Ten Commandments focused on family relationships. Apparently, adultery was rampant during the Biblical Era because the Sixth Catholic and the Seventh Protestant Commandment admonishes sexual relations with anyone outside of a marital union. It is, also, obvious that other forms of barbaric behavior prevailed because the Ninth and Tenth Catholic Commandments and the Tenth Protestant Commandment instructed that a man should not covet his neighbor's wife or any of his neighbor's possessions. Since it is not likely that human laws would have curbed impulses that were driven by strong animalistic urges, it is understandable that (1) only the fear of immediate execution or (2) the fear of God's wrath would have deterred such inclinations; thus, the real world need to curb savage behaviors was, most likely, more a human necessity than it was a spiritual edict. The fear of God's eternal damnation provided *a compelling reason* to motivate those barbarians to transform themselves into civilized human beings.

For a substantial period in human history, *societal necessity*, also, best explains the reason why a woman's virginity has been such a significant moral and religious issue. People who lived during Biblical times had very little knowledge or understanding of venereal diseases such as gonorrhea and herpes, yet they were aware that the only ways to avoid such venereal infections were to either abstain from intercourse entirely or to be sexually involved with only one virginal woman. It was easy for the people living in those eras to conclude that ***God's*** *intention* was to severely punish philandering humans; thus, from the beginning of the Biblical Era until the present day, it has been logical for all humans to conclude that, because *feminine promiscuity* (too often) causes serious health problems (including premature death), it has always made sense to regard a woman's wonton sexual behavior as sinful behavior.

You mentioned gonorrhea and herpes, but you neglected to include syphilis. Why?

There is too little evidence to prove, conclusively, that syphilis existed in the Middle East during Biblical times. The *prevailing theory* suggests that Columbus' crewmen brought syphilis back to Europe and caused a syphilitic epidemic that spread throughout southern Europe at the end of the Fifteenth Century. That does not prove with certainty, however, that syphilis did, or did not, already exist in Europe and the Middle East prior to that time.

Despite the "Columbus Theory", the etiological history of the disease teaches that syphilis derived from the Treponema group of corkscrew-shaped bacteria known as spirochetes; and all spirochetes originated in equatorial Africa and America. It is easy to deduce, then, that these bacteria would have, most likely, migrated to the Middle East millennia ago. Such an inference seems somewhat likely since unsubstantiated evidence of congenital syphilis has recently been found in teeth of the *intact skeletons* of two children who died in the eruption of Mount Vesuvius at Pompeii, Italy in 79 A.D.

In addition, a literal interpretation of Psalm 38: 4-12 reveals a list of symptoms that could be a description of syphilis (as well as leprosy): "no health in my *flesh*…no wholeness in my *bones*…noisome and *festering* are my *sores*…I am stooped and bowed down profoundly…**my *loins* are filled with *burning pain***…I am *numbed* and severely crushed…I *roar with anguish* of heart…my *heart* throbs; my *strength* forsakes me…the very light of my *eyes* has failed me…." It is probable that such a disease would have been regarded as being a *"venereal* leprosy", and the likelihood that syphilis would have been regarded as a form of leprosy (and not a distinctly different disease) is the most plausible reason that there is not a more specific mention of syphilis in the Bible.

Leviticus 15: 1-3 referred to a symptom of "uncleanness" which could readily be interpreted as an early stage venereal disease symptom as well: "Every man who is afflicted with a chronic flow from his private parts is thereby unclean". Leviticus proceeded to enumerate *God's commands* regarding the proper containment, treatment, and prevention of leprotic-type diseases; thus, Leviticus' teachings proved to be a marvelously effective, Old Testament, medical training tool that succeeded in limiting the outbreaks of countless epidemics. If, indeed, syphilis did exist in the Middle East that early in history, and a substantial number of those afflicted humans did suffer rashes and skin pustules, blindness, madness, and premature deaths, it is obvious that stern religious opposition to promiscuous sexual behavior was the most effective strategy that prevented widespread epidemics. *Most likely*, the fear of deadly diseases would have been the *primary*, *real world, basis* for condemning and prohibiting indiscriminate sexual activity. It is even likely (in addition to the many significant religious reasons) that the *primary practical reason* nuns and priests *willingly embraced celibate living* was because of the well-known fact that chaste humans enjoyed healthier and longer lives than those humans who, regularly, succumbed to their carnal urges.

Your explanation has become somewhat confusing. At first, you claimed that God intentionally created humans to have an intense urge to procreate. If that were indeed true, why would God choose to torture sexually active human beings with the pain and suffering caused by various venereal diseases when those persons were guilty of nothing more than behaving in the manner that God created them to behave?

Once again, it is quite obvious that God never intended to create Heaven on Earth. God has always utilized temptation and turmoil in order to sufficiently test His children so that their **true** identities would be defined and revealed to Him. Most likely, after programming humans to have strong urges to procreate, God was not pleased with the behaviors of those prehistoric rapists because they lived lives that caused them to sculpt spiritual frequencies which were unsuitable for ascension to *Heaven*. For the same reason that God cast Adam and Eve out of paradise, God's solution to this dilemma was to cause prehistoric savages to endure the pain, suffering, and regret associated with venereal diseases in order to help them acquire the sensitivity and humility necessary to sculpt *acceptable spiritual frequencies* and, in the process, to learn how to become civilized human (and spiritual) beings.

The first question that should be asked is: How did a venereal disease such as syphilis come into existence? In its original form, it was a fairly benign bacteria that thrived everywhere in the humid heat of a tropical rain forest. When it was carried to distant environments, such as dry deserts or cold mountains, syphilis could have only survived in warm and moist internal areas of a primate's body (such as a woman's womb). Harmful mutations occurred when the original form of that bacteria interacted with other potent bacteria which either existed, or were deposited, inside a female primate's body. Only then, did syphilis become a harmful disease that, first, damaged and, finally, destroyed its host.

The second question to ask is: did these bacterial mutations occur as a result of evolution, or did they occur as a result of divine intervention? It is quite possible that they evolved, independently, without God's control; yet God, nevertheless, chose to utilize those mutations because the damage caused by the resultant venereal diseases did serve *God's greater purpose*. On the other hand, God may have been so displeased with the cruelty and savagery that accompanied the violent and animalistic sexual behavior of those prehistoric rapists (and sodomites) that God felt compelled to impose the types of punishment caused by venereal diseases in order to force primitive humans to have no other alternatives than to cease their barbaric ways. While Genesis 19:24 chronicles that God's anger was so great that He rained burning sulfur (fire and brimstone) on the residents of Sodom and Gomorrah as punishment for their sexual immoralities and perversions, that one event would not have been a *sufficient-enough* punishment to curb the behaviors of all immoral humans, everywhere, for thousands of years. Venereal diseases (which are caused by bacteria and, more recently, by the Human Papilloma Virus), on the other hand, would have provided sufficient, widespread, and continuous punishment. It is interesting to note (1) that, for many centuries, sulfur (including thermal sulfur waters) just happened to be one of the primary compounds used to treat venereal diseases and (2) that Revelations 21:8 warns "the *fiery* pool of burning sulfur, the second death" awaits the "fornicators" and other sinners.

Regardless of whether syphilis mutated as a result of evolution or as a result of divine intervention, the history of venereal disease and the role it has played in the transformation of human behavior demonstrates how God does work in mysterious ways. Bacteria and viruses have always been two significant vehicles which God has utilized to enable sub-atomic, *spiritual energy* (that is devoid of physical world mass and matter) to transcend into the physical world for the purpose of triggering human and environmental changes; thus, it might be inferred that bacteria and viruses are *essential tools* which are employed by God for the purpose of *nudging* humans in the directions that will enable them to sculpt the best spiritual frequencies.

The fact that God would choose to utilize bacteria and viruses as His tools demonstrates that God has elected to, dramatically, limit His direct interaction with humans and has chosen, instead, to behave more like a puppeteer who operates the strings of His creations from behind stage (and out of sight). His reason is quite apparent. If God were to make His existence any more obvious than He already has, God would be besieged by all of the liars and hypocrites who would conceive of innumerable, non-stop, deceptions in order to attempt to dupe God into permitting their entrance to Heaven. Obviously, God is not so foolish. It is God's choice to see people as they truly are (not how they would pretend to be); and God can best do that by allowing the possibility of the existent of Heaven to remain *a debatable uncertainty* for all of His children.

Can you provide any other evidence to support your observation that bacteria and viruses are tools that have been employed by God to transform humans in ways that will guide them to sculpt the best spiritual frequencies possible?

Although any response that I provide can only be regarded as a product of my own speculation, I have, recently, *recognized* that God's reason for re-introducing a relatively new, harmful, virus to human bodies is for the purpose of revealing to humans that both larger and smaller-sized human heads (and brains) did not evolve in the manner theorized by Darwin but, instead, formed, *almost instantaneously*, in the embryos of mothers who had been exposed to a ***particular*** *virus* during the first trimester of pregnancy. While Darwin's Theory of Evolution explains why (1) facial features, (2) the width of hips, and (3) skin colors, for example, evolved differently in separate parts of the world over long periods of time, Darwin's natural selection theory does not provide a convincing explanation which accounts for *the development of human consciousness and spiritual uniqueness*.

God's most recent revelation DOES, however, by disclosing to humans that it is the presence of a particular virus in the womb, *during pregnancy*, which is the *triggering element* that has caused humans to develop those higher-level abilities which make them so different from other primates. It, then, can easily be inferred that *the presence of* ***unique viruses and bacteria*** *in the womb,* ***at particular times*** *during fetal development* (viruses and bacteria which derive from *sub-atomic spiritual energy* that, in its original form, is devoid of physical-world mass and matter), transcend into the physical world, ***specifically***, for the purpose of triggering and shaping ***all mammalian differentiation by way of spontaneous generation***.

The effects of this relatively new virus (named Zika) have, thus, revealed *the* ***true origin of human (mental and spiritual) uniqueness***. Accordingly, since God's most recent revelation (which substantiates *both Christian and scientific theories*) provides a more logical explanation than Darwin's theory, (1) even the most non-religious scientists should be agreeable to acknowledging that this ***Christian Mammalian Differentiation Theory*** **is** ***the, most-likely, scientific explanation which explains why humans are so uniquely different from other mammals*** and (2) all scientists (no matter how reluctantly) should be sufficiently wise to acknowledge the *likelihood* that human transformation is, more likely, the result of an ***intentional cognitive revolution*** rather than ***an accidental and arbitrary evolution***. Despite such a remarkable (eye-opening) revelation from God, it does seem odd that far too few people have, thus far, recognized *God's message* (and the significance of that message).

The Zika Virus is a mosquito-transmitted virus (*first identified* in Uganda in 1947) which causes harm by triggering scattered calcium deposits and microcephaly, a disease which interferes with fetal development that can, *immediately*, cause smaller heads, smaller brains, and brain damage to result in some babies who are born to mothers who had been infected by the virus during the first trimester of pregnancy. Zika attacks and penetrates uterus cells which line and help protect the placenta; this invasion *thwarts* the growth of placental blood vessels and, resultantly, stunts fetal development. The virus, next, migrates to the embryonic brain where it *interferes with* and, thus, damages the stem cells' *normal process* of developing into a functioning organ. In lab experiments that solely tested mice, scientists discovered (surprisingly) that Zika, *randomly,* causes both *abnormally large brain structures* as well as abnormally small brain structures in those tested *mice embryos*. It is likely that God's intention (once the Zika virus' damaging effect in the womb was identified) has been to inspire insightful humans to, correctly, recognize that Zika (***or another similarly acting virus***) must have, **correspondingly, *ENHANCED* human embryonic development *and is, thus, the triggering event which has enabled humans to be blessed with larger and better functioning brains*** than any of their closest mammalian relatives.

Such a revelation, finally, makes God's creation plan much easier for humans to recognize and understand. It appears that His earliest goals had merely been to design, test, and identify those species which could best function, adapt, reproduce, and survive within earth's environment. Only after those initial goals were successfully accomplished did God utilize viruses and bacteria to integrate ***some*** *of those characteristics which reflect His own image* into the consciousness of the human species.

By now, scientists should be pondering how and why a virus could have had such a significant impact on humans yet, then, vanished (or, at least, become totally dormant) immediately after it transformed lower-level primates into thinking, conscious, and spiritual human beings. *My inference* is that the disappearance of the virus had to have resulted from God's *willful act* because, had that virus not vanished, all brains would, by now, be as large as beach balls. Although any evidence which supports my inference can, at best, only be circumstantial, the manner by which certain transformative bacteria and viruses have appeared (*and, then, disappeared*) is almost certain to have been a willful, rather than accidental, consequence of, God-directed, evolutionary events.

Progressive Creationists have long believed that any, nearly instantaneous, species transformation which (1) enhances human embryonic development, (2) results in the growth of larger, more sentient, and/or better functioning brains, and (3) elevates the human species to a much higher mammalian level, only once, *over a very brief period of time* (rather than millions of evolutionary years--and, then, nearly vanishes) is not a species transformation that can, believably, be explained by Darwin's Theory of Evolution. Progressive Creationists (not scientists) have, thus, ***correctly*** *concluded* that there must be a more likely, alternative, explanation.

Instead of condemning and excluding the theories of Progressive Creationism from the classroom, the scientific community should, instead, be joining Progressive Creationists by (1) pondering how and why a virus (similar to the Zika virus) could have had such a significant impact, ***ONLY upon humans*** yet, then, vanished (or, at least, become totally dormant) immediately after it transformed lower level primates into thinking, conscious, and spiritual human beings and by (2) recognizing that Darwin's Theory of Evolution ***cannot possibly be the best explanation*** for the, almost instantaneous, elevation of the human species to its higher mammalian level of consciousness and self-awareness.

By providing an alternative and (*quite possibly*) superior explanation than the Theory of Evolution as to why humans are so uniquely different from other primates, Progressive Creationism has demonstrated itself (in this instance, at least) to be such a sufficiently valid ***theoretical*** *scientific possibility* that it succeeds in uncoupling "itself from its Creationist and, thus, religious, antecedents". There is no legal, intelligent, or moral reason for *Kitzmiller v. Dover Area School District* to have outlawed the inclusion of Intelligent Design Creationism in science classrooms (*even if it were*, in fact, only a "pseudoscientific view" which suggests that certain features of the universe are best explained by an intelligent cause--not by an indirect process such as natural selection) because the inclusion of such insightful, alternative concepts does succeed in stimulating young minds in the same way

Einstein's mind had been stimulated by religious instruction when he was a young man.

Devil's advocates would suggest that the virus became dormant because humans, most likely, developed lifelong immunities as a result of having been infected by the Zika (or a comparable) virus. Does not that explanation seem more plausible?

It *does* seem plausible; however, humans do not, *usually*, develop lifelong immunities after having been exposed, for example, to cold and flu viruses. The fact that Zika (or a similar virus) elevated all of humanity to a higher mammalian level (***only once*** and, then, nearly vanished) ***seems*** *willful* (and not accidental). If the re-introduction of such a virus is, indeed, an intentional Divine act, there is also the possibility that, by allowing man to, finally, understand the effect that the Zika virus (***or a comparable virus***) has on embryonic brain development, God has chosen to herald a new era for human existence by showing scientists how to *increase and/or transform* human brain function for the purpose of allowing humans to evolve, once again, to higher mental, emotional, and *spiritual* levels (and, thus, gain greater control over their animalistic impulses--Original Sin). If my inference is correct (and if, indeed, it is God's will), researchers may soon be able to either reverse-engineer Zika--or utilize a comparable virus (for the purpose of increasing the growth of placental blood vessels, stimulating additional development of embryonic brain stem cells, and, resultantly, *unlocking* unimaginably advanced mental and *spiritual* human abilities). If God does permit scientists to, successfully, reverse engineer the effects of the Zika virus (now or sometime within the next few millennia), humans should recognize that God believes the best way to limit sinful behavior (and, perhaps, prevent humans from destroying Earth) is by, once again, dramatically *enhancing the mental and spiritual capabilities* of all humans--and, thus, reducing the *too-strong influence* of Original Sin.

When (and if) such a metamorphosis occurs, humans should, finally, be sufficiently wise to, gratefully, realize that their transformation is (not the chance result of natural selection but, instead,) solely God's gift--a fulfillment of the Progressive Creationism belief which teaches that *God directly intervenes* in natural order (for the purpose of guiding the course of human evolution) ***only** at key moments throughout history*.

The Zita virus outbreak, thus, does seem to provide the best, most recent, evidence to support my belief that viruses and bacteria are tools which have been employed by God (at key moments throughout history) to transform humans in ways that will help them sculpt their best spiritual frequencies. Despite the fact that my dream did not supply me with *absolute proof* that God does exist, it did, nevertheless, endow me with sufficient intellectual skill to readily refute most atheist and agnostic notions. It is not necessary for Christians to disprove Darwin's theory; instead, Christians merely have to, *first*, point out that Darwin's natural selection theory is not the *correct explanation* which accounts for the development of ***human consciousness and spiritual uniqueness*** and to, *second*, replace Darwin's *presently accepted theory with the more appropriate (and more-likely correct)* ***Christian Mammalian Differentiation Theory***--a combined scientific and religious vindication which ***does, in fact***, *account for the development of human consciousness and spiritual uniqueness*.

You have inferred that by allowing the Zita virus to emerge from its dormancy, God has directly conveyed a significant message to humanity. One of the primary reasons that many humans refuse to believe in God's

existence results from the fact that there is far too little evidence that God interacts with humans in the same way that He, allegedly, interacted with humans thousands of years ago. What is your explanation as to why God no longer directly interacts with humans?

The easiest way to respond is by sharing the following analogy: In 2002, a revolutionary *robotic* house-cleaning tool was introduced. I was so impressed that I immediately bought one. Soon thereafter, I contacted the company in order to make inquiries about the product. I was amazed when I found myself being connected to (and directly talking with) one of the creators and owners of the product. He answered the phone because a customer service department had not, yet, been fully established and because he was interested in receiving feedback regarding his creation so that he could immediately correct all problems and fine-tune the product's performance in order to make it as perfect a product (as quickly as possible). I have always been pleased to know that, by sharing my insights, I *may* have helped.

Since then, the company has perfected the robot, established a customer service department, and earned billions of dollars. Although it is not out of the question that the inventors and owners might still, *sometimes*, answer a customer service phone line, there no longer is a *compelling reason* for them to do so (particularly since they have moved on to other projects). Similarly, it would seem that after thousands of years of tinkering, God has far fewer *compelling reasons* to fine-tune his creation. While (because of sexual immorality) God *may have*, initially, directly caused the destruction of Sodom and Gomorrah, venereal diseases have, subsequently, made God's *direct and continuing intervention* less necessary. I am certain that, by now, God is willing, in most instances, to allow automatic systems oversee His creation; thus, although it is not impossible that God would interact with modern humans and intervene in current, worldly affairs, God's intercessions would be less frequent because God would have far fewer reasons to intercede. If, indeed, God's introduction of the Zita virus is a message to humans, His purpose is to *launch* a distinctively new era for human existence.

The second reason so many people are no longer willing to live religious lives is because there are so many different religions from which to choose. They believe that if God really did exist, there would be only one true religion. What explanation does your dream provide as to why there are so many conflicting religious belief systems?

God's and Jesus' primary concern has been to help humans realize (1) that there is a spiritual existence and (2) that there is a proper way to prepare for that spiritual afterlife. Although Jesus' words have had the most significant world influence and, thus, have been the most beneficial for that purpose, the teachings of other great spiritual leaders such as Moses, Buddha, and Allah (which encourage humans to live good, loving, **truthful**, humble, repentant, and *peaceful* lives) have served God's purpose as well. It has never been God's intention to be worshipped as an idol (*except* in those instances when such *religious focus* helps humans to locate and ascend the salvation pathway). God preference has, instead, *always* been to welcome *all religious belief systems which teach humans "the way" to their spiritual salvation* (by encouraging all human qualities which best assure Heavenly ascension). As long as ***any*** *religion* teaches goodness, and serves God's purpose by guiding humans to Heaven's pathway, God will welcome and embrace that religion. The fact that some of those religions may not recognize Jesus as God is not God's greatest concern.

If you are aware that it is God's will to allow the existence of Heaven to remain an uncertainty in the minds of His children, why are you trying to convince humans that "Heaven is for real" by sharing what you have learned as a result of your childhood dream?

I have already explained my two intentions. The first reason is that I believe that the understandings I gained from my dream can be fruitful for those Christians who are striving to live good lives. The second reason is that I am hopeful that I can help ***some*** humans recognize their own connections with the Holy Spirit and recall the fact that they, too, had similar dream experiences when they were *very* young. Since I am aiming at such a limited audience, I imagine that, initially, only a small number of people will actually benefit from knowing about my dream; thus, I suspect that the majority of humans will, at best, be indifferent. This type of response and acceptance was **true** *even for Jesus*. Neither the moneychangers in the Temple nor the Roman conquerors, for example, were, in any way, impressed by Jesus' inspirations, insights, morality, divinity, and goodness. I do not believe that the world has changed so much from then until now. There are countless modern-era people who are equivalents to those moneychangers and those merchants who cheated buyers inside the holy temple. I doubt if many of those types of modern-day transgressors will be, positively, influenced by my spiritual insights (regardless). Nevertheless, I am hopeful that the understandings that I gained as a result of my dream ***might*** *help some* ***good*** *humans when they are in need of* ***practical*** *spiritual guidance.*

You have explained that many aspects of sexual morality result more from real world necessities than God's religious mandates. If that is the case, is not the condemnation of

promiscuity just as great a sin as the promiscuous act itself? For example, during the Victorian Era, young women would have had their lives and reputations destroyed (even after having been raped) if they did not remain virgins. Why was such unyielding condemnation regarded as proper Christian behavior?

That question is the theme of the Victorian novel, *Tess d'Urbervilles* (a sympathetic portrayal of a "fallen woman"), first published by Thomas Hardy in 1891. The subtitle, *A Pure Woman Faithfully Presented*, made clear that the novel was an attack on Victorian Christian morality.

Tess is a touching, and beautifully written, tale about an attractive, yet impoverished, sixteen-year-old girl, Tess, whose family is led to believe they are distantly related to an affluent, titled family. What Tess does not know is that the wealthy family had purchased that title and, thus, is not related by blood. After seeking an introduction, Tess is provided a job as an elder guardian by Alec, a man she believes to be her cousin; however, Alec soon seduces, rapes, and impregnates Tess.

Tess returns home in shame to give birth to a child, Sorrow, who shortly, thereafter, dies. Since her opportunities to live a good life were stolen from her because of her *sexual sin*, she is reduced to laboring as a field worker for farmers. While working as a dairy maid, she meets the love of her life, Angel, and they marry; however, when they confess their sins to one another, Angel cannot forgive Tess for having had a child before marriage and suggests that they separate. Angel goes to Brazil, and Tess returns to harsher work and an even harder life.

Tess, once again, encounters Alec who, by this time, has become an evangelical minister. He pursues her and asks her to marry him, but she despises him too much. Before long, however, her father dies, her mother is ill, and her family is evicted from their home. Destitute and desperate, Tess is forced to turn to Alec for help and, ultimately, lives with Alec as his mistress after Alec convinces Tess that Angel will never return.

Overwrought with regret, Angel does return in order to be reunited with Tess; but he is too late. When they meet, Tess sends Angel away. Consumed by rage, she confronts and kills Alec by stabbing him in the heart. Angel assists Tess's escape, but she is quickly caught, tried, and executed; thus, ends the tragic life of a totally innocent human being whose suffering and death is, *entirely,* the result of intolerant *Victorian* ***Christian*** *morality.*

If the story of *Tess D'Urbervilles* were, indeed, a **truthful** depiction of events during the Victorian Era, it would serve as a compelling and convincing condemnation of Christian excess, cruelty, and prideful self-righteousness. For decades, *Tess* has been essential college English Literature reading. The ***initial*** *reason* for inclusion of such a *slanted, anti-Christian*, selection was to help young Christian minds develop higher-level thinking skills by teaching students the ability to *recognize and understand* ***all points of view*** in order to help them learn how to arrive at insightful and correct conclusions. Such skills, thus, were particularly important in helping Christians recognize ***that*** *spiritual moment* when sinless intentions have the potential to transform into sinful behavior.

Decades ago, students would have been well versed in Christian moral teachings; and *Tess* would have provided an effective, higher-level, intellectual counterpart. Regrettably, for more than forty years, most references to Christian beliefs and morality have been either (1) condemned or (2) excised from both undergraduate and college-level educational programs. *The Crucible*, for example, (an **allegorical play**--written by a non-Christian--which *critically attacks* both the, alleged, fanaticism surrounding (1) a single Puritan trial in the late1600's and (2) the McCarthy Senate hearings in the early 1950's) is, ***curiously***, considered to be essential reading for high school English students. On the other hand, far too many works of literature which reinforce Christian values or teach about Christian heroes have been eliminated. Even worse, students are no longer being equipped with the valuable lessons and tools that can be gained from studying insightful writings such as William Shakespeare's *The Merchant of Venice*, a play which helps decent human beings acquire essential skills for recognizing, confronting, and thwarting the evil schemes, vengefulness, mercilessness, and **untruthful** intentions of non-Christians, anti-Christians, and make-believe Christians (who are ***not*** guided by the same moral principles although they may, *very convincingly, pretend* that they are). As a result, college students are being taught, ***only***, a dumbed-downed, one-sided, propagandized, anti-Christian point of view. No longer is any effective attempt being made to help students develop sound moral foundations and higher-level skills. With *Tess* (and with far too many other areas of college curricula), the only indoctrinating message a college student is required to retain is that people who earn diplomas should be both suspicious and contemptuous of Christian religious beliefs. As a result, unfortunately, too many college graduates are no longer allowing themselves to be guided by Christian values and, thus, are foolishly exerting far too little effort into sculpting the best possible spiritual frequencies for themselves.

Should not students be made aware of the dangers of religious extremism and governmental excesses that could lead to tyranny?

The problem with *The Crucible*'s lessons, for example, is that the allegory misrepresents history. Although it is **true** that Senator McCarthy's tactics were dishonest and heavy-handed, his improper behavior was minor (and forgivable) compared to the significant issues that modern revisionists have chosen to erase from historical records. Not a single reference to the mass murder, less than two decades earlier, (by way of starvation, torture, and firing squads) of between seven and ten million Eastern European **Christian** landowners is ever included in *The Crucible*'s lessons; nor is there a single acknowledgment that the **truthful** purpose for the McCarthy hearings was to assure that such mass murder would not be duplicated in the United States. McCarthy's purpose was to identify, and thwart, the conspiratorial intentions of those influential and powerful members of America's non-Christian and anti-Christian minority who advocated (and, *secretly*, worked to instigate) similar political upheaval and mass murder in this country.

Although it is ***true*** *that* ***some*** *innocent people* were falsely accused by McCarthy, ***most*** *of those other persons pursued by McCarthy* were not the harmless victims that *The Crucible*, and propagandists, have portrayed them ***all*** to be but, instead, were traitors to this country who advocated, and worked *secretly* to foment, violent revolution and mass murder in the United States as well. What is most amazing is that the **true** purpose for the McCarthy hearings (and all facts concerning the Eastern European, anti-Christian, holocaust) have been so successfully misrepresented, obscured, and **removed from history** that few Christians in the United States even know that between seven and ten million Christians, primarily of Germanic and Slavic descent (more than one third of whom were *children*), had been tortured and murdered in the 1930's for no other reason than the fact that they were *Christian* landowners.

It would, certainly, make sense that all outraged (and more civilized) European countries would have (1) invaded that Ukraine region (the bread basket of Europe) for the purpose of putting an end to the greatest holocaust the world has ever seen and (2) punished those persons who were responsible for the world's greatest mass murder. Any such invasion would have been spurred by the *Old Testament*, ***Hebrew***, *mandate* which demands the taking of "an eye for an eye". If this is the **true**, and primary, reason for Germany's pre-World War II invasions, why have Americans been taught a version of World War II history that, ***entirely, misrepresents the*** **truth**? Sadly, even though this mass murder occurred at a time when the United States was in the throes of The Great Depression (and the United States had maintained a, steadfast, isolationist policy), it is puzzling that Great Britain and the United States (a country composed of more than forty million German Americans--America's largest minority) would have (within less than ten years) become allies with the evildoers responsible for those mass killings.

American students have been successfully brainwashed into believing that (1) the excesses of the McCarthy hearings and (2) the improper execution of ***twenty*** *Puritan innocents* in 1692-1693 are noteworthy illustrations of extremism, yet ***the mass murder of between seven million and ten million Germanic and Slavic, Christian, innocents*** **in the 1930's,** ***by non-Christians, is insignificant***. Why?

You have just explained that The Crucible is such a dishonest representation of history that, essentially, it is merely anti-Christian propaganda. If what you have explained is true, this country has an obligation to remove The Crucible (and others works like it) from the classroom, exclude the involvement of all publishing companies that have chosen to, dishonestly, brainwash (rather than properly educate) America's youth, and remove accreditation from all educational institutions that facilitate and/or mandate indoctrination rather than education. Many other works of literature can teach allegory more

competently. There is no justifiable reason that so few people in the United States have any knowledge (1) of the Twentieth Century, Eastern European, anti-Christian holocaust, (2) of those persons responsible for causing the atrocities, and (3) of the impact those mass murders may have had on subsequent European events which led to World War II and events which occurred during World War II. Is this form of educational dishonesty the underlying reason why you have, also, noted that Tess does not, truthfully, depict the Christian morality of the Victorian Era?

Tess D'Urbervilles is a *work of fiction*--a *tale* that was ***entirely contrived*** by Thomas Hardy. Properly educated humans must be taught to be able to recognize the differences between (1) fiction and reality *and* (2) **truth** and propaganda. Regrettably (and **puzzlingly**), far too few students who have earned ***advanced*** *degrees* in recent decades have been taught how to develop that ability. If actual events had occurred *exactly* as Hardy had written them (and an innocent woman had been deceived and raped), such an incident would have *truly* amounted to a tragedy; however, Tess's life story is a concoction.

In real life, it would be difficult to imagine why any aristocrat would have had to rape any peasant girl because noblemen (regardless of whether they were ugly, old, rotund, or mean) were regarded in the same fashion that rock stars are regarded today. The reasons why, virtually, *any peasant girl* would have been willing, and eager, to engage in a sexual dalliance with *any nobleman* were numerous. Even if the encounter were brief, that girl would have had (at least for one night) the opportunity to experience the life of a wealthy noble woman--that is reason enough; yet, an even stronger incentive stemmed from the (ever so slight) possibility that the nobleman might fall in love and marry her. Virtually any peasant girl would have welcomed a pregnancy when a nobleman was the father of her bastard child because it would have insured permanent financial stability for her, her child, and her family. Even without a pregnancy, at the very least, the peasant girl would have cemented a personal connection with a wealthy and influential person--a source for help in the event that she should experience future legal, employment, or financial crises.

Although it is possible that a woman who experienced, only, a one-night intimacy might have felt rejected and, thus, alleged that she had been used (or worse), such a claim was unlikely to have ever been **truthful** (or believed). Regardless of whether she portrayed herself as a victim, such a woman's spiritual frequency would have been molded, more likely than not, by self-serving and exploitative energy than by the spiritual energy of a victim. In real life, a tragedy similar to Tess's would have been exceedingly improbable and infrequent.

In addition, there is the issue concerning the death of Tess's child. Although infant mortality rates were quite high, the overwhelming majority of good and devoted Christian mothers seemed to be able to keep their children alive (regardless); thus, any bastard child's suspicious death would have caused most to infer that the mother was both unfit and uncaring. Sadly, in those difficult times, it was not unusual for an impoverished mother to smother or drown her babies. Such behavior, obviously, would have had a far more detrimental effect on the molding of such a parent's spiritual frequency than the (modern-era) act of aborting an unborn child; thus, in an effort to help all to save their souls, it was not unreasonable for Christians to have been highly skeptical (and critical) of parents whose *bastard* infants experienced unexplained deaths.

As for Angel's behavior, his disappointment with Tess's confession did not necessarily result from his Christian teachings because any man believes that he has a right to know the **truth** about his wife's background *before* he marries her. Despite having had no involvement with Tess's misfortune, Angel would have, nevertheless, been sentenced to the same level of condemnation and social exclusion as Tess. In addition, Angel would have had good reason to be suspicious of the circumstances surrounding the baby's death.

These issues were minor, however, in comparison to the fact that Tess was no longer a virgin. This meant that there was a possibility that Tess might have transmitted a venereal disease to Angel which could, possibly, have caused him to experience a horrible, long-suffering, death within as few as twenty years. Regardless of Victorian morality, Angel had every, real world, reason to feel as if he had been betrayed by Tess.

Upon his return from Brazil, however, it is not likely that Angel was still an innocent man. It is doubtful that he would have remained chaste all of that time after having been exposed to promiscuous Native American and African American women who had never been guided or inhibited by Christian teachings and values. Sadly, it is a virtual certainty that Angel would have returned to Tess with syphilis in his body. That being the possibility, Angel's concern about transmitting a life-shortening disease to Tess, apparently, did not matter as much as when he thought that she might have, conceivably, transmitted such a disease to him.

Finally, there is the issue of Alec's murder. Despite the fact that Hardy depicted events in a manner which causes any reader to have great empathy for the heroine, Tess did *commit* ***murder*** *in a fit of passionate rage*. Such a murder is, almost always, a savage act; and such barbarism will, negatively, influence the sculpting of any person's spiritual frequency no matter how exculpating Hardy's sympathetic point-of-view may have made her *act of murder* seem.

Hardy's method of, convincingly, transforming facts into a *contrived fiction* is not dissimilar to the way American and world history have been transformed (since the 1960's) into a series of dishonest and incomplete tales which have been fabricated for the purpose of (1) fermenting unjustified social changes, (2) forcing the majority Christian culture to tolerate non-stop, inexcusable, barbaric misconduct in American society, (3) stripping Christian children of their traditional beliefs and values, and (4) demanding that the majority Christian culture condescend to the transfer of massive amounts of their accrued financial wealth and security to others. A properly educated young person must be taught how to *perceive the* ***truth***; sadly, that is no longer happening in public schools, colleges, and universities in the United States. Regrettably, the United States has, as a result, been forced to re-enter a (modern-era) "Dark Age".

You have still provided no justification for the stern behavior of Victorian Christians.

Victorian Christian behavior requires far less defense than any other societal behaviors which existed elsewhere in the world, at that time, because Victorians formulated a value system which molded the most moral, advanced, and civilized Nineteenth Century society. That morality was based more on Old Testament wisdom (which originally was a canonical collection of Holy Hebrew Scriptures) than it was based on the teachings of Jesus. The objective of the stern interpretations of those Old Testament instructions was to save "the many" even if it were at the expense of "the few". That approach is just the opposite of modern-day thinking where, non-Christian, socialist activists choose to put "the many" at risk even where there is only a slight likelihood of saving "the few". For example, governmental agencies finance the relocation of drug dealers and their families to stable and decent neighborhoods (hoping that good environments will, somehow, correct their behaviors); however, such misguided social engineering has, *repeatedly*, ***only*** resulted in the destruction of additional communities and schools, dramatic property value declines, an out-of-control barbaric tyranny that severely threatens public security and safety, the creation of a massive number of new drug addicts, and the destruction of countless innocent lives. Despite the irreversible damage caused by such tyrannical social engineering, those ***harmful***, socialist, programs are not allowed to be challenged and are never terminated. Victorians were aware that the only way to foment positive societal change was by being sternly intolerant toward all types of misconduct. That is the ***truthful*** reason why Victorian efforts to improve society succeeded; but modern efforts, continually, fail.

Victorians knew, for instance, that the only effective way to curtail the ravages of venereal diseases was to *insist* that women remain virgins until married (and stay faithful after marriage); the most effective tool for accomplishing that goal was societal condemnation (and exclusion) of those women who did not remain chaste. Victorians, also, demanded that husbands provided security for their virginal brides and their children for a lifetime. Men who failed to do so faced societal condemnation and exclusion as well. Orphans were also a Victorian concern. It was difficult enough for society to care for children who had no close living relatives, but it was quite another issue to have to provide for those waifs who were born out of wedlock or had been abandoned by their parents. *Only the harshest forms of condemnation* proved successful at curtailing such behaviors. If some Victorians did not deport themselves properly, they were totally excluded from "decent" society until such time as they corrected their behaviors. There were very clear societal rules for all areas of life (from cleanliness to eating, speaking, and interacting with those other persons who were trying their best to be decent human beings). In other words, Victorians codified, and attempted to be guided by, Old Testament teachings in order to assist as many persons as possible to both locate and, then, travel upon the Heavenly pathway.

While Hardy was correct to criticize mean-spirited, hypocritical, and prideful people who used Christian morality as a *weapon to, unfairly, abuse distressed humans*, Hardy (as well as other anti-Christians) was wrong to be critical of stern Victorian values which were based on Hebrew teachings and traditions. Those moral rules successfully uplifted the lives and souls of most Victorians because ***truthful*** *Christian values and behaviors* were far less sinful (and far more enriching) than any of the alternative values, behaviors, and imperatives that predominated, throughout the world, during that Era.

You have stated that truthful Victorian Christian values were less sinful than other value systems that prevailed, throughout the world, during the Victorian Era. Is your concept of sin the same as traditional Christian beliefs?

My concept of sin runs parallel to Christian philosophies. Christians have, traditionally, believed that humans sin when they go beyond set boundaries and, thus, "miss the mark" for God's standard of righteousness as defined in the Bible and as guided by moral principles. Christians also believe that, since God has shared His love by showing His children how to live in peace and harmony, sin is a transgression which has the potential to destroy an individual's connection with God's love and God's Spirit within. The English poet W. H. Auden summarized this point when he observed that, "All sins tend to be addictive, and the terminal point of addiction is *damnation*".

The Catholic Church defines sin even more specifically. Catholics believe there is either "Mortal Sin" (a grave, intentional violation committed with *full knowledge and deliberate intent* which causes spiritual death) or "Venial Sin" (a sin that can be forgiven). At Romans 3:23, Paul says, "All have sinned and fall short of the glory of God"; because at Romans 3:20, Paul explains that no one will be declared righteous, *merely*, by observing the laws of God. Instead, Paul teaches that, by understanding God's laws, *humans are provided a* ***tool*** *to help them recognize their sins so that they* may ***attempt*** *to make amends and repent for those sins*, hence: "no one will be justified in God's sight through observance of the law; the law does nothing but point out what is sinful". In other words, it is not sufficient to "talk the Christian talk"; it is, instead, *essential* to "walk the Christian walk". The Church, thus, recognizes that avoiding sinful behavior requires more than merely observing God's laws. While, for example, it can be helpful to memorize and recite Biblical passages, it is far more important for ***true*** *"followers of the way" to* ***internalize Christ's teachings*** *and make them* ***innate*** *parts of their identities*; thus, in order to avoid sin, humans must ***fill their souls with truth****, love, goodness, humility, and peace (and remain connected with the Holy Spirit within).* It is clear that most Christians believe God will severely punish sinners; thus, in order to avoid the potential fate of eternal damnation, devout Christians strive not to violate *any* of God's mandates.

My dream has taught me, however, that God does not want His children to fear Him. God would prefer that His children *demonstrate their gratitude for their spiritual consciousness by* ***choosing*** *to live decently*. My dream has also revealed that God is not a vengeful God because vengeance does not exist in Heaven; thus, it has been my belief that God seldom, if ever, negatively judges His children. Instead, each individual has the free will to be solely responsible for his or her own eternal spiritual destiny.

The concept which teaches sinners to ***fear the wrath of God's eternal damnation*** *is, merely, an effective lesson,* ***created by humans****,* to provide sufficient uplifting motivation and instruction to those people who might, otherwise, have chosen to live sinful lives. Despite such teachings, each individual is, ***solely***, responsible for the sculpting of his or her own spiritual frequency. Once sculpted, that person's spiritual identity is fully defined. There is no reason, at that point, for God to *pass* ***vengeful judgment*** because "the die had already been cast". A human, merely, ***automatically***, ascends or descends to the "room" which is most suited for that person's ***true*** *spiritual identity*. Many Christians refer to Romans 2: 5-11, for one example, as proof that Judgment Day will be that day when God unleashes His *wrath* upon sinful humans, yet a more thoughtful analysis of those verses, instead, reinforces *what my dream has taught*: "the just judgment of God will be revealed when He will repay every man for what he has done: eternal life for those who strive for glory, honor, and immortality by patiently doing right; wrath and fury to those who selfishly disobey the **truth** and obey wickedness. Yes, affliction and anguish will come upon every man who has done evil.... but there will be glory, honor, and peace for everyone who has done good.... ***With God, there is no favoritism***". Paul teaches that the Bible provides excellent instructions and pathways for all humans who earnestly wish to ascend to the best possible Heavenly "room". My advice is that all humans should shun wicked sin and, instead, attempt to locate and, then, walk upon the Heavenly pathway for as long as they possibly can.

Earlier, you were asked (1) if you thought that the institution of marriage might be threatened because of this highly promiscuous modern society and (2) if you believed

that these types of human misadventures might, also, have some form of negative influence on humans' "spiritual stability" and "the molding of spiritual frequencies". You never answered those questions. Instead, you explained that the complete answer concerning sexual promiscuity, love, and marriage is far more complicated because most of the Old Testament prohibitions guiding sexual interaction were, more likely, practical rules created by humans to enable barbarians to live peacefully, safely, and healthfully together in civilized communities than they were mandates ordered by God. Will you please, now, finally explain which aspects of human sexual behavior might be sinful?

Proverbs 23:7 in the King James Version of the Bible states: "For as he thinketh in his heart, so is he". This passage presents a good starting point because the verse teaches that sin originates in people's minds (for humans are what they think). Christ explained at Matthew 5:27-28: "You have heard the commandment, 'You shall not commit adultery'. What I say to you is: anyone who looks lustfully at a woman has already committed adultery with her in his thoughts". More than anything, it is thoughts and emotions which exercise the greatest influence upon the sculpting of most spiritual frequencies (because people think non-stop). Since I have already mentioned, for instance, the impact a single altruistic act can have on a martyr's spiritual frequency, it seems possible that, **sometimes**, *highly charged (sexual) thoughts **might***, also, exert strong influences upon the sculpting of spiritual frequencies.

While the longing of one unmarried person to make love with another unmarried person cannot be sinful (because God instilled that desire and joy, as a gift, in all of his children), sexual longing is, nevertheless, the strongest (continuous) life force that impacts humans' spiritual frequencies. Decent humans must, then, be *prudent* in the manner by which they choose to activate and utilize that energy. Christians have always been encouraged to express, *only*, feelings of love, kindness, goodness, respect, **truth**, and decency when they make love (or think about making love). By so doing, their spiritual frequencies will be sculpted by Heavenly energy (*despite* their, animalistic, sexual urges). The best way for Christians to achieve such a result is to *attempt* to restrict their intimacies to, *only*, those persons they are able to *truly* appreciate, care for, and/or love. When two partners exchange equal levels of affection and goodness with one another over the course of a lifetime, there is a much greater likelihood that both partners will be able to ascend to the same "room" in Heaven and be together for eternity.

In contrast, those countless sexual thoughts, urges, and behaviors which are not generated by thoughtfulness, respect, and affection must be some of the most sinful influences upon spiritual frequencies because it is the ***character*** *of a person's thoughts and feelings* that **truthfully** defines that person's spiritual identity. If, for example, a person, dishonestly, claims to love a potential sexual partner in order to convince that person to engage in sexual activity but, instead, feels only negative thoughts or feelings, *those corrupt impulses* will have a very powerful, and damaging, influence on the sculpting of that deceiver's spiritual frequency. Treating another human as a sexual object for the purpose of satisfying a sexual desire is lustful; thus, even though that fraudster may, *ordinarily*, observe God's laws and may, *almost always*, attempt to maintain the ***appearance*** *of decency*, that type of deceit reveals, and sculpts, the **true** nature of that person's soul. The best safeguard, then, is to restrict sexual thoughts and activities to situations where only *honesty, respect, and affection* are possible.

Are you saying that those persons who engage in evil or deviant sexual thoughts and behaviors are condemning themselves to hell?

Not necessarily, I have already explained that it, *usually*, takes a lifetime to sculpt a personal spiritual frequency; thus, *rarely* will one act or time period be determinative in the creation of a frequency. God knows that, because of Original Sin, most people will behave improperly during their lives; as a result, God's plan (and God's teachings) do allow for those sinners to transform themselves for the better (should they choose). The problem is that far too many people, consciously, choose not to be good or to transform themselves for the better; this is *particularly* ***true*** when they are attempting to satisfy their sexual urges.

The dilemma for those humans who choose to secretly succumb to sexual activities which involve ***evil*** thoughts, urges, and actions is that such behaviors (which usually remain unchanged and, thus, typically define those individuals for their entire adult lives) are not secrets on the spiritual plane. If, for example, (1) some persons take pleasure in dominating others by inflicting pain, torture, and/or humiliation while engaging in sexual activities, or (2) if they choose to fantasize about sadistic and other hurtful deeds, there is no other endeavor that more clearly defines their spiritual identities than ***those types*** *of sexual thoughts and behaviors*. Even though sadists, for example, are quite skillful at masking their ***true*** *natures* from other humans, it is impossible for them (1) to conceal their ***true*** *natures* from their spiritual frequencies and (2) to prevent their desires and cruelties from, eventually, dominating every aspect of their lives and their after-lives. Such impulses and urges are so strong that, ultimately, sadistic evil becomes totally consuming (both in the physical world and on the spiritual plane). If sadists were, indeed, wise, they would make every effort to transform themselves for the better. Regrettably, very few do. Instead, there has been a concerted effort to transform sadism into a socially accepted behavior (the primary reason, of course, is that sadists have an insatiable lusting for an infinite quantity of new, willing, and submissive partners).

It is difficult to determine which is more sinful: (1) the actual sadistic acts or (2) the desire to promote such a lifestyle in order to corrupt the innocent. The theme of several recent number-one, bestselling novels is just such a promotion. The book series suggests that it is quite normal and wonderful for submissive sexual partners to be tied, whipped, controlled, and humiliated because those types of deviant sexual activities are "fun" and "so enjoyable". I am aghast (1) as to why such a book series would have, *allegedly*, sold more than one hundred million copies and (2) as to why the majority of purchasers would have been women. This is quite a disconnection from the traditional perception which has portrayed women as being "sugar and spice and everything nice".

In reality, it is very unlikely that any human can ***play*** *sadistic and masochistic characters* without being, seriously, spiritually damaged (because the ***distinctions*** between those types of, *savage, role-playing emotions* and *real emotions* are, virtually, non-existent on the spiritual plane). It is also difficult to believe that, at the conclusion of such self-destructive behavioral activities and "games", the involved parties could, possibly, feel anything other than complete revulsion for one another. Sadly, even though humans have a lifetime to sculpt the best possible spiritual frequencies, far too many, willfully, choose *only to be bad.* Those persons who have chosen to define themselves by their unrepentant sadistic natures are souls who will ultimately descend to "rooms" that are crowded with beings whose frequencies have been sculpted by similar inclinations. Even if their *descents* to their appropriate "rooms" do not take them entirely to hell, it is very unlikely that any of those sadistic spirits will be pleased with their final, *eternal*, destinations.

Regrettably, it is not only sadists who choose to utilize violence as a form of sexual expression. This distinction results from the fact that some men and women are so *animalistic* (by nature) that they are not able to emotionally perceive the difference between brutality, cruelty, and the sexual act. These humans are controlled more by an overwhelming need to vent aggression (even toward their sexual partners) than by a willingness (and an ability) to share affection and goodness with them. While sadists' acts are usually guided by some primitive level of evil, ***cerebral***, activity, this savage behavior results from nothing other than pure ***animalistic compulsions*** (a state of existence where there is indifference to all but avaricious physical appetites). God has little tolerance and understanding for those humans who allow themselves to be, overwhelmingly, consumed by such urges; thus, there are few desirable *Heavenly* "rooms" awaiting humans who allow their spiritual frequencies to be sculpted by such barbarism.

Have you concluded that dishonesty and sadism are the only types of sin associated with sexual activity?

I am sure that there are countless other animalistic behaviors that can (because of the presence of sexual energy) amplify sin in both men and women. I am not, however, an expert regarding the full breadth of those types of sins because I have never had any desire to engage in them. I was, for example, amazed to learn of the large number of humans who, willingly, choose to participate in sadistic and masochistic sexual activities. Since such behavior is so *spiritually* defining, it is not merely my hubris that makes me know, *with certainty*, that I will not be encountering ***any of*** *those types of deceased souls in the afterlife* (regardless of what spiritual fate awaits me).

In an effort to more directly answer your question, however, I will, briefly, review ***a few** of the* **numerous** *sexual misbehaviors* which damage spiritual frequencies. For example, it should be obvious that when men drug or intoxicate women (for the purpose of raping those women), those men cause as much spiritual harm to their own frequencies as they cause physical and emotional damage to their victims. Violent rape becomes even more amplified, with spiritual evil, when the sexual attack is a group activity which includes several attackers and a sole, defenseless, victim. Regardless of whether (1) those men are fully prosecuted for having committed a criminal act or (2) those men escape all worldly punishment, it is not difficult to recognize the degree of permanent damage that they have, also, caused their *own* spiritual frequencies.

It would be silly, however, to presume that women are *always* sexual victims because they, too, are guilty of committing *damning*, sex-related, sins. For example, women who utilize and exploit their sexual allure for the purpose of separating men from large amounts of money and/or drugs are also creating spiritual frequency problems. This is especially **true** when they claim to be in love but, instead, are merely being dishonest and manipulative. Frequently, those types of women (1) *intentionally* become pregnant for no other reason than to assure themselves lifelong financial support and, too often, (2) accuse one of their *many* sexual partners of being the father of their unborn child yet, in reality, have no idea who the real father might be. Pretending to love, when there is no genuine capacity for love, causes severe frequency damage; thus, such behavior creates a lasting chasm between those women and God's acceptance.

An even more serious spiritual transgression occurs when women *falsely* accuse innocent men of rape. Those types of women, apparently, take pleasure in knowing that if their false accusations are sufficiently convincing, they will succeed in both (1) committing perfect crimes and (2) destroying the lives of innocent men. Evidentially, such dishonesty gives some women a sadistic sense of empowerment. Too often, they successfully deceive everyone into believing that they are victims when, in fact, they are diabolical aggressors. Such evil intentions will, sadly, define those women for eternity; and they will (with certainty), ultimately, ***descend*** to those "rooms" where they truly belong.

There are countless-other extreme and bizarre behaviors which cannot be excluded when sexual sins are being identified. For example, persons who become obsessed with body excrements or develop fetishes toward physical objects or body parts (and then connect those obsessions with their sexual urges and activities) also cause considerable spiritual harm for themselves because worldly (self-absorbing) cravings for perverted pleasures create such a profound spiritual imbalance that those forms of unhealthy appetites weaken resistance to temptation and cause a disconnection from too much of their innate spiritual goodness. ***Gluttonous*** and ***lustful*** *obsessions with physical world "things"* are two of the Seven Deadly Sins. When these twisted obsessions are amplified with sexual energy, they, regrettably, ***too often define*** *misguided souls*.

Sexual betrayal is another spiritually damaging deed (regardless of whether the infidelity is committed by the husband or the wife). An additional facet of betrayal occurs when one of those partners chooses to regard the other mate as a slave, a servant, or a victim--rather than as an equal. Partners who make loving vows of commitment to one another (but have no honest intention of keeping those vows) *do* spiritually define themselves and *do* disappoint God because *infidelity is an affront to* **truth**. As far as the sculpting of one's spiritual frequency is concerned, it is the *spiritual betrayal of trust and commitment* (even more than lust) which makes adultery one of the gravest sins among those cited in the Ten Commandments (the lustful sexual act, hence, is reduced to an ancillary characteristic of the sin). Since it is more the willingness to contemplate betrayal (and less the willingness to contemplate fantasies of a sexual dalliance) that is the most sinful **adulterous** behavior, ***spiritual betrayal*** *is the* ***true*** *focus of Jesus' message* when Jesus taught that anyone who looks, lustfully, at a woman has already committed *adultery* with her in his thoughts (even though it is **true** that *lust*, an intense and uncontrolled sexual desire--and one of the Seven Deadly Sins, may exacerbate the sinful nature of such thoughts).

Finally, there is, perhaps, no greater sexual sin than the act of *knowingly and intentionally transmitting a sexual disease to an unsuspecting partner*. What should be a moment of shared affection and goodness is, instead, an intimacy in which *one* ***evil*** *participant* causes severe injury to an innocent partner (at the moment when that partner is most trusting and vulnerable). Such a deed is, particularly, sinful when the disease spreads life-threatening, terminal, afflictions such as AIDS and/or other venereal viruses that are known to cause cancers. This intentional act is one of the most glaring examples of a mortal and, thus, unforgiveable sin.

To summarize: *these types* of sexual behaviors are human misadventures which generate such powerful negative influences that they damage both (1) *human emotional stability* and (2) *the capacity to sculpt* ***good*** *spiritual frequencies*. All of the aforementioned examples (and countless others) illustrate ***some*** *of the reasons* why the Christian religion has provided guidance to (1) identify what is, *most likely*, God's expectation of righteousness when humans are engaged in sexual and intimate activities, and to (2) help humans remain on the best spiritual pathway when they are succumbing to their sexual urges. It does not matter if modern media and/or societal influences are, cleverly, convincing the majority of Americans to abandon their traditional Christian beliefs; each individual is, nevertheless, fully responsible for being the "captain" of his or her own soul (even when engaged in sexual activity).

My, *nutshell*, summary explanation is that a sexual desire or act, in and of itself, cannot be a sinful activity. Instead, thoughts, feelings, and behaviors (which are devoid of love, goodness, kindness, **truth**, respect, and decency--yet energized and magnified by sexual energy) ***can*** *be* sinful and, thus, *can*, *possibly*, cause significant damage to any person's spiritual frequency. My belief is that there is no need to feel guilt, or seek forgiveness, for having sexual desires as long as love, kindness, goodness, respect, **truth**, and decency are the strongest types of feelings and spiritual thoughts that accompany those sexual urges.

You have already expressed concern about the, undemocratic, manner by which homosexual marriages have been forced upon an overwhelmingly disapproving Christian majority; yet, now that homosexual marriage have been deemed by the Supreme Court to be a Constitutionally protected right, you have failed to include, or discuss, homosexuality as sinful sexual behavior. Is that because you believe that homosexuality is not sinful behavior?

The complete answer to any question concerning homosexuality is lengthier and more complicated than might readily be expected because there are far too many distinct homosexual behaviors, thoughts, and urges; and each of those distinct manifestations of homosexuality is accompanied by its own unique measure of sin or goodness. If the Biblical account of God's destruction of Sodom and Gomorrah is a correct history, sodomy could not have been the *sole basis* for God's disenchantment with the citizens of those cities because God would have never condemned, or punished, two human beings who ***loved*** *one another* merely because they engaged in same-sex intimacies. Genesis 19; 1-13 reveals that God destroyed the cities because evil men of Sodom attempted to commit *forceful* homosexual rape upon two messengers from God; thus, *the focus of God's rage would have, most likely, been directed at those* ***other*** *types of* ***more sinful*** *thoughts, impulses, and behaviors that, invariably, accompany wanton sexual excesses and cruelties.*

It is easy for all humans to understand clearly defined sins such as those enumerated in Proverbs 6:16-19: "There are … things the lord hates, yes, seven are an abomination to him; Haughty eyes, a lying tongue, and hands that shed innocent blood; A heart that plots wicked schemes, feet that run swiftly to evil, the false witness who utters lies, and he who sows discord among brothers". It is far more difficult, however, for most humans to recognize that *instant* when innocent behavior transforms into something more diabolical. Since homosexuality is, now, being praised as a desirable lifestyle and, as a result, there has been no *honest* public analysis of those aspects of homosexual behavior which are sinful, it could prove helpful (and instructive) to examine and understand the, most likely, reasons why God and Jesus would be disappointed with any contemporary culture that chooses to be steered by an immorality which is comparable to the decadence that consumed Sodom and Gomorrah. Just because modern media and governmental influences have ***forced*** society to accept the belief that *aberrant lifestyles* should no longer be regarded as improper, that does not mean that God concurs. God's disenchantment with such activities results from the fact that too many of the thoughts, urges, and behaviors sculpted by such transgressors fail to connect with the frequencies which guide humans to spiritual salvation;

thus, any valid examination of homosexual behavior requires an analysis of those thoughts and urges:

To begin, the primary, practical reason homosexuality has never been encouraged is because homosexual relationships do not breed children. At Genesis 1: 28, the Old Testament conveys God's command to "Be fertile and multiply". During times when this world was vastly underpopulated, homosexuality would have been regarded as a form of societal suicide--a serious threat to the survival of the human species; thus, homosexuality is not behavior that any wise society would have ever advocated. In addition, throughout most of history, the strongest opponents to homosexuality would have had to have been females (because survival would have been far too difficult for any woman who did not have the support and protection of a male). Mothers would have trained their sons to believe that heterosexual relationships were the *only appropriate types of interpersonal unions*.

A small percentage of people have always, nevertheless, chosen to quietly pursue homosexual lifestyles; and, throughout history, *most* have been allowed to do so without societal interference. Some of their acquaintances may have questioned the nature of the living arrangements of two "spinsters" or two "confirmed bachelors"; however, few of those acquaintances ever really cared. Most people have always been willing to "mind their own business" and "live and let live"; nevertheless, because homosexuality has been regarded as an *alternative lifestyle*, it has always been considered prudent for homosexuals to pursue that lifestyle as discretely as possible.

The Catholic Church has long been grateful for those caring humans who exercised that discretion by choosing to sublimate their homosexual urges (in the same way that heterosexuals sublimated their sexual urges) by taking vows of Chasity and redirecting their sexual energies to prayers and good deeds. By so doing, it is clear that such decent humans, regardless of their homosexual inclinations, have always been able to sculpt some of the very best spiritual frequencies imaginable.

Of course, there have also been many historically significant, world famous, homosexuals who have made outstanding contributions and, thus, are remembered for their good works and not their sexual lifestyles. Clearly, no fair-minded Christian (or God) would have failed to recognize the goodness of any decent human (regardless of whether that person privately chose to pursue an alternative way of life) *as long as that person's lifestyle did not cause harm to the rest of society.*

In recent times, however, the majority of homosexuals are no longer willing to live "discrete" lives. The stigmas and societal pressures that made them feel as though they were being forced to conceal their homosexuality were no longer tolerable; thus, from the 1950's until the present, homosexuals have fought for, and won, equal rights in all areas of life--including marriage. The most serious, unintended, consequence which results from the validation of homosexual marriages, however, is that the accompanying marriage licenses create a permanent homosexual identification registry in the public records. (Who can possibly guess what type of future harm such a registry might potentially cause)? This is a dramatic departure from the *cautious behavior* of previous Christian generations that had, always, ***wisely*** chosen to ***protect*** *the privacy* of homosexuals by refraining from publicly broadcasting the identities of those individuals.

An additional reason Christians have always had doubts about the wisdom of validating homosexual marriages is that Christians have been aware that the overwhelming majority of homosexuals (including those who have lived together under the same roof for extended periods of time) have, repeatedly, confessed to their non-homosexual family members that they have no intention of restricting their sexual activities to monogamous relationships. The desire to have sexual trysts with scores of partners of the same sex has always been the focus of, *virtually all, sexually active homosexuals*.

Even though it is universally known that the homosexual lifestyle is a promiscuous lifestyle, there will be (successfully orchestrated) dishonest rebuttals accusing anyone who would make this correct observation as being a hater and a bigot. How do you respond to such a propagandized accusation?

Regardless of whether a union is heterosexual or homosexual, *betrayal and absence of* ***truth*** *in any relationship* have always been sinful. Homosexual adultery is no less sinful than heterosexual adultery. That reality makes it difficult for Christians to understand the wisdom, morality, and the societal need to legitimatize the *majority* of homosexual marriages when the overwhelming number of partners in such unions has no intentions of remaining faithful. Virtually all propagandized claims to the contrary are dishonest.

Where and when did the impetus for the acceptance of the homosexual lifestyle originate?

The ***impetus*** *that triggered a* ***successful*** *homosexual revolution* originated on college campuses in the 1960's and 1970's. Students were manipulated into believing that, in order to be "evolved and well-educated humans", their minds had to be reasonable, balanced, moderate, and (above all) *tolerant* toward all unpopular issues; thus, efforts were continually made to convince college students that *the "well-*

educated" did not condemn ***anything*** that was, at that time, considered aberrant by the moral majority. (Those young minds were *brainwashed* into believing that "evolved and properly educated" college graduates were totally accepting and "tolerant" of *all* behaviors--particularly those which had not, historically, been fully embraced by Christians).

For many years, I (like most other college graduates) succumbed, unquestioningly, to that philosophy before I, finally, realized that such a belief system was nothing other than a *propaganda scheme*. The, underlying, reasoning principles for that *ruse* require a total absence of all, higher-level, analytical thinking skills. That "non-questioning" process could not possibly have produced an "evolved or well-educated" person because it has always advocated ***blind obedience***, and ***mindless acceptance***, of virtually everything mandated by others (particularly non-Christians, anti-Christians, and make-believe Christians).

At 1 Corinthians 2:15-16, Paul taught that a *spiritually* well-educated human, by knowing the mind of Christ, can *discern* spiritual truth: "the spiritual man…can appraise everything…." All properly educated college students (regardless of whether they are Christians or not) should be taught *comparable secular abilities* in order to cultivate sufficient keenness of perception so that they can, also, develop higher-level skills which enable them to, ***correctly***, *distinguish and select* those ideas which are **true** and appropriate from those which are not. When this type of discerning analysis is applied to the homosexual revolution, doubts arise as to whether society's acquiescence to the embracing, and mainstreaming, of the homosexual lifestyle is in ***anyone's*** *best interest*.

What incidents caused you to become somewhat skeptical of the merits of the homosexual revolution?

It was during the early 1970's when I, first, became somewhat suspicious of the psychological compulsions which controlled, far too many, homosexuals. By then, homosexuality had been fully accepted by most educated communities and all major American cities. Except for certain legal issues such as hospital visitation rights, inheritance rights, and marriage, the homosexual revolution had been won. It seemed as though homosexuals were free to live "happily ever after". That, regrettably, is not what has since happened.

At that very same time, a large number of homosexual "leather bars" began opening across the country. The purpose of those bars was to provide a meeting place not only for those men who sought anonymous homosexual sex but, also, for those men who sought partners willing to participate in, sadistic and masochistic, homosexual activities which included torture. When I became aware of those types of bars, I, immediately, questioned the underlying reasons why homosexuals would choose to pursue such a lifestyle. ***At that time***, most homosexuals *claimed* that they were gay because they had an *innate sexual revulsion* toward the opposite sex. Over the ensuing years, that explanation has transformed into the (more politically correct) *claim* that most homosexuals had been born with genitalia that was incompatible with their (psychological and emotional) *gender identities*. If that were, indeed, correct, why, then, did homosexual behavior mutate into *sadistic and masochistic* homosexual behavior (and worse) at the very moment in history when homosexuality had achieved widespread tolerance?

When you make statements like that, are you not, really, being nothing more than a homophobe, a hater, or worse? In addition, are these the types of statements that a true Christian would make?

Most often, *homophobia* is regarded as an ***irrational*** fear (that is, sometimes, based upon religious beliefs) and is, usually, manifested in expressions of contempt, prejudice, aversion, and hatred. If (1) the National Coalition of Anti-Violence Programs (NCAVP) is, indeed, correct in reporting that 20-25% of lesbian and gay people experience hate crimes within their lifetimes and (2) ***self-admitting*** *homosexuals* (who compose little more than three percent of the population) were the victims of, approximately, nineteen percent of all hate crimes in 2010 (*for no other reason* than they chose to, peacefully, pursues an alternative lifestyle), any **true** Christian would be both outraged and supportive.

My suspicions and concerns, however, are not based on *irrational fears*. My concerns are, instead, grounded upon a number of *appalling* episodes which have occurred since the 1970's that should not have been "sent down the memory hole" (a concept first introduced in George Orwell's novel, ***1984***, where indefensible, and embarrassing, events were altered and/or made to disappear from history) for no other reason than the fact that those events provided an honest, yet very damning, account of the lifestyles of *far too many homosexuals*.

Since the 1970's, I have suspected that homosexuals are, indeed, born with different impulses and urges; however, I have long doubted that those, innate, impulses are limited, merely, to sexual behavior. I have ***feared****, instead, that far too many homosexuals* are, actually, born with a compulsive need to be deviant (or, in some cases, even evil) and that living ***clandestine*** homosexual lives had been, until the 1970's, the most effective way for those persons (with *an* ***obsessive*** *need to be different*) to satisfy that compulsion. If my suspicions are correct, that would mean that, at the very moment homosexuality was no longer regarded as being a deviant activity, many homosexuals would have felt compelled to pursue an, even more extreme, alternative lifestyle (with new, and distinctly unacceptable, social behaviors) *in order to continue to satisfy their **innate** aberrant urges*.

It should not seem surprising, then, that a very large percentage of the homosexual community has recently moved to the forefront of many radical movements which attack and attempt to eliminate all Christian influences and institutions--as well as all other stable, just, and moral aspects of our society. Christians must realize that people who share these types of mental disorders have, repeatedly, worked to destroy stable societies *for centuries* because they have always been more driven by their deviant compulsions than they have been motived by any type of moral principles.

If, indeed, a large proportion of the homosexual community does engage in extremely improper (or criminal) behavior, there is no justifiable reason to allow that community (or its supporters) to conceal such behavior and, then, insult and dismiss any critic (who might disagree by expressing *valid concerns* about that misconduct) as being a homophobe. Sadly, the following examples are ***just a few instances*** which illustrate the compelling reasons why *certain aspects of the homosexual lifestyle require greater, and more honest, societal scrutiny*.

The first disturbing example, also, began during the 1970's (at the very same time that (1) the homosexual lifestyle was gaining widespread acceptance and at the very same time that (2) numerous leather bars were coming into existence). A significant number of homosexuals were booking ***sex**-junket vacations* to Haiti for the purpose of engaging in sexual acts (and quite possibly sadistic acts) with, under-aged, African-Haitian ***boys***. Society needs to, openly, ask this question: if homosexual men had, indeed, been born with, ***only***, a predisposition which compelled them to engage in same sex copulation, how, why, and when did

(1) the urge to sexually pursue young boys and (2) the urge to engage in sadistic acts originate?

Soon thereafter, a new (mysterious--yet deadly) venereal disease began ravaging the North American homosexual community. By 1980, that disease was isolated and identified as Acquired Immune Deficiency Syndrome (AIDS). Its etiological history is similar to syphilis. Both originated as benign microorganisms in Equatorial areas and, then, mutated. When carried away from their sources of origin, both diseases could have only survived in warm, moist interior portions of the human body. The differences are that AIDS is triggered by a sexually transmitted *virus* (not a bacteria); and the warm, moist, interior portion of the body where the North American, homosexual, AIDS virus thrived was the anus (not the vagina). The virus was acquired in Haiti and, subsequently, widely spread throughout the United States' homosexual community (beginning in 1970 in New York City) after North American adult homosexuals performed anal sex with Haitian ***boys*** and, then, returned home to continue pursuing their promiscuous, and indiscriminate, sexual lifestyles with numerous other men.

As the epidemic grew, it was clear that the best way to stop the spread of the disease was to quarantine those with AIDS because the majority of those infected (**sinfully**) refused to curb their *promiscuous lifestyles* in any way. In the heat of the quarantine discussion, an AIDS infected (closeted) Florida dentist, Dr. David J. Acer, committed one of the most evil acts of domestic terrorism (and serial murder) in the history of this country. He, ***intentionally***, gave AIDS to six of his dental patients (including a teenage girl). His acts were clearly intentional because there is no way that an *accidental transmission* could have possibly occurred (even once) based upon the type of treatment he had provided his patients. Since he knew that he would soon die from AIDS, his purpose was to send a *terrorist's message* to this entire country by making everyone aware that there were numerous other *closeted homosexuals* who were ready, willing, and able to cause a widespread AIDS epidemic among the general population if any, state or Federal, governmental agency were to *quarantine even one homosexual*. As a result of that blackmail, homosexuals were allowed to continue to widely spread their diseases to ***hundreds of thousands*** *of innocent victims* despite the fact that, in the beginning, the disease could have, easily, been *eliminated* by quarantining ***a few thousand*** *infected* ***homosexuals***. In 1985, (five full years after the identification of the disease and fifteen years after its introduction to this country), AMFAR reported that 15,527 known cases had resulted in only 12,529 deaths. By 2013, the Center for Disease Control estimated that 1,194,039 United States citizens had been diagnosed with AIDS and that 658,507 people with an AIDS diagnosis, subsequently, died (**at the expense of billions of *non-homosexual taxpayers' dollars*** for research and treatment costs).

Sadly, no effective effort was made to protect the general heterosexual population from AIDS exposure. Media, continually, insisted that (1) tainted blood transfusions and (2) needle sharing among addicts were the two primary causes for the rapid spread of the disease into the heterosexual community. Although that explanation is, somewhat, **truthful**, it is incomplete. The ***primary reason*** that AIDS jumped, so quickly, into the general population is that it was *maliciously disseminated by AIDS infected homosexuals and bisexuals (whose evil and maniacal intentions were the same as Dr. Acer's)*. It is, then, fortunate that AIDS is not as easily transferred to unsuspecting victims during heterosexual, vaginal, sex as it is during homosexual, anal, sex (because anal abrasions and ruptured hemorrhoids more readily facilitate the virus' entry into the bloodstream). Had AIDS been as easily transferred heterosexually, the number of infected Americans would, by now, be in the tens of millions (if not hundreds of millions). Nevertheless, it is a deplorable fact that evil, AIDS-infected, homosexuals continued to spread the disease by (1) ***intentionally*** sharing infected needles and (2) by, ***knowingly and deliberately***, causing the AIDS virus to enter the bloodstreams of unsuspecting victims when they, ***shamelessly***, donated tainted blood.

Sadly, too, virtually all **truthful** versions of those events (some of the most horrible events in America's history) have been made to disappear. Why? There are, for example, no longer any accounts of the Haitian sex-junkets or the Haitian boys. Most reports now available to researchers either portray Dr. Acer as a social activist or suggest that his deeds were unintentional. One of America's most relied upon, and trusted (sic), investigative television news sources even attempted to discredit the teenage female victim who died from AIDS shortly thereafter. Clearly, **it is *not irrational fear, prejudice, or hatred that motivates Christians to be opposed to evil homosexual behaviors***. These aforementioned, horrendous, deeds (and their continuous cover-ups) are unacceptable to all decent human beings (including most homosexuals).

The majority of people who defend homosexual rights believe that it is necessary to protect the rights and freedoms of all (even those people who represent unpopular views, behaviors, and lifestyles). How could you, possibly, find fault with their desire "to do the right thing"?

"The road to hell is paved with good intentions" may not be a Biblical passage, but it does provide an appropriate initial response to that question. If people choose to support a social movement, they have an *obligation* to know what they are, actually, supporting. There has ***never*** been a balanced discussion or analysis of the homosexual revolution. Anyone who might have a dissenting point of view, no matter how valid, has been confronted and silenced by a propaganda machine that makes those which existed in Communist U.S.S.R. before and during the Cold War seem amateurish. It is unlikely that the majority of people (including most lesbians and many male homosexuals who support homosexual rights) are even aware of the **true** history of AIDS.

The failure to quarantine that small number of homosexuals who had traveled to Haiti and/or were identified as having AIDS in 1985 (for the purpose of protecting the general population) is still another example of the *far too many instances* where governmental decision-makers have (within the past fifty years) sacrificed hundreds of thousands of innocent people (by destroying and ending their lives) in order to provide, questionable, benefit to a ***very undeserving few***. Why was it acceptable to deny all of those victims *their* basic human rights? The question to be asked is: "Would the majority of people (including fair-minded homosexuals) still support such a movement once they have been made fully aware of all of the sordid **truthful** facts?" Sadly, sadism, Haitian sex-junkets, the blackmailing of America, and the intentional dissemination of AIDS are not the only examples of improper homosexual behaviors that have aroused Christian concerns; and *none of those concerns are based upon,* ***irrational, homophobia***. What is most tragic (*for the spiritual destinies of those types of homosexuals*) is that ***none*** of their alternative sexual behaviors and urges can, possibly, help them sculpt the most desirable spiritual frequencies.

***

(In order to correctly explore and explain the next, regrettable, example of homosexual impropriety, it is

necessary to digress--and briefly review--those relevant historical events which provided the backdrop that facilitated such misdeeds).

***

Beginning in the late 1960's, America's youth was bombarded with propaganda from media, college campuses, musical idols, and cinema which proved to be very alluring, society-altering influences. That movement, cleverly orchestrated by non-Christians and anti-Christians (who were *directly linked* to that Fifth Column which Senator McCarthy had failed to, successfully, thwart in the early 1950's) encouraged American youth to protest against the United States' involvement in the Viet Nam conflict, support civil rights and anti-apartheid activities, accept socialism and Marxism, use drugs, embrace promiscuity, and reject their parents' cultural, religious, and moral values. It proved to be a total success at undermining and replacing the principles and beliefs of the Christian generation that had fought for this country and won World War II. The societal transformation that resulted could not have been any greater (or more damaging) if the United States had lost a World War to the Communist U.S.S.R. and had been, thereafter, occupied by a tyrannically hostile enemy army.

Although I, too, was beguiled by the movement (because that type of "social involvement" had, *initially*, been portrayed as being *concerns* that any good Christian youth would choose to help correct), I, almost immediately, became *somewhat suspicious* when I attended my first anti-war "peace" rally. One of the *highlight speakers* was a leader of the American Communist Party. Since I knew that anti-Christian Communists had been responsible for the murders of between seven and ten million, defenseless, Christian land-owners in the Ukraine (approximately thirty years before) in the 1930's (and ***many*** millions more Christians in the Soviet Union), I immediately questioned the purpose of the Communist Party's involvement because it made me realize that the anti-democratic and anti-Christian movement Senator McCarthy had ***ineffectively*** *confronted* in the early 1950's had, *once again, reemerged from the shadows.*

Thereafter, I (foolishly) remained socially in touch, aware, and in support of my "Hippie" friends; but I was (smartly) no longer interested in being a leader or active participant. As that Marxist movement grew, I learned that the most effective enticements to new, younger recruits were the lures of free drugs and "free love" (often group sex). How could any unattractive, self-conscious, hormonal teenager resist such easily accessible *forbidden temptations*?

Prior to1968, most American soldiers who served in Viet Nam (***truth*****fully**) were Christians of European descent. During that time, America fared well. After 1969, a necessary, all-inclusive, multi-cultural military draft proved disastrous for America's military efforts because too many of those drafted soldiers (1) preferred getting high on hardcore narcotics and (2) are known to have, frequently, killed their platoon leaders while on patrols (by "fragging" them--killing them with fragmentation grenades for the purpose of making the murders appear to be the results (1) of accidents or (2) of engagements with opposing forces) rather than risk the possibilities of encountering and fighting Viet Cong guerrillas. Regrettably, most of those platoon leaders had been reared in Christian families of European descent yet most of their murderers had not. Because of the untenable behavior of those *traitorous* draftees, military leaders had no other choice than to, abruptly, withdraw from Viet Nam before victory had been achieved. That extraction resulted from the fact that America's *multi-cultural* conscripts were, completely, out-of-control in every way.

The Christian community should obligate itself to either prove or disprove the **truthfulness** of those (wide-spread) allegations of *traitorous behavior* because, if **true**, the United States' military (by (1) concealing ***most*** accounts of the assassinations of those Christian officers and (2) not pursuing and prosecuting their murderers) has, thus far, been able to avoid paying ***appropriate*** lifetime earnings-compensation damages to the entitled families of those murdered Christian officers. Should ***any*** *additional instances* of these odious historical accounts be verified, such a conformation would prove the military's behavior to be just another, very odd, way that the United States has demonstrated its ingratitude for sacrifices made by Christians to this country. In summary, as incredulous as this condensed explanation may sound, it is a more correct historical account of the late 1960's and early 1970's "Hippie" and "Anti-Viet Nam War" movements than the propagandized version that, presently, appears in America's high school and college history books.

Do you really believe that the United States military would even admit to your version of historical events?

The United States military has several good (self-serving) reasons for never honestly admitting the complete **truth**; however, recent military deployment decisions have, nevertheless, unintentionally verified this, correct, historical account. Beginning at the turn of the Twenty-first Century (before the United States' military involvements in Afghanistan and Iraq escalated), national mainstream media, regularly, reported (and praised) the dramatic increase in *diversity* in all branches of the military services. Remarkably, the reporting of such stories vanished just as soon as soldiers were *deployed into combat* in Afghanistan and Iraq. What has been *most notable* about Afghanistan and Iraq military operations, since, is *the dramatic reduction in* *diversity among those soldiers in* ***combat units*** *that have been commanded to the front lines (to risk their lives for this country).* The overwhelming majority of those soldiers are clearly, once again, Christians of European descent; yet that fact seems to have escaped mainstream media's interest entirely. The media does still, nevertheless, ***demand*** that (1) officer training candidates and (2) the military personnel who control drones and submarine-based nuclear missiles (the weapons that could, most readily, be turned upon our own citizens) be composed of the very same multi-cultural personnel that military leaders have not been able to rely upon (and trust) to fight in Afghanistan, Iraq, and Viet Nam. Why?

You are not, *foolishly*, claiming that only Christians of European descent have died while serving in the military for this country, are you? There are, for example, Hispanic-Americans who have, heroically, fought and died for this country as well.

That would be a very ungrateful and dishonest claim. Clearly, *decent citizens of* ***all*** *backgrounds* have lost their lives while serving for the United States' Armed Forces; however, I should not have to mention that (1) most Hispanic-American soldiers *and heroes* are, also, of European Christian descent and (2) the percentage of those soldiers who have died for this country has ***always, disproportionately, been Christians of European descent***. I, also, should not have to point out that truck drivers, quarter masters, and support staff do not, usually, risk their lives *on the front lines* in the same way that combat soldiers risk their lives even though (because of suicide attacks and hidden road bombs) support staff *has*, ***recently***, become, ***somewhat****, more* vulnerable to attacks than in the past.

You assert that your explanation is the most correct historical summary of that era, yet is not your version, at best, anecdotal?

The disclosure that our multi-cultural draftees were out-of-control and getting high on drugs can easily be verified; however, the widespread knowledge that officers were shot in their backs and/or fragged by their own soldiers remain anecdotal because all witnesses to the murders became accessories to those crimes just as soon as they failed to, officially and **truthfully**, report what had happened. Over the years, however, some of those involved have, nevertheless, made a sufficient number of, unofficial, boastings and acknowledgments of their misdeeds. By now, the majority of those murderers must, themselves, have died from old age. Although mainstream media would never choose to investigate the remaining living soldiers who were members of alleged *"ambushed"* patrols, the Christian community should make every effort to locate and interview those soldiers who might now be willing to unburden their souls so that (1) a **truthful** history can be written and (2) the aggrieved families can, finally, receive just compensation and closure.

Your military explanation seems to have *detoured* from your *digression*. What other historical homosexual issues are relevant?

Once the Viet Nam conflict came to an end, many of those *instigating socialist, Marxist, and Communist activists* searched for the optimal new arenas from which they could continue disseminating their socialist, Communist, and anti-Christian agendas. Many pursued careers in areas such as media so that they could acquire the power to both limit and maintain control of all national discussions (fake news).

Others chose educational administration so that they could continue to propagandize and brainwash children by controlling the educational process; or publishing so that they could put themselves in the position to rewrite history; or law so that they could rewrite America's laws. Those who pursued careers in finance, constantly, conceived and implemented ploys (such as the Derivatives and Sub-prime mortgage schemes) that succeeded in separating massive amounts of accrued Christian earnings and retirement savings from those trusting Christians who had gained their financial stability by way of hard and decent work. It is noteworthy that this country has, as yet, made no effort to properly investigate the financial regulators (too many of whom were non-Christians, anti-Christians, and/or make-believe Christians) and to properly return the trillions of dollars that were stolen from Christian investors on the premise that the financial institutions responsible (most having also been controlled by far too many non-Christians, anti-Christians, and make-believe Christians) were "too big to fail". Until such time as that stolen money has been returned to the *proper owners*, every Christian investor who lost money is justified in believing that he or she *remains* a victim of a continuing criminal enterprise.

Still, other activists (despite the fact that they were not very religious) realized that the best way to continue spreading their ideology was by taking advantage of the prosperity, authority, and influence that Christian ministries would provide them. It was so easy to disguise socialist propaganda as Christian belief; thus, from then until now, far too many sermons (which seem to have been written more by *secular* humanists than Christians) have instructed that good Christians, unquestioningly, should give *all* that is theirs to others (regardless of whether those beneficiaries are *deserving*).

It is **true** that Isaiah 58: 10-12 teaches, "If you bestow your bread on the hungry and satisfy the afflicted; then light shall rise for you in the darkness, and the gloom shall become for you like midday" and Matthew 26: 34-36, in describing The Last Judgment, quotes how Jesus will judge: "Inherit the kingdom prepared for you from the creation of the world. For I was hungry and you gave me food, I was thirsty and you gave me drink. I was a stranger and you welcomed me, naked and you clothed me. I was ill and you comforted me, in prison and you came to visit me".

Despite the wisdom of such wonderful Christian beliefs, too little attention has been devoted, however, to other *important* Christian teachings such as those expressed by Paul in Paul's Epistle to the Galatians at 6:10 when he advised: "let us do good to all men--but *especially those of the household of the faith*," or Matthew 7:6 which revealed Jesus' warning, "Do not give what is holy to dogs or toss your pearls before swine. They will trample them underfoot, at best, and perhaps even tear you to shreds". These teachings *should be **equally utilized** to guide modern Christians* because the hardships and levels of desperation faced by the poor during the time of Christ were, dramatically, more severe and unjustified than those difficulties faced by today's poor (who are free and have equal opportunity in the world's richest country).

The *primary* church purpose should have always been (1) to help its own "hungry", "thirsty", and "naked" members make *the very best connection **with their spiritual frequencies*** and (2) to help those ***sincere Christians*** accomplish that goal by focusing, primarily, on ***strengthening Christian families and Christian communities***. Regrettably, that has not been happening for decades; thus, it is not surprising that, because of *far too many **dubious** modern church agendas*, the number of Christians who have remained active churchgoers has declined. Decent Christians should have never been "exploited", "trampled underfoot", or "torn to shreds"; but that is what has been happening since the 1970's. Sadly, too, it was during that time period when an even more extreme level of homosexual impropriety succeeded in damaging both (1) the lives of many innocent Christian victims and (2) the stability of the Christian church.

The *primary event* involved the Catholic Church, which was rocked by one of the most damaging scandals in its history. Numerous priests (1) were accused of having sexually molested young boys and girls (yet overwhelmingly ***boys***)--national media has (puzzlingly) chosen not to report accurate percentages of male-female molestations; and, thus, has chosen to conceal this scandal's most relevant fact); and the Catholic Church (2) was accused of having covered-up those molestations for decades. Victims were awarded billions of dollars in legal judgements or settlements; and, with each legal result, more victims came forward to reveal their victimizations (and to collect their financial rewards--an amount which, by now, has been estimated to be *far in excess* of three billion dollars). The financial costs to the church were so great that parishes and schools had to be closed; and many Catholic charitable services had to be curtailed or terminated. (It is sad that the massive sums of money paid in those judgments or settlements came from the *contributions* of decent Christians whose ***only*** *intentions* were to help others who were ***truly*** in need).

Non-stop, year after year, condemnation of the Catholic Church (by mainstream media--fake news) stirred a national outrage that caused a continuous barrage of contempt, ridicule, and distrust to be directed toward ***all priests*** (even though the overwhelming majority of Catholic priests were entirely innocent and had only lived decent, good, and giving Christian lives).

It is worth restating that during the entire time of the scandal, mainstream media (fake news) chose to ***ignore*** and, thus, ***conceal*** *the most significant factual detail*: the rogue priests guilty of the molestations (and the church officials responsible for cover-ups--in instances where cover-ups had occurred) were, almost entirely, homosexuals. Although (over a period of many years) national newspapers, magazines, television, and radio outlets were bombarded with evidence urging them to *honestly* report the ***truthful*** *details* of the scandals, very few, if any, media outlets ever did. Because of media's continuous dishonest and malicious behavior toward the Catholic Church, it is difficult to believe that a free press (one which supports and allows the ***truth*****ful** exchange of ideas) could, possibly, still exist in the United States. It appears as though mainstream media's (successful) diabolical agenda was to coerce innocent, heterosexual Christians to surrender billions of their dollars to (far-too-many) not-so-innocent members of the homosexual community. Remarkably, during that time-period when media was condemning the ***entire*** *Catholic Church rather than, merely, the guilty four percent of homosexual priests and church officials* (a number that, coincidentally, closely parallels the percentage of ***admitted*** homosexuals in the general population), media was also engaged (puzzlingly) in a parallel propaganda campaign that *supported homosexual agendas* such as those which demanded, for example, (1) that, openly gay, homosexuals be ordained as Protestant ministers and (2) that, openly gay, homosexuals be permitted to serve as Boy Scout leaders. Despite mainstream media's hypocrisy and lack of values (and the *chilling effect* media's propaganda had on the general population), there has never been an ***appropriate*** *challenge or analysis of mainstream media's improper misrepresentation of the* ***truth*** *concerning* ***homosexual misconduct*** *in the Catholic Church*. Why?

Although the Catholic Church has always been aware that some priests would have pursued homosexual lifestyles had they not joined the priesthood, the Church has, also, always been cognizant that, throughout history, the overwhelming-majority of those priests had lived Christian lives despite the torment and struggle that their sexuality may have caused them. For centuries, the Catholic Church has been grateful that so many ***decent*** *homosexuals* had taken their vows of chastity seriously and had remained devoted Christian priests.

Throughout history, also, in those instances when homosexual (and heterosexual) priests may have sexually sinned, the Church has been no less agreeable to forgiving those priests' sins than the Church has, ***always***, *been willing to forgive the sins of all other transgressors*. Even though the Church's, so-called, cover-ups had more to do with the Church's desire to encourage and support all sinners' efforts to repent (and, also, to protect all of the victims' reputations), mainstream media propaganda disregarded the clergy's legal right to not testify against confessors of sins and, instead, *convincingly portrayed* **the entire Catholic Church** *(instead of* **the guilty homosexuals***) as having been a willing accomplice to every one of those sexual crimes*. In all fairness, the Catholic Church had *no way of knowing* that (1) the *intentions* of a sizable number of "post-Hippie Era" priests were very different from those of previous generations or that (2) many had chosen to join the priesthood more for socialist and Communist ideological reasons than religious reasons or that (3) some were not even religious or that (4) a small percentage had no intention of remaining celibate regardless of their vows to the Church and God.

Before we go any further, you just stated that one of the reasons for the Church's cover-up was to protect the victims' reputations. How could you possibly make such a ridiculous statement?

The real question that should have been asked (but never was) is: How could ***so many*** *boys have been sexually molested, yet* ***so few*** *of them had ever sought help from their parents or the police when the molestations were occurring*? The generally accepted answer is that ***all of the boys*** *were so traumatized* (and were caused to feel so ashamed) that their extreme emotional injuries made them too fearful to seek help from anyone. In all instances where this had been the ***truth*****ful** reason, multi-million dollar awards *were appropriate.* This is particularly **true** when higher Church officials, *actively, made attempts to cover-up reported molestations*, solely, because those officials were also homosexuals. However, *one* of the primary reasons that so many *Hippie-Era*, non-religious, homosexuals chose to join the priesthood was because the duty of hearing young boys' confessions provided them opportunities to identify and make personal connections with those adolescents who confessed to either having homosexual interests or having engaged in homosexual activities; thus, in many instances, the homosexual-molesting priests confined their sexual pursuits to those boys who had, during confessions, indicated that they, too, had homosexual inclinations. While forty-percent of the molested boys were between the ages of eleven and fourteen, the largest percentage were older than fourteen and had already chosen to pursue (and were actively engaged in) homosexual lifestyles. These were the *primary* ***truthful*** *reasons* (1) why this scandal had not been exposed decades before and (2) why ***a very small number*** of non-homosexual Catholic Church officials, also, chose not to draw excessive attention to those boys' activities. In all instances where the homosexual priests developed relationships with, sexually active, homosexual boys, it is difficult to understand (1) how those involvements (although, in many cases, illegal) could have, possibly, been traumatizing or (2) how the boys could have been so damaged that ***all*** were deserving of ***multi-million dollar*** verdicts ***from the ninety-six percent of the, not guilty and non-homosexual, Catholic Church*** (which had no way of knowing that those *private*, *intimate*, *illegal*, *and homosexual* relationships were occurring).

Of all of the parties involved in this scandal, who caused the most damage to their own spiritual frequencies?

Obviously, those adult homosexual men who betrayed the church (and their vows) for the sole intention of molesting innocent children (and remained unrepentant) are those who would have done the most harm to their spiritual frequencies because those actions, alone, were sufficient to have defined their spiritual identities completely. This is particularly **true** in instances when priests took joy in knowing that they had ***corrupted*** *young, and very innocent, children.*

It is unlikely, however, that most of the priests involved in the scandals were that evil. The reason is that no matter how unscrupulous their initial purposes for becoming priests may have been, the majority had, nevertheless, been positively changed by the Church and, thus, spent the substantial portion of their lives performing, far more, good deeds than most other human beings. For the ***truly*** *repentant priests*, their sexual misconduct would have sculpted only a small portion of their spiritual frequencies; thus, the overall, lifelong, levels of goodness in their souls would have, nevertheless, remained the ultimate determiners of their spiritual fates.

Certainly, all of those emotionally damaged boys were victims. Oddly, it is possible that their victimizations actually helped them to, spiritually, sculpt more perfect frequencies. Since their shame and emotional trauma only resulted because they were strongly attached to those spiritual tethers which contained the most goodness, their ordeals would have, surely, enabled them to heighten their connections with that goodness and, also, with a more desirable Heavenly "room".

On the other hand, those *homosexual* boys who *falsely* claimed to have been victimized (in order to gain millions of dollars in payments) could, quite conceivably, have caused greater damage to their own frequencies than any other participants. Their spiritual behavior could, possibly, be likened to the behavior of those females who (1) falsely accuse blameless men of rape, (2) are believed, and, thus, (3) succeed in destroying the lives of those innocent men. In *almost all instances*, mock victims are spiritual transgressors.

How could you possibly assert that any child* molester's *victim could be a transgressor?

My recollection of comments made in the late 1950's by some of the wilder (and more out of control) Catholic boys I encountered during my childhood in an urban environment (many of whom were bullies) has provided me some insight because I remember those groups of boys, even then, making snide quips about improper sexual interactions between altar boys and priests. What is most memorable is that I also remember those same boys boasting, unrepentantly, about traveling to the downtown bus stations (sometimes posing as shoeshine boys) for the purpose of making easy money by, briefly, joining older homosexuals in bathroom stalls. The emotional and spiritual problems of those boys (and boys like them) could not have been caused by priests; and it is unlikely that any homosexual predator-priest could have, seriously, exacerbated their preexisting mental and emotional damage.

My suspicion is that it was knowledge of the behavior revealed in those homosexual boys' confessions that motivated some priests to transform their sexual fantasies into realities because the only way that so many priests could have molested without detection (for such a long period of time) was by, *carefully*, identifying and preying upon those boys who, more likely than not, would have been willing sexual participants. As a result, ***at least some*** *of the damage claims* made years later, for the purpose of gaining windfall monetary awards, had to be corrupt and, thus, even more *spiritually* damaging to those boys. In such cases, I would advise all mock victims to return their ill-gotten money to the church in order to begin the process of redeeming their souls and healing their damaged spiritual frequencies.

That sounds very harsh and judgmental. Did any other anecdotal events occur during your childhood which may have influenced your observations, and conclusions--that many homosexuals are driven more by a compulsive need to be deviant than they are by their sexual urges?

There was one significant childhood event which has *provided* ***insight*** and helped me to conclude that the compulsive need to be deviant could, possibly, be the prevailing impulse which controls the behavior of a substantial number of homosexuals. That experience began when, at the age of fifteen, my mother decided to send me to the YMCA to, belatedly, learn to swim. It proved to be one of the most important experiences of my life because I met a group of older lifeguards, swimming instructors, and lifesaving instructors who became some of the very best influencers (and role models) I have ever known. They, kindly, taught me so well that I was able to be hired there as a lifeguard in little more than a year.

In addition to teaching me how to swim, my best YMCA friend (and role model), generously, taught me the value of, individualized, cross-training physical activities such as weight lifting, jogging, and swimming. The life lessons that I learned at the YMCA from him (and the others) have remained with me and have proven to be some of the most positive and important influences in my entire life. I am still very grateful to all of them for their guidance.

At the same time, I was aware that some of my friends had attracted older mentors who befriended and demonstrated great interest in the welfare of those friends. To a degree, I was, somewhat, jealous because I wished that I, too, might have demonstrated the type of qualities that would have attracted the interest of an older, caring, mentor; but that never happened. Since I was already aware of my friends' good qualities, I, fully, understood why older men would have recognized their outstanding attributes as well. I, merely, concluded that I was not, yet, perceived as being the same caliber of person as my friends; and I accepted that fact.

The urban decimation that resulted from the non-stop unrest, murder, and violence which began during the1960's in large American cities forced the YMCA to close. That, plus busy lifestyles, resulted in our losing contact with one another (or so I had thought); thus, more than forty years passed before I noticed a newspaper *editorial obituary* summarizing the life of one of my older friend's mentors (whose lifelong success merited a picture and a tribute of nearly one thousand words). The obituary motivated me to, finally, locate that friend and offer my condolence. His response to my well-meaning intentions, however, proved to be the most startling, and unexpected, confession I have ever had admitted to me.

After a brief update regarding his wife, his children, and his church work, he, methodically, bared his soul. *(It is only because he--and all of those other older friends--have since passed away that I am willing to convey his confession).* He revealed that when he processed his mentor's personal effects, he discovered a treasure-trove of pictures and movies of his mentor engaging in homosexual intimacies with numerous men and boys, love letters to and from many men, and a large collection of sadistic and homosexual sex toys. When I, innocently, asked my friend how he had not been able to recognize his mentor's homosexuality for more than fifty years, he confessed that the two of them had been sharing an *open* homosexual relationship since the 1960's (when he was still a very young teenager).

While struggling to conceal my shock, I inquired about those other teenage friends who had, also, attracted mentors at the YMCA. He disclosed that they, too, were homosexuals. Dumbfounded, I next asked, "Are you telling me that everyone I knew at the YMCA was a homosexual?" His delighted response was, "Pretty much!" Although I still hope that his confession was *not **truth*****ful**, his explanation made more sense than any other account that he might have provided. His revelation, finally, did clarify for me the, most likely, reasons why (1) I had not attracted the attention of a mentor and why (2) my YMCA friends and I had not stayed in touch.

Even now, I cannot understand the reason for the confession. Perhaps, he had just inherited a fortune and, thus, no longer felt a need to mask his **true** nature (I don't know). I have heard of instances where closeted homosexuals waited until their wives were dying of incurable diseases before they confessed their homosexuality and admitted that their marriages had been shams because they had never been capable of loving (or being faithful) to women. Such admissions (much like Judge Blackmun's) were always motivated by the *perverted desires to experience the sadistic "thrills"* which resulted from, ***finally***, revealing the **truth** (about their lifelong patterns of dishonesties, betrayals, and deviancies) to their trusting victims. Perhaps, that was my friend's reason as well. Whatever his motivation, it is clear that he felt so, sufficiently, insulated that he no longer deemed it necessary to conceal his secret life from me.

I, next, inquired about my best friend (and role model) since, as a teenager, that friend had vented, non-stop, disapproval toward all homosexuals (and often expressed a desire to engage in "gay bashing"). In response, I was informed that his anti-homosexual behavior had merely been a charade. That explanation, also, made sense because, even when we were young, I had been puzzled as to why that friend would have spent so much time and energy being preoccupied with a homosexual lifestyle that any normal person would have, merely, tolerated or ignored. After more than fifty years of puzzlement, the, most likely, honest reasons for his obsessive preoccupation became apparent. The first reason for his anti-gay diatribes would have been to divert and quash all suspicions and rumors which might have arisen concerning his own sexuality. His second reason would have been to gauge reactions to his anti-gay comments and behaviors in order to help him, more clearly, identify other closeted homosexuals.

That ***truth*****ful** explanation of his deceptive behavior has caused me to reconsider the statistical basis for the nineteen percent of all, alleged, hate crimes that are being committed against homosexuals. I, now, must wonder how many of those attacks are actually being committed either by closeted homosexual sadists or by consenting partners who had participated in sadistic homosexual "games" (or other deviant activities) that went too far.

Regrettably, the revelation that was most disappointing to me came next. I was informed that several of those homosexual boys, whom I believed were my friends, had been, anonymously, selling their sexual services to, countless, older homosexuals on a regular basis; and, when they did, all had agreed to assume my name and reveal details of my life as a way of, convincingly, concealing their own identities (for no other reason than the fact that I was one of the few among them who was not homosexual). If this revelation were **true**, that would mean that their inability to be faithful friends, or to live **truthful** and decent lives, had, apparently, caused my reputation to be destroyed (without my knowledge) for no other reason than I had ***not*** *chosen* to participate in their ***evil*** *life choices*.

If the types of boys who had been involved with homosexual priests behaved similarly, it is unfathomable to comprehend why *any of them* would have been deserving of multi-million dollar payoffs from the Catholic Church since it would be difficult to comprehend how any of them could have, possibly, been victims.

You realize that this account of a very small number of YMCA mentors will, most likely, cause society to become highly suspicious of all mentors despite the fact that the behavior of virtually all other mentors is above reproach?

That would be a mistake because, until the 1970's, most urban YMCA's and YWCA's *required same-sex* ***nude*** *swimming*. In retrospect, it is obvious that it was the nude swimming policy that attracted *those types of mentors*; thus, it is regrettable that, despite the presence of the word "Christian" in the name of the organization, YMCA swimming pools and shower areas were allowed, for decades, to be *prime hunting grounds* for homosexuals and pedophiles. This is the **true** meaning of the lyrics in "YMCA", a popular 1970's Disco song (that was sung, originally, by a homosexual septet whose stage costumes represented "gay fantasy personae") which proclaims that (1) *men can find everything they might want to enjoy there, and that* (2) *men will be able to* ***"hang out" with boys*** *at the YMCA*.

It might easily be inferred that betrayal by a group of friends (you trusted) is the reason for your disapproval of the homosexual lifestyle. Is it?

Their duplicity has caused me great sadness, disappointment, and confusion because, despite the fact that I will always be grateful for the help and kindness I had received at the YMCA, I have, unnecessarily, been made to realize that the, ***inbred****, sexual urges and emotional compulsions* of those friends had prevented them from, ever, being capable of trustworthiness or decency (even when being guided by a positive YMCA influence). It is unsettling to be forced to recognize that the kindness that I thought had been genuine, most likely, resulted from nothing more than an effort to carry out procedures outlined in a YMCA instructors' manual; thus, it would have been my choice to have never been made aware of such a ***disappointing*** **truth**.

Even worse, my friend clearly revealed that he had lived his entire life deceiving and betraying his wife, his children, his friends, his church, and others--even though such betrayals (and absences of **truth)** had never been necessary. It would seem as if his need to maintain a secret, dishonest life was just as compelling an inclination as his homosexual urges. This realization, *thus*, is one of the primary reasons I have concluded that many homosexuals are driven as much by compulsive needs to be deviant as they are by their sexual desires. My friend, regrettably, had been sculpting his spiritual frequency in the same ***untruthful*** manner for his entire life. By the time that he had reached his mid-seventies, his spiritual frequency must have been so, completely, defined (by the most, spiritually, self-destructive behaviors possible) that his eternal fate had already been determined; thus, it saddens me, most, to have been made to realize that he and those other (now deceased) YMCA friends had distinctly different spiritual destinies awaiting them and that, as a result, there is no chance that they and I could, possibly, reunite in the same Heavenly "room" after my death.

My friend's confession opened my eyes to other situations where closeted homosexuals have, puzzlingly, risen to some of the highest levels of power and influence. I have long been mystified, for example, as to how so many "outed" homosexual politicians and judges who had, supposedly, undergone thorough "vetting" processes, could have ever been elected and appointed. (What is even more frightening is the realization that most "closeted" political leaders have never been "outed"). I would presume that they, too, had had wealthy and powerful mentors (such as the exposed leader of the disgraced Lincoln Project) who facilitated their climbs to power for the, most likely, reason of thwarting the Christian majority's political influence and, thus, undermining this country's democratic representation. It is regrettable that far too many homosexuals have fronted for both corrupt and/or criminal organizations either because (1) they had pursued lifestyles that, readily, made them prone to blackmail victimization or (even more likely) because (2) they (much like Hollywood actors and actresses) had proven to be far more willing (and capable) of living duplicitous lives than most other humans.

Sadly, *such deviant impulses are never harmless but, in fact, are the triggers for the aberrant behaviors of troubled humans* who take pleasure in deceiving, betraying, and harming those persons who had, *unwisely*, placed trust in them. Although Timothy was speaking of all types of evil humans, it would be mindful to be guided by 2 Timothy 3:4 where he warns, "They will be treacherous, reckless, pompous, lovers of pleasure rather than God as they make pretense of religion but negate its powers. Stay clear of them". By means of Timothy's advice, insightful Christians have not been irrational "homophobes" (as accused) but, instead, have always understood that it is unwise to place *complete trust* in humans who have, willfully, chosen to live *deviant and deceptive lives.*

Can you provide any additional reasons as why you believe that many homosexuals (1) might be driven as much by a compulsive need to be deviant as they are by their, alleged, inborn gender misalignment and (2) how such a compulsive need might be harmful to others?

I have long wondered why (because of the massive amount of violent and sadistic homosexual rape that, *allegedly*, has been taking place in some prisons) no one has examined the obvious connection which exists between homosexual and criminal behavior. The first question that must be asked is: are those inmates committing violent homosexual attacks because such acts are, merely, additional means by which they choose to vent their innate sociopathic and psychopathic hostilities; or, instead, are such criminal behaviors, merely, out-of-control expressions of innate, yet often suppressed, homosexual urges? In other words: where (in the minds of aberrant humans) do homosexual compulsions end, where do the urges to commit criminal acts begin, and to what degree might these two inborn, deviant, compulsions overlap?

There is no better example of this conundrum than the psychosexually (and incongruously) conflicted mental state of Omar Mateen, the mass murderer of forty-nine defenseless humans (and the attempted mass murderer of fifty-three additional defenseless humans) at the Pulse homosexual nightclub in Orlando, Florida on Sunday, June 12, 2016. Although he justified his motive by pledging allegiance to the Islamic state, it is puzzling as to why he, for years, repeatedly visited online homosexual dating sites and patronized homosexual nightclubs that were over one hundred miles from his home if he had not, in fact, been a closeted homosexual sadist. No one will ever be able to know (for certain) because none of his *likely homosexual partners* will ever come forward to provide evidence that this mass murderer was, in fact, a closeted homosexual; however, ***the likelihood that he was a closeted homosexual sadist is more probable than not***--*despite the fact that* (like my YMCA friend) *he was both a father and husband.*

The reason this question about prison rapes must be asked is because of how unlikely it is that heterosexual and non-violent prisoners would be, willfully, raping one another. In the absence of any more valid explanation, the most plausible inference is that the overwhelming majority of violent prison rapes are being committed by homosexual and bisexual sadists. It follows, then, that if all prison rapes were to be properly included in national hate crime statistics (as they should be), that data might reveal that the preponderance of all hate crimes in this country are, actually, crimes being committed by homosexuals against heterosexuals. Since ***admitted*** homosexuals compose little more than three percent of the population, this statistical data, shockingly, reveals a dramatically disproportionate percentage of criminal behavior among homosexuals and, thus, explains *the most obvious reason* why Christians have remained somewhat skeptical about, mindlessly and unquestioningly, ***embracing all aspects*** *of the homosexual lifestyle.*

The second question to be asked is: since it is so easy for prison officials to end these sexual atrocities, why, then, are all prison rapists not punished (and stopped) by being *permanently* segregated from other inmates? Would not the mere threat of twenty additional years of imprisonment (and unending isolation) thwart most rapists? The solution is so obvious that the continuous failure by (at least some) prison officials to prevent vicious homosexual rapes seems intentional.

The Christian perspective is that homosexual prison rapes are heinous and must be prevented; thus, if there is ever evidence that any official in authority allows a prison rape to occur (even if by way of gross negligence), that official is equally as guilty of the crime and, thus, must be charged, prosecuted, and imprisoned as an accessory to that rape. Despite the absence of all rational, moral, or justifiable reasons, there are still some prisons which have, puzzlingly, been allowed to remain playgrounds for homosexual sadists for far too long. Why?

Why do you believe that such homosexual prison atrocities have been allowed to continue?

The primary reason for the, alleged, tens of thousands of yearly prison rapes results from the fact that mainstream media, America's (designated) public watchdog, has failed to effectively instigate reform by graphically spotlighting, and condemning, *those forms* of sexual crimes. Instead, media has helped to perpetuate those prison barbarities by successfully brainwashing the general population into accepting violent ***homosexual*** *rapes* as being the *humorous*, inevitable, and justifiable consequences for imprisonment even though (1) few of the victims are homosexuals and (2) even fewer have committed sufficiently serious crimes to justify such an odious form of (physically and emotionally damaging) violent, cruel, and unusual punishment.

While Constitutional protection facilitates freedom of the ***printed*** press, it is remarkably puzzling that (1) all (but, *possibly*, one) major media outlets are presently controlled by a single non-Christian influence and that (2) there has been, virtually, *no* ***effective*** *mainstream media voice (for more than fifty years) which has fairly and clearly represented any aspect of the* **intelligent** *Christian perspective.*

It is this anti-Christian mainstream media voice, for example, which has, most recently, been brainwashing young girls by fabricating and, then, perpetuating the lie that ***all*** "modern" adolescent girls ***must*** experience a "teenage lesbian stage". In order to successfully accomplish this latest form of orchestrated child corruption, mainstream media has been stage-managing the public homosexual confessions of young singers and actresses who had, previously, been marketed and, thus, recognized as teenage role models. After all, if an influential teenage idol has experienced a lesbian phase (and she publicly claims that it is wonderful), shouldn't every naive teenage girl be influenced to follow her deviant sexual lead? Disturbingly, it appears, now, that young boys are the newest targets for the propaganda.

The problem which results from the broadcasting of this dishonest indoctrination (as with the glorification of teenage drug use) is that most young girls never emotionally recover from exposure to such damaging (formative years) sexual experiences and, thus, find it difficult (if not impossible) transitioning into the roles of *well-adjusted and capable* wives and mothers. The acts of encouraging young girls to experience such corrupting and harmful influences, at such young ages, is nothing other than a clear attempt to destroy young lives and, thus, destabilize the foundations of the Christian family structure. Despite these obvious evil intentions, the dissemination of this form of harmful propaganda remains unchallenged and, thus, continues to succeed.

For centuries, *committed parents* have wisely, and correctly, warned their sons and daughters of how difficult it is for *promiscuous young women* to, successfully, transition into the roles of capable and devoted mothers and wives. Despite the fact that recent media and educational influences have undermined this parental advice, such wise counseling must, once again, become the prevailing form of societal guidance utilized to dissuade young girls from blindly embracing damaging promiscuous experiences (especially teenage lesbianism).

Nationwide, a united Christian community has to expose, confront, and stop ***all*** *non-Christian, anti-Christian, and make-believe Christian media agendas* which are so devoid of fairness that they suppress honest debate and the expressions of legitimate ideas. The Christian community must make certain that those persons, institutions, and ***advertisers*** responsible for such damaging propaganda are ***no longer allowed to control, and dictate, any societal beliefs and norms in a democratic country that is populated, overwhelmingly, by a Christian majority***. Once the scoundrels responsible for these forms of societal corruptions are properly confronted and stopped (and media **truthfulness** and decency are restored), countless forms of societal problems (including homosexual prison rapes and ill-advised teenage lesbianism) will decline dramatically.

CHAPTER FIVE

THE SEVEN DEADLY SINS

You have created the self-righteous impression that you already know you are going to ascend to one of the most desirable Heavenly "rooms" while the rest of humans (including, perhaps, your deceased YMCA friends) are going to have a more difficult time. Is this not prideful hypocrisy?

If that is the impression I have created, it is an incorrect impression. I am aware of how easy it is for any person to appear to be a great humanitarian when condemning the sins of others while concealing his or her own misconduct; so, please be assured, it has never been my intention to be that hypocritical. Marcus Cicero was correct to conclude, "It is the peculiar quality of a *fool* to perceive the faults of others and to forget his own". I have lived as a human being for more than six decades; thus, it would have been impossible for me not to have sinned.

Because I have been guided by such a powerful, spiritually instructive, dream since the age of seven, I have far fewer excuses for any of my sins because I cannot use spiritual ignorance as an excuse. At Luke 23: 34, Jesus urged God to: "Forgive them, Father; for they know not what they do". I cannot expect such absolution to excuse any of my transgressions. It is most likely that all of *my* sins will be judged far more harshly than those sins committed by the "unknowing"; thus, it should be obvious that I have no ordained right to judge anyone.

When Jesus confronted the moneylenders in the Temple, he was not *judging* the souls of His fellow Hebrews; instead, He *merely* ***criticized their behaviors*** and urged them to change their sinful ways. My analyses of *modern* behaviors are no different. If Jesus made clear at John 12: 47 that he: "did not come to judge the world, but to save it", I would be a very foolish human to think that I might possess some special license to pass judgment on others. The sole purpose for my willingness to provide answers during this interview is to help steer others onto the correct salvation pathway. That does not necessarily certify, however, that I have already, successfully, been allowed to enter that pathway myself.

As for those of my deceased YMCA friends who may have lived closeted-homosexual lives, I doubt that they had abandoned very many of the *better human qualities* that I had always known them to possess; so it is doubtful that their homosexuality, *alone*, would have prevented them from having achieved ascension to Heaven. Sadly, however, because of the differences in our lifestyle choices, it is *improbable* that, upon my death, we will find each other in the same Heavenly "room".

To briefly summarize: those human qualities which sculpt the best human frequencies **(truth, love, goodness, humility, and peace)** are the spiritual qualities which, most often, were missing in the previous homosexual discussions; and it is the absence of those qualities in human living experiences which makes the possibility of ascension to Heaven more problematic.

When you were asked if you believed that homosexuality is sinful, your initial response was that the answer would be lengthier and more complicated than might readily be expected. Your explanation was, indeed, lengthy and complex. Why was this answer more thorough than any of your previous answers?

The reason for the thorough review was to illustrate how difficult it can be for most humans, in this modern-era, to recognize where, how, and when goodness ends and sin begins. Such knowledge is *paramount* because the ***only way*** humans are going to be able to sculpt the best possible spiritual frequencies is by understanding God's expectations and, thus, the manner by which God (*not contemporary culture*) approves or disapproves of various human thoughts, impulses, and behaviors. If Matthew 7: 13-14 is to be believed, the conduct of far too many humans is so unacceptable to God that few will be allowed to enter the "strait gate" of Heaven: "The gate that leads to damnation is wide, the road is clear, and many choose to travel it. But how narrow is the gate that leads to *life*, how rough the road, and *how few there are that find it*!" (If Matthew's verses are correct, it is quite possible that there are far fewer "rooms" available in the vicinity of Heaven than there are available in the vicinity of Hell).

The best way for humans to develop the spiritual insight that will guide them *to avoid damnation* was explained by Paul in 1 Corinthians 2: 1-16 (particularly at verse 10) when Paul taught that: "God has revealed this wisdom to us through the Spirit"; thus, Paul at 1 Corinthians 6: 19 made clear that *God's* ***true*** *intentions* can be found in the innermost recesses of *our own minds and our own souls* once we have developed the ability to hear God's voice: "You must know that your body is a temple of the Holy Spirit, who is within--the Spirit you have received from God". At Romans 8: 7-9, Paul further explained, "The flesh in its tendency is at enmity with God: it is not subject to God's law. Indeed, it cannot be; those who are in the flesh cannot please God. But you are not in the flesh; you are in the spirit, since the Spirit of God dwells in you".

The purpose of the extensive homosexual discussion was to illustrate how ***worldly*** *preoccupations* have the potential to create enmity with God; thus, whenever, for example, human beings choose to, *primarily*, identify themselves as homosexuals, they are indicating that they have succumbed to their bodies' impulses and cravings and, thus, have foolishly caused themselves to be "*in the flesh*" **and not** "*in the spirit*".

Previously, I had alluded to my *inner spiritual voice* when I revealed that I have always been aware that I have been guided--*not controlled*--by my very own, powerful, spiritual tethers. My explanations (1) of the lifelong process of sculpting spiritual frequencies and (2) of the spiritual tethers which connect individuals to specific Heavenly "rooms" are explanations which may help modern humans, more completely, understand what "*your body is a temple for the Holy Spirit, who is within*" actually means.

The best way to develop the skill *for hearing and being guided by God's spiritual goodness* (and, thus, connect with the most desirable spiritual tethers) is to, first, understand and internalize *Christ's lessons* for **truth**, peace, love, humility, and goodness. Although it is **true** that *all humans* (*including non-Christians*) have the capacity to possess these virtues and, thus, *have the potential to hear God's spiritual voice*, the most direct (and *easiest*) ***way*** to succeed is by properly understanding, embracing, and internalizing the righteous examples emphasized in Christ's teachings. In addition, if humans are going to be successful at, correctly, understanding the distinctions between good and evil (and appropriate and inappropriate conduct), higher-level, analytical thinking skills ***can*** (possibly) provide a second beneficial tool. Such skills enhance the likelihood that humans will be able to discern God's words by helping to filter immoral ideas from their minds, to eliminate confusion and temptation in their thoughts, and, thus, to achieve the necessary level of internal peace in order to recognize and understand God's quiet spiritual voice amid the engulfing static of worldly corruptions.

In summary, the goal of my thorough explanation is merely to provide a *first example* of the manner by which God, *most likely*, scrutinizes all human follies and sinful behaviors (*not just* ***some*** *homosexual behaviors*). Regardless of how readily any society is willing to, superficially, praise and embrace worldly foolishness, Matthew 7: 13-14 makes clear that God expects more from those of his children who seek ascension to the most desirable "rooms" in Heaven. God expects his children to ***attempt*** *to live more like Jesus in every possible way* (not as deviants). 1 Peter 1: 14-16 instructs: "As obedient sons, do not yield to the desires that once shaped you in your ignorance. Rather, become holy *yourselves* in *every* aspect of your conduct, after the likeness of the holy One who called you; remember, Scripture says: 'Be holy, for I am holy'."

You have discussed truth as being the most important human quality; however, you have yet to say very much about love, goodness, and peace. Does your concept of peace vary from the conventional Christian view?

Christian religious teachings have provided such *complete wisdom and insight* regarding love, goodness, and peace that the words of Christ and the lessons in the Bible are sufficient. At best, I can only offer insight as to how modern humans *might* better bond with those virtues. The concept of peace to which I am referring does differ from the broader Christian view which is as equally concerned with peace within a community, peace that results from civil order, and peace which exists when there is an absence of war. My narrower concept refers to the internal peace that humans must be able to realize if they are to succeed in locating and connecting with the best *spiritual tethers* within themselves. This peace was explained by Jesus at John 14:27 when Jesus said: "Peace I leave with you, my own peace I give you, ***a peace the world cannot give***; this is my gift to you". With these words, Christ made His followers aware that the peace "frequency" was ***one*** *of the primary pathways to salvation* and affirmed, thus, that a strong spiritual connection with the Holy Spirit can be realized by those who maintain appropriate peace *within their own souls.*

The pursuit of internal peace is not only a significant Christian objective; such peace has also been one of the primary objectives for virtually all of the great religions. Christians who strive to achieve internal peace, thus, can greatly benefit, for example, from the Buddhist wisdom which teaches that peace is best achieved when humans succeed in freeing themselves from greed, hatred, fear, delusions, ignorance, and all other worldly *cravings*--passions--and--attachments.

Peace is the calm which emerges in the presence of balance and order. Christians understand, then, that personal peace can best be realized when humans are able to eliminate all internal and external conflicts by ***balancing and ordering*** their thoughts, feelings, urges, and deeds with sufficient quantities of goodness, **truth**, love, humility, contentment, moderation, psychological health, and analytical clarity. This is why Proverbs 11:1 warns that, "A false ***balance*** is an abomination to the Lord".

The most effective means (by which to achieve such peace, order, and balance) results when Christians master the ability to ***recognize and avoid sins*** **(particularly the notorious Seven Deadly Sins: gluttony, lust, greed, pride, sloth, wrath, and envy)** ***at their inceptions*** because all seven of those sins are examples of excessive desires and indulgences which attract and motivate Satan and can, *unwittingly*, convert what would, otherwise, be *peaceful*, normal, and acceptable behaviors into sinful activities. Such *understanding* and *awareness*, then, help humans to maintain *spiritual balance and order* ***within*** by guiding them to distinguish (1) when and where the frequency tethers for peace and goodness separate from them and (2) when and where the frequency tethers for sin attach.

My dream has taught me that the reason why these seven sins are so significant is because all seven are behaviors which are the fuels that extinguish goodness and ignite transgressions. (The Seven Deadly Sins, therefore, are the building blocks upon which most other, more grievous, sins arise); thus, it makes sense for righteous Christians to develop the ability to, instinctively, *recognize* ***that moment*** *when sin originates* so that they can prevent sinful tethers from exercising control (and creating "a false spiritual *balance*" within them).

This is the primary reason why Christians have utilized corporeal punishment (not as an excuse for venting animalistic aggressions against weaker and more defenseless humans but, instead,) as a means of teaching their children (and misguided adults) the importance of, *immediately*, identifying and avoiding sin. In contrast, rather than supporting and recognizing the importance of corporeal discipline, modern secular society's prohibitions against such punishment have proven to be extremely damaging to the young. By preventing parents from ***training*** *their children to* ***INSTINCTIVELY recognize appropriate limits***, it is secular society's total lack of standards and values which are the primary causes that steer the young to drug and alcohol addiction, promiscuity, reckless and criminal behavior, non-learning, apathy, selfishness, materialism, sloth, and countless other forms of *imbalanced*, sinful, and out-of-control behaviors that disappoint God.

Although it would be presumptuous for me to attempt to reinvent Christian lessons that the Church has, so ably, been teaching for several thousand years, I do believe that a more, in-depth, examination of the Seven Deadly Sins will help to better explain what my spiritual tethers have taught me as they have guided (not controlled) my behavior throughout my life; thus, the following explanations are the reasons (*how?* and *why?*) I believe those Seven Deadly Sins can be so harmful:

1. Gluttony is included as one of the Seven Deadly Sins because ***excessive*** yearning for food (and other worldly pleasures) leads to *over*-consumption. While eating is a life-essential, sinless activity, gluttony is a ***disproportionate fixation*** *with physical things*; and that form of *worldly addictive obsession* creates such a profound *spiritual imbalance and disorder* that it weakens the glutton's resistance to evil temptations, causes the glutton to lose the ability to link with the Spirit within (as well as the most desirable Spiritual Afterlife) and, thus, to lose the ability to recognize God's quiet spiritual voice. At Philippians 3:19, Paul warned of the dangers of gluttony: "Such as these will end in disaster! Their god is their belly and their glory is in their shame. I am talking about those who are set about the *things of this world.*"

It is insufficient for humans to merely expect God to "lead us not into temptation and deliver us from evil" because all Christians who seek salvation are obligated to develop (on their own) the spiritual strength to resist those temptations and evils. This is why, in December, 2017, Pope Francis suggested that the words of the Lord's Prayer should be changed to "Do not let us enter into temptation" in place of "lead us not into temptation" because Pope Francis explained, "I" (a human being) "am the one who falls" (and, thus, am responsible for my sins); "It is not Him pushing me into temptation".

2. Lust: When God created humans, He included essential survival impulses such as yearnings for sexual gratification;

however, whenever any of those desires transform into such disproportionate, self-absorbed cravings for pleasure that they cause humans to disconnect from the Spirit within, lustful sin is the result. **Lust**, therefore, transforms acceptable sexual desires into sinful behavior because the pursuit of *immoral urges* often leads to, out-of-control, activities which ignore all harmful consequences. At 1 Corinthians 6: 9-10, Paul teaches: "Can you not realize that the unholy will not fall heir to the kingdom of God? Do not deceive yourselves: no fornicators, idolaters, or adulterers, no sexual perverts, thieves, misers, or drunkards, no slanderers or robbers will inherit God's kingdom". At 1 Corinthians 6: 17-19, Paul concludes: "But whoever is joined to the Lord ***becomes one spirit with him***. Shun lewd conduct. Every other sin a man commits is outside his body, but the fornicator sins against his own body. You must know that your body is a temple of the Holy Spirit, who is within--the Spirit you have received from God. You are not your own". Regardless of whether sexual desires are heterosexual or homosexual, the best way to shun lewd conduct and maintain the best connection with the Holy Spirit within is by (1) bolstering peaceful and ***truthful*** impulses, and (2) exercising *ordered restraint* when succumbing to human urges.

3. Greed is a similar sinful compulsion; however, greed is more a lusting for worldly possessions such as money and material objects. While pursuits for necessities that include food, shelter, warmth, and security in old age are *usually* sinless, the intention to possess material items of earthly value, beyond the need for basic survival and comfort, is excessive and can, very quickly, create a disorder which results in a disconnection from the Spirit within. Far too many transgressors deceive themselves into believing that it is, merely, *harmless human nature* that causes them to, willingly, commit sin in order to get (by any means necessary) those material items they desire. 1 Timothy 6: 9-

10 warns, however, that: "Those who want to be rich are falling into temptation and a trap. They are letting themselves be captured by foolish and harmful desires which drag men down to ruin and destruction. The love of money is the root of all-evil. ***Some*** men (and ***some*** women) in their passions for it have strayed from the faith, and have come to grief amid great pain".

One of the most paradoxical situations in modern America results from the fact that the Republican political party (a party that, most ***traditionally***, embraces those principles which 1 Timothy 6 warns against) is the political party *claiming* to be the defender of the Christian faith. By making that claim, the party has been able to entice far more voters to support its political agendas even though (1) few, if any, ***traditional*** Republican agendas could possibly be recognized as being based upon Christian principles and even though (2) the party has done virtually nothing (until the election of President Trump) to strengthen Christian influences within a country that, continually, becomes more materialistic and corrupt.

It would seem as though ***traditional*** Republican Party principles have missed Matthew's admonitions at 6: 24: "No man can serve two masters. He will either hate one and love the other or be attentive to one and despise the other. You cannot give yourself to God and money". Nothing is more likely to separate a man from the *Spirit within* than those questionable activities which, frequently, facilitate and accompany the acquisition of wealth such as bribery, deception, collusion, betrayal, blackmail, exploitation, violence, intimidation, abuse of power, misuse of knowledge, and/or a total disregard for harmful repercussions to society. It is fortunate, then, that President Trump has guided the Republican Party to embrace more Populist and ***Christian*** beliefs.

Are you, then, advocating that all American Christians should be Democrats?

Although, at one time, the Democrat Party used countless *deceptive* ploys for the purpose of enticing the Christian vote, the Democrat Party could not conceal its contempt for the Christian religion (and the majority Christian culture) for very long; and the, regrettable, result is that the United States stopped being a Christian Democracy in the 1960's (soon after John F. Kennedy was elected President). If Christianity is to survive in a country that is presently controlled by (what appears to be) a corrupt (Christian-loathing) minority, Christians will have to regain political control of this country by (1) either *insisting that* ***all*** *Republican Party agendas reflect Christian values* or (2) by establishing an entirely new *secular* political party that is based on the most sound, and *worldly-practical*, Christian beliefs and, then, by (3) winning the majority of elections (state-by-state) until Christians have *regained* nationwide control of this country's governmental system.

You have not yet said anything about pride.

4. While some have claimed that **Pride** might be the most serious of the Seven Deadly Sins, pride is, also, one of the trickiest sins to identify and understand. Self-confidence and personal contentment have always been some of the more desirable human qualities (because self-satisfaction is an essential aspect for realizing internal peace). In his wonderful book, *The Power of Positive Thinking*, Norman Vincent Peale employs Biblical teachings to reveal how humans can find personal peace through the realization of positive self-assurance. My two favorite verses emphasized by Peale are from Romans: 8:31: "If *God* be for us, who can be against us?" and Philippians 4:13: "I can do all things *through Christ* that strengthens me". Both are **prideful** Christian mantras that do help reinforce the connection with the Spirit within. It would seem, then, that as long as self-contentment helps to achieve order and balance (and strengthens a connection to the Spirit within), prideful feelings can be desirable; however, the moment such ***delusions*** *of self-importance* separate a person from the spirit within, that is the crux where goodness ends and sin begins. Psalm 10:4 of The King James Version reminds us that, "The wicked, *through the pride of his countenance*, will not seek after God. God is not in all his thoughts".

When *excessive* confidence or glorification of oneself above others rises to the level of ***conceit, self- righteousness, or haughtiness***, a spiritual disconnection occurs because of a misguided sense of personal importance; and that fallacy leads prideful humans to disregard, disrespect, disobey, and, thus, separate from the guidance of the best possible tether (the Spirit within). 1 Corinthians 4: 7 reminds us that pride results when humans decide to take credit for those benefits they have received from God and, thus, choose to self-worship rather than be grateful to God for those wonderful blessings: "Who confers any distinction on you? Name something you have that you have not received. If, then, you have received it, why are you boasting as if it were your own?" Proverbs 16: 17-19 warns: "The path of the upright avoids misfortune; he who pays attention to his ***way*** safeguards his life. Pride goes before disaster, and a haughty spirit before a fall. It is better to be humble with the meek than to share plunder with the proud".

Wasn't it this type of Christian, prideful, intolerance that Thomas Hardy condemned in <u>Tess</u> <u>D'Urberville</u>?

Hardy's concerns focused attention upon the actions of those, *seemingly*, *merciless Christians* who used Biblical teachings as *cruel and heartless weapons* against the most downtrodden and vulnerable in Victorian society; however, Hardy's criticism failed to, in any way, *evenhandedly acknowledge* that those stern Victorians, by refusing to tolerate or accommodate *sinful behaviors*, were remarkably successful at civilizing (and, thus, saving the souls of) a large number of wayward humans. The question, then, focuses on whether God would have regarded such Victorian harshness as ***prideful** sin*; and *that* answer *depends* upon whether Spiritual disconnection occurred as a result of any of those unyielding Victorian behaviors.

The Fifth Catholic Commandment (and the Sixth Protestant Commandment): "Thou shall not kill!" affords a sufficiently accurate analogy for purposes of answering that question. Wise men have been able to recognize and conclude that not all forms of homicide are equally as sinful because innocent humans who kill entirely in self-defense or by unavoidable accident could not possibly be guided by the same evil spiritual tethers as those persons who commit premeditative murders.

The purposes of stern Christian mandates have always been to *save* as many sinners as possible. The best way to accomplish that has been by vigorously opposing *all forms* of sinful behavior; thus, in those instances where prideful Victorian sternness was utilized *solely for the **noble purpose of uplifting society***, no separation from the Spirit, within, was likely to have occurred. In instances where abuse of the downtrodden resulted primarily from evil, self-serving, or sadistic conceit, that prideful behavior would have caused a Spiritual disconnection.

In summary, the behavior of most Victorian Christians would not have been nearly as offensive to God as the behavior of Thomas Hardy; nevertheless, Thomas Hardy's observations have proven to be helpful by reminding well-meaning Christians of the need to avoid excessive, prideful, behavior by choosing to utilize ***Christian discernment*** rather than ***animalistic judgment*** when making efforts to save those sinners who have fallen.

What qualifies sloth (laziness) to be one of the Seven Deadly Sins?

5. Sloth: When Pope Gregory, in AD 590, revised and consolidated earlier recognized vices into what are presently The Seven Deadly Sins (for the purpose of identifying those human behaviors which most frequently--*yet unwittingly*--trigger more grievous sin), **Sloth** focused on humans (1) who chose to avoid *essential* work and obligations, ***and*** (2) who chose to refrain from utilizing their minds (and the gift of *consciousness*) in an appropriate manner that would please God.

While rest and relaxation are vital for maintaining a healthy life and, thus, cannot be sinful activities, Genesis 2:15 provides two essential reasons why sloth is included as one of the seven sins: "The Lord God then took the man and settled him in the Garden of Eden, *to cultivate and care for it*"; and Genesis 1:28 commands: "*…fill the Earth and subdue it*". It is because of these mandates to support society (by properly *utilizing the gift of consciousness*) that so many Biblical passages remind humans that *slothful behavior is a demonstration of sinful ingratitude for that gift.*

Proverbs 22: 6 advises humans to: "Train a boy in the way he should go; even when he is old, he will not swerve from it"; thus, the Old Testament teaches that (along with all other Christian values) a work ethic should be instilled in the young, beginning at the earliest age possible. One of the most beneficial modern teaching-aids for helping children understand the necessity for a conscientious work ethic is the 1934 cartoon (available on the internet), "Walt Disney's Silly Symphony-The Grasshopper and the Ants", a delightful re-creation of an enduring Aesop Fable. While the ants industriously prepared for winter, the grasshopper played his fiddle and danced. When winter arrived, however, the ants were safe, well fed, and warm; but the grasshopper was (*unnecessarily*) cold, hungry, and near death. It was only the ants' goodness (and their willingness to rescue the grasshopper) that saved that *slothful* grasshopper from his folly.

This cartoon is a wonderfully effective tool for demonstrating to children the primary reason why all humans should utilize their God-given gifts to willingly work when industry is necessary. Numerous Biblical verses, repeatedly, reinforce this concept by reminding humans of God's disdain for indolence. Proverbs 10: 5, for example, instructs that, "A son who fills the granaries in summer is a credit; a son who slumbers during harvest, a disgrace". This notion is re-emphasized in Proverbs 12: 11, "He who tills his own land has food in plenty, but he who follows idle pursuits is a fool". Ecclesiastes 10: 18 (in the King James Version) cautions of the sinful result of such laziness (both literally and metaphorically): "By much slothfulness, the building decays; and through idleness of hands the house drops through"; thus, Proverb 18: 9 warns, "He who is slothful in his work is a brother to him who *destroys*"; and Proverb 13:4 concludes: "The soul of the sluggard craves in vain, but the *diligent soul* is amply satisfied".

Although these *and* ***many other*** *Biblical verses* emphasize the necessity for essential work, *physical* laziness is only one aspect of this sin because God also expects all humans to develop and utilize their mental and spiritual God-given abilities; thus, the refusal to perform (or a carelessness in the performance of) moral, spiritual, and legal obligations are examples of slothful behavior as well *and* are the most significant proofs of sinful ingratitude for the gift of consciousness.

When humans deliberately decline to be as conscientious and self-disciplined as possible, they are being slothful; thus, *mental* sloth is both (1) the willful choice to refuse to properly utilize God-given gifts and talents and (2) the intentional decision to remain foolish and uncaring for the purpose of pursuing only self-indulging, animalistic, pleasures. Since mental sloth causes humans to neglect God's and Jesus' teachings, Thomas Aquinas observed that sloth "…is evil in its effect, if it so oppresses man as to draw him away entirely from good deeds".

Sloth, then, is one of the controlling urges which accompany most forms of sinful misconduct. It is, for example, slothful human nature which facilitates the downward spiral into drug addiction and/or alcoholism. It is also slothful urges (1) that cause "accidental" yet unwanted pregnancies, and impulsive slothful solutions (2) which, subsequently, prompt the willful decision to abort such pregnancies.

Because sloth is a *primary, animalistic, impulse which impedes humans from connecting with the most desirable spiritual frequencies*, it is important to be mindful (once again) of two guiding **truths**: (1) If humans are going to be successful at, correctly, understanding the distinctions between good and evil (and appropriate and inappropriate conduct), the highest *possible* levels of analytical thinking skills are essential. Such skills *enhance the likelihood* that humans will be able to discern God's words by helping to filter immoral ideas from their minds, to eliminate confusion and temptation in their thoughts, and, thus, to achieve the necessary level of internal peace in order to recognize and understand God's quiet spiritual voice amid the engulfing static of worldly corruptions. The Buddhist tenant that "peace is achieved in the absence of ignorance" correctly summarizes this *universal **truth***. (2) At 1 Corinthians 2:15-16, Paul taught that a human, by *knowing the mind of Christ*, can ***discern*** *spiritual truth* because: "…the spiritual man can appraise everything…." (***Discernment*** means keenness of insight and the ability to perceive. It stresses the power to *distinguish* and *select* that which is ***true*** and *appropriate* from that which is not). God's test expects all humans to demonstrate their gratitude for the gift of consciousness by *adequately* developing their *mental abilities* so that they can utilize their *spiritual discernment* to help identify and, thus, avoid as much temptation and sin as possible. That, regrettably, is far less likely for those humans who, willfully, choose the slothful path; and that, as a result, is why sloth has been included as one of the Seven Deadly Sins.

You have not yet discussed wrath.

6. Wrath: One of the most significant reasons humans must be, steadfastly, aware of the distinctions between good and evil results from the fact that we are all spiritual beings who exist within primate bodies which are controlled by animalistic instincts, urges, and desires. God's purpose for creating such a reality for us is to help God determine which impulses dominate and, thus, define our identities. God's hope is that we develop such ***spiritual strength*** that we are able to utilize and control our life-essential animalistic talents rather than be ruled by them; as a result, when we allow ourselves to succumb to our body's impulses and cravings (and permit them to sculpt our identities), we sin and fail God's test.

Few savage compulsions dominate humans more than *anger*. While the venting of anger (in the absence of sin) *can be* an essential way for all humans to (periodically) effectively release an excessive buildup of aggressive feelings, *uncontrolled* and continuous anger has the potential to be one of the most extreme, unhealthy, and harmful of all animalistic impulses. James 1: 19-20 advises: "Know this my beloved brothers: Let every person be quick to hear, slow to speak, and slow to *anger*; for the *anger* of man does not produce the righteousness of God". This is particularly **true** when that anger is of a **wrathful** nature: a strong, stern, and fierce type of anger that is so deeply resentful that it demands vengeance and punishment. Desire for retribution provokes such strong evil passions of resentment, rage, irritation, selfishness, and self-interest that wrathful passions have the potential to *permanently damage* the spiritual identities of wrathful sinners.

From the earliest age, I have, innately, known to avoid being wrathful against those persons who, unreasonably and unjustifiably, choose to attack and harm me. The reason is that I have always recognized that the *primary instinctive reason for any such act of aggression* is to force a victim to fight back and, thus, be (as equally) transformed into a *spiritually corrupt human* as the attacker had already, willfully, chosen to be. I have, also, recognized that when I did not fight back in the same wrathful manner, the savage impulses that had, originally, been directed at me, *almost, always* turned inwardly and resulted in some form of self-destructive outcome for the attacker. Proverbs 17: 13 teaches: "If a man pays back evil for good, evil will never leave his house"; thus, it has always made sense to observe the lesson of Proverb 20: 22 which advises: "Do not say, 'I'll pay you back' for this wrong! Wait for the Lord and he will *deliver you*". Notice that Proverb 20: 22 makes clear that the Lord will "*deliver*" *me* rather than "*wreak vengeance*" for *me*.

This is one area of spiritual understanding where my dream has caused me to perceive God's intentions differently from the conventional Judeo-Christian belief. Despite this distinction, I have always known that my dream's wisdom can help make God's ***true*** intentions clearer and, thus, easier for persons of all religions to accept. My dream taught me that the spiritual force which, ultimately, consumes and punishes an evil attacker is not *God's wrath* (because God is not wrathful) but, instead, derives directly from the evil tether that the transgressor drew to himself and connected to his soul; thus, what the Old Testament, frequently, refers to as "God's *wrath*" is *actually* the price that Satan demands, in exchange, as payment, from any human who had, willfully, chosen to connect with one of Satan's *stronger* tethers. Satan (*not God*) demands that ***his evil must be disseminated*** (*most frequently for the purpose of corrupting innocents*); thus, when a sinner fails *in any effort* to unleash Satan's energy, that fallow evil overwhelms *every* sinner's consciousness and remains a permanent part of *every* sinner's soul *to such a degree* that "good" tethers can be disconnected and, thus, thwarted from, any longer, positively influencing that wayward person.

My dream has, also, made the **true** meaning of Christ's instruction at Matthew 5: 39 clearer to understand and accept: "When a person strikes you on the right cheek, turn and offer him the other". Christ's guidance was not meant to encourage humans to behave as masochists and, thus, ***always submit to the domination of evil humans***. Instead, the objective of Christ's advice was to remind us that our ***primary*** *purpose is to* **save our *own* souls**; and, ***whenever possible***, we should not allow ourselves to be drawn to the same evil tethers (or allow ourselves to be influenced by the same wicked impulses) that had already consumed those sinners who, unjustifiably, chose to attack and victimize others (***because*** Satan does not serve humans--instead, misguided humans serve Satan). Ephesians 4:26, advises, "If you are angry, let it be without sin. The sun must not go down on your wrath; *do not give the devil a chance to work on you*". Romans 12: 19, thus, consoles: "Beloved, do not avenge yourselves; leave that to God's wrath, for it is written, "'Vengeance is mine; I will repay' says the Lord".

Again, my dream has made clear that "Vengeance is mine" does not, ***literally***, mean that God will extract vengeance on a victim's behalf either immediately *or* on Judgment Day". Instead, my dream has taught me that since wrath makes humans vulnerable to demonic influence, "vengeance is mine" means: ***only God*** *has the capacity to remain holy while being vengeful*; thus, Christians are advised (***whenever possible***) ***to trust in God's will*** rather than seek wrathful vengeance on their own. In summary, since demonic tethers deceive willful sinners into sculpting *corrupted* frequencies, God does not have to intervene and unleash wrathful vengeance against wrongdoers because those transgressors have, already (by way of self-destructive choices), *permanently harmed their souls.*

Are there not instances when wrathful behavior is necessary?

Obviously, there are times when an individual or a society must either defend or perish. When attacked to a point where serious and permanent injury has resulted (or could, possibly, result), there is no other choice than to obey Old Testament tenets by *wrathfully* responding, in kind, for the purpose of thwarting the resultant damage of such attacks. According to Psalm 97: 10, "The Lord loves those who hate evil". ***Righteous*** *wrathful behavior* is expected, then, when humans acknowledge their duty to God and fulfill their obligation by not only hating such evil but by confronting and permanently foiling such evil. ***Necessary*** *wrath* is perceived, reluctantly, by God as being sinless; however, humans must *proceed cautiously* because when wrathful responses result from little more than hurt feelings and other trivial worldly concerns (and there is *no* ***righteous*** *justification for such imprudent behavior*), wrathful responses are sinful and permanently damaging. This is particularly **true** when such wrathful responses are unleashed upon large numbers of blameless victims.

Are Muslims who wage "Jihad", by committing mass murder against large numbers of innocent people, unleashing righteous wrath or are they, instead, sinful, mass murderers?

Despite (***untruthful***) denials, large numbers of Muslims are taught, from the youngest ages, that they are justified (and obligated) to ***murder*** all humans who disagree with what they believe. There is the possibility that such a faith system fails to recognize God's **true** purpose for granting *free will* to humans: life on Earth is God's testing laboratory. He has, *intentionally*, given humans *the freedom to determine their own spiritual destinies* (to be sinners should they desire and to *repent* when they are ready). Muslim willingness to murder other humans for having a different point of view (rather than allowing those humans the opportunity to *fully* sculpt their frequencies) is one of the most trivial justifications (among all possible worldly reasons) for seeking *destructive vengeance*; thus, such wrathful murder clearly connects with (and is driven by) ***demonic tethers, ONLY***. If God did not want his children to remain free, and to think and act as they please, God would have never created humans with the ability to exercise *free will*; thus, it is not possible that God could encourage (or forgive) humans for imposing a vengeance that God would never execute Himself.

Well-meaning Muslims might possibly recognize that the world was far more savage prior to the Seventh Century (that time when ***God's truth*** was revealed). There were demonic-type religions such as those practiced by the Aztecs, Incas, and Mayans where idol-worshipping priests would select, rape, brutalize, and *silence* young virgins by offering those innocent lives to pagan *idols* and *gods*.

"Conan the Barbarian" (a 1982 film which was based on Robert E. Howard's 1930's series of tales of a ***fictional*** Hyborian Age) depicts a barbaric, pre-historic era where humans who sought salvation were invited to contribute all of their worldly possessions to *Set* (a snake god) and wait, patiently, for their chance to achieve spiritual *splendor*. When their time did arrive, innocents were sacrificed, butchered, and eaten for fresh meat because their "*saviors*" were (in actuality) murderers, cannibals, and thieves.

Although the "Conan" events were **fictional**, there had been *numerous, self-styled, religious sects* that behaved similarly, in every part of the world, prior to the times of Christ and the Great Prophet; and it is for ***those types*** *of sinful behaviors* that God would have advised His followers to wage war on ***those types*** *of idols* (and the evils they represented). Demonic forces, so totally, dominated those false religions (and idols) that *righteous* Muslim vengeance (***at that time***) would have, indeed, been *necessary and appropriate in order to protect the world from the evils that* ***psychotic and sociopathic mentalities*** *had, sinfully, unleashed.*

In contrast, most balanced (sane) humans no longer worship false idols. *All* of the remaining great religions of the world share the same intention of elevating humans for the purpose of directing them toward Heaven. The fact that God has *encouraged* more than one great religion to exist demonstrates that God has *sanctified multiple pathways which lead to Him*; and God's expectations are that all humans should be free to follow that path which best suits them without fear of reprisal from other humans who are compelled more by, *mistaken*, *demonic compulsions* than by God's blessings. It should be clear that any modern religious belief which attracts (and is appealing to) humans who are controlled by, ***psychotic and sociopathic***, ***animalistic urges*** could not possibly be a belief that is either sanctioned by God *or* leads to spiritual salvation.

The remaining deadly sin is Envy. Why is envy included as one of the Seven Sins?

7. Envy: To begin, it is noteworthy that envy is the only Deadly Sin which is also included as two of the Ten Commandments by the Catholic religion and one of the Ten Commandments by the Protestant religion. Deuteronomy 5: 21 instructs: "You shall not *covet* your neighbor's wife. You should not *desire* your neighbor's house or field … nor anything that belongs to him"; thus, by having been included as (either one or two) Biblical Commandments, it is clear that **Envy** has remained one of the most persistent "unwitting" sins in Judeo-Christian societies since before the time of the Great Exodus.

The primary reason that Envy is included as one of the deadly sins is because it is motivated, almost entirely, by malicious and animalistic impulses which cause spiritual imbalance and disorder; thus, the more envious a person chooses to be, the greater the chasm between that person and the spirit within. Envy is an uncomfortable urge which causes both a strong resentment toward another person's assets, qualities, advantages, accomplishments, reputation, or good fortune and an unreasonable desire, *triggered by malevolence*, to unjustifiably take possession of those benefits for oneself. It is an irrational and shameful coveting since the resentment exists, only, because the envious person refuses to acknowledge the possessor's right to his or her own assets. Envy has the potential to cause such great feelings of inadequacy and unhappiness that it cannot coexist in any human who possesses ***true*** *spiritual wisdom.*

James 3: 14-17 explains, "Should you…nurse bitter jealousy and selfish ambition in your hearts, at least refrain from arrogant and false claims against the **truth**. *Wisdom like this* does not come from above. It is earthbound, a kind of animal, even devilish, cunning. Where there are jealousy and strife, there also are inconstancy and all kinds of vile behavior. Wisdom from above, by contrast, is first of all innocent. It is also peaceable, lenient, docile, rich in sympathy, and the kindly deeds that are its fruits, impartial and sincere". James makes clear that envy is such a sinful urge that it causes a disconnection from the best spiritual tethers.

Some humans, however, believe (and are quite possibly correct) that *benign* envy has the *potential* to generate constructive results. If, for example, a person covets a friend's possessions or accomplishment so much that the envious desire *motivates* that person to be less slothful and to utilize God-given abilities for the purpose of, competitively, obtaining and achieving just as much (or more) through one's own hard, *sinless* work, then benign envy *could possibly* result in, desirable, worldly and personal outcomes.

Benign envy, for example, might have been the strongest human catalyst that has triggered widespread acceptance of the principles of Democracy because (1) *equal opportunity for all* short-circuits the need for wars (generated by envious passions) which inevitably result from social disparity and because (2) Democratic equality and freedom *removes all justification for* ***destructive*** *envious behavior* since Democracy facilitates and, thus, allows everyone to have equal and fair opportunity to achieve *any* desired goal.

Do you believe that benign envy is the spiritual impulse which most influences those humans who insist upon transforming this world into socialist or communist societies?

In recent history, a large number of humans, including (puzzlingly) far too many Christian ministers and priests, have insisted that Socialism (and even Communism) are the political systems which ***Christians*** *should prefer* because those activists *allege* that socialist beliefs, more correctly, reflect God's and Jesus' intentions. Regrettably, since this deceptive propaganda is so false, it readily reveals how its proponents fail to understand (1) God's intentions and (2) the ***true*** *goals* of socialist and communist systems. Such inappropriate advocacy causes most, insightful, Christian to suspect that the primary reason, too many, modern-era clergymen have chosen careers in Christian ministries is to exploit the power and influence of the Church for the purpose of instigating unjustified political and social upheaval rather than guiding Christians to salvation.

It is correct that Christian goodness requires decent humans to help others who are *truly and* ***justifiably*** *downtrodden (and in need)*. Isaiah 58: 10-12 teaches that, "If you bestow your bread on the hungry and satisfy the afflicted, then light shall rise for you in the darkness; and the gloom shall become for you like midday". Matthew 26: 34-36 concurs by revealing what Jesus will say at The Last Judgment to those who are saved: "Inherit the kingdom prepared for you from the creation of the world. For I was hungry and you gave me food, I was thirsty and you gave me drink. I was a stranger and you welcomed me, naked and you clothed me. I was ill and you comforted me, in prison and you came to visit me".

Christians must remain mindful, however, that the hardships (and levels of desperation) faced by the poor, during the time of Christ, were dramatically more severe and less justified than those difficulties faced by modern-era poor who are free, are allowed equal opportunity, and are given more than sufficient governmental aid by the richest country in the history of the world. In fact, those who are now regarded as being the most impoverished have a far more advantaged existence (in every way) than the wealthiest humans who lived during Jesus' era. It is difficult, then, to understand why anyone would demand that charitable Christians (who had, willingly, created a Democratic and free society) should, additionally, *be forced to give* ***equal*** *amounts of what is theirs to others* who have deliberately chosen to live decadent and slothful lives rather than have properly utilized their God-given abilities to adequately provide for themselves and their families. The ***envious*** motivational urges (which insist that all humans are ***equitably entitled*** to everything a society can provide) derive from some of the most sinful and malevolent human impulses imaginable.

Overwhelmingly, far too many who demand such a political system are people who had intentionally chosen (1) to live ***slothful***, idle, sinful, and/or criminal lives; (2) to harbor greedy, ***gluttonous***, and ***envious*** desires to exercise control over worldly goods which they have no right to possess; and (3) to demonstrate a willingness to unleash ***wrathful*** *destructive holocaust* upon other, harder-working, innocent humans in order to unjustifiably seize undeserved worldly assets, qualities, and advantages for themselves even though they have lived in a *free* society and have been provided an *equal opportunity* to achieve whatever they wish to achieve. There is nothing benign about this form of envy.

Since such human intentions vary so distinctly from God's and Jesus' teachings, it should not be surprising that communists and socialists have, throughout history, ***forced secular beliefs*** upon Christians (starting with their children), waged (declared and undeclared) war against Christians and the Christian religion, and, in some instances, committed mass murder against Christians for no other purpose than to steal the benefits that Christians reaped as a result of having chosen to live industrious lives. In a 1954 interview,

Evangelist Billy Graham discussed the ***true*** *goals* of Communism. A paraphrase of his remarks explains that either Communism must die or Christianity must die because it is actually a battle between Christ and anti-Christ. In effect, Communism (and some forms of Socialism) are political systems which choose to enslave (and even kill) the most decent humans in order to seize the benefits of their hard work for the purpose of ***briefly satiating*** *the unjustified whims of society's most sinful.*

Considering the degree to which socialist ideas have been promoted and embraced by some Church leaders and America's media since the 1960's, all Christians who have disagreed with socialist principles have been accused of being insensitive to the struggles of America's poor. Do you believe that is true?

If God's intention for humans is to provide *themselves* the opportunity to attach to the best tethers and frequencies (for the purpose of molding the most desirable eternal spiritual identities), it is unlikely that God could be pleased with those humans who fail to properly utilize the gifts He has provided them. Since it has never been God's purpose to create Heaven on Earth, God expects humans to be strengthened by the struggles they face rather than to use those struggles as excuses and justifications for choosing to live ***envious***, ***slothful***, ***wrathful***, decadent, and evil lives.

While **true** Christians, willingly, embrace charity, kindness, and understanding, the good spiritual frequencies and tethers that are associated with those emotions and deeds only attach to those humans who extend charity and understanding to the *deserving (not to those humans who, instead, unjustly and ungratefully exploit those kindnesses).* God expects spiritually evolved humans to *attempt* to overcome their worldly conditions--not succumb to them *or* to use them as excuses for choosing sinful paths; thus, while God expects Christians to help America's ***deserving*** *poor*, God's greater expectation is for the *undeserving poor* is to abandon their ***envy*** and ***sloth*** and to *elevate* ***themselves*** through hard work and decency (rather than submit to sin and, thus, sentence themselves to eternal damnation).

Instead of uplifting humans, Socialism and Communism facilitate and encourage the perpetuation of the lowest forms of human behavior; thus, these types of governmental systems could not possibly be God's favorites. While it is **true** that any society which allows a privileged class to exploit and restrict the freedoms and opportunities of the poor is a tyrannical and indecent society, there is no more tyrannical and evil form of government than a communist system which allows the most sinful members of society to exploit and, essentially, enslave its most decent, hard-working, and talented; thus, neither Socialism nor Communism can ever successfully prosper (in the long term) because, ***in all instances***, the primary intention of the largest percentage of its more sinful citizens is, solely, ***to enviously ill-use and plunder the work-results of others***. This, then, inevitably triggers a permanent downward societal spiral because it causes the most decent and industrious citizens to reduce their efforts so much that, ultimately, they produce and contribute on the same dysfunctional and sinful level as the most slothful citizens. At that point, the only way a Socialist or Communist government can prevent itself from unraveling is by spying, restricting most freedom, and, tyrannically, terrorizing its citizenry.

Despite such **truth**, it has not been *entirely* impossible for ***certain*** highly taxed, socialist leaning, yet Capitalist, Democracies to have prospered after having integrated ***some*** *socialist* policies within their *competitive* economic systems. This integration *has* succeeded in ***small*** *(and homogenous) countries* such as Sweden and Denmark, for example, where the majority of citizens descend from the same familial tribe of *equally* moral, industrious, disciplined, and devoted Christians; thus, admittedly, there are, indeed, *limited ways* by which ***some*** socialist-type policies can, successfully, be incorporated without destroying a free and moral Christian society.

***

To summarize this "Seven Deadly Sins" discussion: it must be noted that although most insightful Christians have always known that living ***moderate*** lives is the best way for them (1) to maintain spiritual order and balance and (2) to avoid sin, Christians must, nevertheless, also be aware that if they are going to *fully succeed at avoiding "unwitting" sin*, it is essential for them to, likewise, continually remain conscious of that *exact instant* when they might disconnect from the Holy Spirit within. Understanding the harm that results from embracing any of the seven "deadly" behaviors helps Christians to constrain those ***excessive*** *desires and indulgences* which attract Satan and enable him to transform into sin those *behaviors* that would, *otherwise*, be peaceful, normal, and acceptable conduct. Developing such understanding, then, (1) should be one of the *primary life-goals* for all decent human beings who desire to remain connected to the very best spiritual frequencies for their entire lives and (2) should, also, be among the primary lessons taught to children--starting at the earliest ages.

CHAPTER SIX

THE TEN COMMANDMENTS

You have just stated that envy is not only one of the Seven Deadly Sins but is, also, a sinful behavior admonished by one Protestant Commandment and two Catholic Commandments. Now that you have completed your discussion of the Seven Deadly Sins, would you, next, be willing to share your insights regarding the Ten Commandments as well?

It would be presumptuous and haughty for me to ever represent myself as being a Christian expert or advisor. For more than two thousand years, ***numerous*** *inspired humans* have *devoted their lives* to the effort of fully grasping and, then, revealing the meaning of God's and Jesus' teachings. I could never pretend to possess their degrees of insight, spiritual guidance, devotion, and goodness.

My in-depth discussion of the Seven Deadly Sins was for the purpose of *emphasizing the importance of being able to,* **immediately, recognize that instant** *when harmless behavior transforms into sin* so that all decent humans might utilize their spiritual strength to avoid as many transgressions as possible. ***Some*** of my insights have been gleaned from the lessons that I have learned (at least, in part) from wiser, inspiring, Christian teachers; thus, it is inappropriate for me to *pretend* that I could, possibly, possess a more insightful understanding of those Commandments than the, countless, great Christian teachers who have preceded me.

While that may be true, you have, nevertheless, already, repeatedly provided fresh understanding which helps Christians perfect their spiritual wisdom. The insight that you have acquired from your dream has, for example, (1) furnished a coherent and accurate account as to why Communism and Socialism could not possibly be God's preferred governmental systems because both are motivated more by the covetousness forbade by the Commandments than they are inspired by God's goodness. Although most Christians have always been aware of those facts, the non-stop, one-sided, socialist propaganda that, continually, brainwashes modern society has effectively thwarted most Christians from successfully challenging and correcting that misinformation. Your explanation is so clear that it can readily be utilized by Christians to help them explain and fortify their Christian beliefs.

You have shared helpful insight regarding several other Commandments as well. For example, you (2) clarified the Sixth Catholic Commandment (the Seventh Protestant Commandment) by explaining that the most sinful aspect of adultery is not so much lustful behavior as it is the betrayal of commitment and the absence of TRUTH; thus, you have made clear that even though lust is recognized as being one of the Seven Deadly Sins, lustful thoughts and actions could not possibly be the primary reason for that Commandment's condemnation of adultery because, if they were, all other promiscuous behaviors should have been included in that Commandment as well (but were not). Your repeated emphasis of the importance of TRUTH has provided sufficient understanding for Christians to recognize that it is the willful abandonment of TRUTH and fidelity in the marriage commitment which so displeased God that He included adultery as one of the Ten Commandments.

You have also been quite helpful (3) in delineating the distinctions between sinful murder and forgivable homicide

by explaining, in simple terms, that the sin associated with the killing of another human being (including the aborting of an unborn child) derives, primarily, from the emotional and spiritual intent which caused that death rather than the fact that a life had been lost. This, then, explains why the Protestant Church chose to change the word "kill" to "murder" in the wording of the Commandment. Your explanation has, also, made Christians aware that God recognizes grossly negligent and extremely reckless behavior which results in harm or death as being equally as sinful as willful sin; thus, God is just as disinclined to approve or forgive the malevolent, unjustified, slothful, and harmful stupidity of His children (Adam and Eve, for example) as He is unwilling to forgive their intentional evil actions.

In addition, you (4) drew attention to the fact it is not just the worshipping of false idols addressed in the Second Protestant Commandment which displeases our Creator because the true reason for living Christian lives is to understand and internalize God's and Jesus' teachings for the purpose of sculpting the best possible spiritual frequency which connects humans to the most desirable Heavenly "room". You have made clear that it has never been God's "preference" to be solely worshipped as an idol (except in those instance when such religious focus helps humans to find and ascend the salvation pathway). You did this by reminding us of Jesus' warning at Matthew 7:21:"Not everyone who says to Me, 'Lord, Lord,' shall enter the kingdom of Heaven" and emphasizing to Christians that, merely, having faith and believing that Jesus is God (and worshipping God and Jesus as idols) could not, possibly, be the sole reason for God to grant eternal salvation to any human.

Although you may believe that the insights you have gained as a result of your childhood dream are not as

discerning as those of the many great Christian minds which have preceded you, your fresh insights are so easy to grasp that they do help Christians better understand their faith. You have, already, discussed four of the Commandments. Would you, then, be willing to share your practical explanation for the Commandments' instruction as to why humans should not steal?

The *Seven Deadly Sins* discussion cannot, as yet, have been completed if I am to answer this question because the willingness to steal and, thus, commit a *more significant sin* results when several of those Seven ***Deadly*** Sins intertwine and create an even stronger (and more controlling) evil compulsion. To explain: thieves, typically, allow themselves to be driven by ***gluttonous*** and ***greedy*** hungers which cause them to crave materialistic items beyond basic survival needs (yet thieves are too ***lazy*** and impatient to work for what they desire); thus, rather than be conscientious and self-disciplined for the purpose of avoiding both mental and physical ***sloth***, thieves choose, instead, to ***enviously***, malevolently, unjustifiably, and criminally take possession of those items even if (in some more extreme instances) they must utilize ***wrathful*** and destructive violence in order to succeed in their sinful endeavor. The willingness to steal, then, is an illustration of how easy it is for humans to commit ***grievous*** *sin* when they allow themselves to be dominated by ***a combination of*** (otherwise less controlling) ***animalistic urges at the same time***.

To illustrate: in most instances, the type of tethered spiritual connection which results from having committed one of the *Seven Deadly Sins* is relatively weak and, thus, is quite often as insubstantial as a single thread of fiber; however, when multiple weak strands of sin are meshed in a manner that is similar to the way rope fibers are intertwined, the evil tether which results has the potential to become as robust as an inescapable noose. It is possible, then, that whenever a potential thief exercises sufficient restraint to curb *even one of those impulses* (sloth or greed, for example), the remaining interconnected urges weaken and are far less likely to result in criminal and sinful behavior. In summary, thieves (as well as all other sinners) are, most permanently, spiritually defined when they allow themselves to be controlled and transformed by multiple interconnected animalistic urges because, sadly, it is that, willful, acceptance of those animalistic behaviors which attracts, and strengthens connection with, the *demonic tethers* that can, lastingly, block misguided humans from *ascending* the Heavenly pathway.

Are you saying, then, that all acts of theft are equally as sinful?

No, of course not--in his novel, *Les Miserables*, Victor Hugo, sympathetically, *portrays* a central character, Jean Valjean, who, because he has no other alternative, steals bread in order to prevent his family from starving. Jean Valjean is not motivated by any combination of gluttony, greed, sloth, envy, or wrath; nor has he succumbed to any other sinful compulsions. Instead, his deed is *a selfless act of necessity* that is performed for the purpose of preventing innocents from dying. Despite the fact that he breaks a law and is prosecuted and punished for doing so, behavior that results because of such exigent circumstances is never offensive to God. Nevertheless, it must be recognized that (1) *Les Miserables* is, merely, *a work of **fiction*** and that (2) Victor Hugo ***manufactured*** *a set of circumstances* which provided no other viable options. In a free society, however, there are almost always adequate alternatives to the commission of criminal and sinful acts; thus, it is fortunate that there are far fewer real-life situations similar to those faced by Jean Valjean.

Do you believe that drug addicts who commit crimes as a result of their addiction will be forgiven because of their exigent circumstances?

I am certain that God is even more enraged with this modern society's *lusting for drugs* than He had been with the sexual practices of the sodomites at Sodom and Gomorrah. Despite the fact that God must be disheartened for every soul that is lost because of addiction, God does not exercise control over the manner by which human beings (as a result of free will) sculpt their spiritual frequencies. Humans are masters of their own fates ***and*** the captains of their souls.

The spiritual downfalls of addicts, thus, can, also, best be understood by recognizing the role that a comb*ination of the Seven Deadly Sins* plays in enabling ***weak-minded*** *individuals* to, willingly, succumb to drug addiction. Those who are ***foolish*** *enough to become addicts*, freely, surrender their intelligence, values, conscientiousness, and self-discipline to the influences of a type of mental ***sloth*** which causes them to ***gluttonously lust*** for ever-increasing levels of physical-world pleasure until the ***gluttony*** becomes an out-of-control fixation. At that point, they resort to other sins such as stealing in order to, continually, satisfy their cravings; thus, by stealing, they succumb to additional ***gluttonous***, ***slothful***, ***envious***, and, perhaps even, ***wrathful*** sins in order to, successfully, satisfy their ***lusting***. As they do, they commit an ever-increasing number of sins; and the *all-consuming demonic tether* to which they are attached becomes ever-more powerful, *and controlling*, until such time as they totally disconnect from their own spiritual identities and, thus, transform into lost souls.

Is it possible that, with rehabilitation, addicts have the ability to recover their lost souls?

Rehabilitation enables addicts to improve but *never recover*. They spend the rest of their lives being dependent on other, non-euphoric, drugs such as Methadone because, regrettably, they have, *permanently, lost control of, at least, one aspect of their spiritual identities*; and that loss makes it far more difficult for any of them to effectively sculpt the most desirable spiritual identities. That is why one of the, truly important, modern-day Christian missions must be to make life in this world an addiction-free existence. Since society has learned that criminalizing drug and alcohol use (*without* ***appropriate, immediate, and effective punishment***) in a free (as opposed to a totalitarian) society only creates a highly profitable, unlawful, industry which enables a large number of very evil humans to become incredibly wealthy and, thus, powerful enough to control every important decision to be made for that (no longer free) society, Christians must, once again, exercise an even more dominant influence by (1) effectively convincing all weak-minded humans to avoid drug use entirely, by (2) ***seriously punishing*** those responsible for drug proliferation, and by (3) *identifying, confronting, and stopping* ***all*** of those who work so hard to corrupt the lives of others.

Why do you believe that the Catholic Eighth Commandment (and the Protestant Ninth Commandment) decrees that Christians should not bear false witness against their neighbors?

The Commandment is still another significant means by which God has conveyed the importance of ***truth*** to His children. At John 14:6, Jesus explains: "I am the way and the ***truth*** and the life. No one comes to the Father except through me". Ephesian 4: 24-25 teaches that all humans who wish to sculpt the best possible spiritual frequency and ascend to the most desirable Heavenly "room" must: "...put on that new man created in God's image, whose justice and holiness are born in ***truth***. See to it, then, that you put an end to lying; let everyone speak the ***truth*** of his neighbor".

In contrast, then, those persons who choose to be false witnesses do not sculpt frequencies which emulate (or connect with) the Father. Proverb 25: 18 advises that "Like a club, or a sword, or a sharp arrow, is the man who bears false witness against his neighbor"; and Proverbs 19: 9 warns that "The false witness will not go unpunished, and he who utters lies will perish". Even worse, such dishonesty (regardless of whether it is (1) merely idle gossip and slander *or* (2) highly damaging false testimony in judicial proceedings) is almost always accompanied by additional *Deadly Sins* which widen an ever-more permanent chasm between that false witness and God.

Any animalistic desire to ***untruthfully*** cause harm to a neighbor is, too often, fueled by ***envious*** and ***wrathful*** impulses (and, sometimes, by ***gluttonous*** and *greedy* ***lusting*** for undeserved and unjustified worldly gain as well). It is worth repeating, then, that ***envy*** is (1) an urge which causes both a strong resentment toward another person's assets and good fortune *and* (2) an unreasonable desire, *triggered by malevolence and dishonesty*, to unjustifiably cause harm and punishment to that person for the purpose of separating that person from those benefits. W*rathful* anger, too, provokes such strong, *dishonest*, evil passions of resentment (which demand vengeance and punishment) that such passions also have the potential to permanently damage the false witness's spiritual identity.

A ***recent scientific study*** concerning brain scans of the ***amygdala***, the almond-shaped group of nuclei located deep and medially within the temporal lobes of the brain which (1) plays a primary role in the processing of memory, decision-making, and emotional responses (by responding to unpleasant emotional experiences) and which (2) is a part of the limbic system structures that are involved with emotions (particularly those related to survival, memory, motivation, and appetites), published in *Nature Neuroscience 19* on October 24, 2016 (1727-1732), by a team of British neuroscientists (Neil Garrett, Stephanie C. Lazzaro, and Tali Sharot), explained that even the most innocent forms of lying can trigger permanent physiological changes in the brain: "signal reduction in the amygdala is sensitive to the history of dishonest behavior, consistent with adaptation". Those brain scans revealed that the amygdala region becomes less sensitized after every falsehood (no matter how inconsequential the dishonesty may seem) to a point where the brain becomes indifferent (and ***deadened***) to the absence of **truth**; thus, neuroscientific research has uncovered physiological evidence which verifies long-held Christian beliefs. Those researchers concluded that lying is a "slippery slope: What begins as small acts of dishonesty can escalate into larger transgressions". *Every untruth*, so completely, damages the spiritual tethers which directly connect human souls with Heaven that, *eventually* (*and inevitably*), all pathways which lead to the most desirable Heavenly "rooms" will become so obstructed that they will cease to exist.

Far too many modern-era transgressors, nevertheless, deceive themselves into believing that it is, merely, forgivable human nature which causes them to *greedily* pursue material items and worldly benefits they desire (by any means necessary) including by bearing false witness. It is unfortunate they do not realize that when they succumb to their body's impulses and cravings (and *permit their sins to sculpt their identities*), they fail God's test.

At John 8: 44, Christ (while referring to Satan) states: "… he brought death to man from the beginning, and he has never based himself on ***truth***; the ***truth*** is not in him. Lying speech is his native tongue; he is a liar and ***the father of lies***". In summary, Christ makes clear that it is Satan (not God) who is the father of those scoundrels who, willfully, choose to bear false witness; thus, regrettably, when sinners dishonestly cause undeserved wrong to their neighbors, they cause even greater spiritual injury to themselves.

Previously, I referred to two instances when false witnesses are perceived as victims and, thus, receive worldly benefit and societal approval despite the fact that their decisions to bear false witness cause them everlasting spiritual damage. Those women who *falsely* accuse men of rape, are believed, and, thus, succeed in destroying their victims' lives were the first example; and the homosexual boys who had, in fact, been pursuing homosexual lifestyles since their early teens by having engaged in sexual activities (that included prostitution) with scores of other men (but, in order to be made instant millionaires by the Catholic Church, *dishonestly swore* that their lives had been destroyed by predator homosexual priests) were the second example. These are just two illustrations of the many successful bearers of false witness who may not be *worldly* victims but, nevertheless, are ***spiritual transgressors*** because their types of, willful, ***untruthful*** behavior cause such irreversible damage to the amygdala that they instigate (1) a permanent separation from God and (2) an everlasting connection with Satan. This, then, is why the Commandment decrees that humans should refrain from bearing *false* witness.

Are you claiming, then, that all women who testify against rapists and all boys who testified against homosexual priests are false witnesses?

Of course not--clearly, ***truthful*** victims are, ***in fact***, victims.

What are the insights you have learned from your dream regarding the First Commandment, "You shall have no other God before me"?

The Ten Commandments are the foundation upon which Judeo-Christian religious beliefs arise. For that reason, the First Commandment should be recognized as being more a *fundamental Mission Statement* for both religions than as being a *command* because: (1) Earth is a crossroads between Heaven and hell, (2) there are an infinite number of tethers to which humans can connect as they sculpt their frequencies and define their spiritual identities, and (3) humans have been granted *free will* so that they are not, in any way, restricted from connecting with those tethers which are, uniquely, appropriate for them. It has, thus, been my belief that because God has granted *free will* to His children, God has chosen to *guide* rather than *command* them.

The problem which results for humans (when they utilize that freedom to connect with whichever tethers they choose) is that only a small number of those tethers link humans to optimal "rooms" in Heaven. It is, then, worth recalling the warning from Matthew 7: 13-14: "The gate that leads to damnation is wide, the road is clear, and many *choose* to travel it. But how narrow is the gate that leads to *life*, how rough the road, and *how few there are that find it*"; thus, the practical reason why *free-thinking* Christians should avoid worshipping and connecting with *false gods* is because ***righteous*** Judeo-Christian convictions are the beliefs which ***best*** guide them to the "gate that leads to *life*". It, therefore, makes no sense for humans to, instead, attract and connect with tethers that entice them to worship ***false*** *gods* whose *temptations* lure them to damnation. This is the ***primary*** *reason* why humans have been ***encouraged*** by The First

Commandment to worship, only, ***THE ONE TRUE GOD OF GOODNESS***.

You stated that The Ten Commandments are the foundation upon which both Jewish and Christian beliefs arise. Despite the fact that the two religions are the most similar of the world's greatest religions, Christianity and Judaism, nevertheless, have dramatically different belief systems. How does your dream knowledge reconcile the distinctions between the two religions?

Briefly, Christians believe that Jesus is the **Messiah** who fulfills the Old Testament's *Messianic Prophesies* (Isaiah 7: 14; Psalm 22: 14-19, etc.); but Jews, *generally*, are not willing to recognize the possibility of Jesus' divinity because (1) Jews do not believe the Messianic Age has yet arrived (just as Christians do not believe that Christ's second coming has arrived) and (2) Jews believe Jesus to have been a human being who was only one of several *false prophets* who had claimed to be the Messiah.

Christians, in response, have chronicled the ***many ways*** by which the events in Christ's life ***prove*** that He is the ***one true Messiah*** described in Isaiah 52: 13 to 53: 12. Isaiah 7: 14, for example, foretells that the Messiah will be born to a virgin; and Matthew 1: 18-25 describes how Jesus' birth fulfills that Prophesy. A few of the *many other examples* of Old Testament Prophesies and Christian proofs are: the Messiah shall be born in Bethlehem (Micah 5: 2 and Matthew 2: 1-6); the Messiah shall be a prophet (Deuteronomy 18: 18 and Matthew 21:11); the Messiah will be rejected by his own people (Isaiah 53: 3 and John 7: 40-44); the Messiah will have his side pierced (Zechariah 12: 10 and John 19: 34); and the Messiah will be tortured and crucified (Psalm 22: 1-18 and Luke 23: 32-35; John 19: 33-34; and John 19: 23-24).

Although Christians are satisfied that Christ's life does fulfill ***most*** *of the many Messianic Prophesies*, unconvinced Jews elect, instead, to believe that these Christian verifications are, at best, (1) inconsistent with God's words and meanings and (2) incomplete (because Jesus did not fulfill ***all*** *of the, essentially required, Messianic predictions*). Judaism, also, does not recognize Jesus as the Messiah because Jews do not believe (1) in the *Holy Trinity*, (2) in abstract spiritual beliefs and thoughts such as the ***nature*** of God and the ***afterlife*** (Jews have no definitive or official beliefs regarding any such abstract subjects but, instead, are concerned, primarily, with human *action*--based upon 613 commandments given by God in the Torah--as well as long-standing Jewish customs) or (3) that humans are born *with original sin* and are, thus, inherently evil and in need of salvation.

Jews believe in Maimonides's Second Article of Faith which states that *their God is an absolute and unparalleled* ***unity***. In addition, they have faith in *the Torah's translation* of Deuteronomy 6: 4 which states: "***Hear Israel***, Hashem is our God, ***Hashem is one***" and trust that this verse, *correctly*, echoes the intention of the First Commandment and, thus, eliminates the possibility for accepting a *Trinitarian Doctrine* which recognizes the Father, Son, and Holy Ghost as being "**one**". Most notably, Jews, steadfastly, insist that ***no human***, including Jesus, (1) should claim to be God *or*, more importantly, (2) should be worshipped as an idol.

Jesus responded to ***those legitimate Jewish concerns*** during the Sermon on the Mount (Matthew 5:17) when Jesus explained His role: "Do not think that I have come to abolish the law and the prophets. I have come, not to abolish them, but to fulfill them". With that statement, Jesus explained the **true** *purpose* for God's Messianic Prophesies as promised in Deuteronomy 18: 18-19: "I will raise up for them a prophet like you from among their kinsmen, and will put my words into His mouth; He shall tell them all that I command Him. If any man will not listen to my words which He speaks in my name, I myself will make him answer for it".

My dream has enabled me to understand Jesus' meaning by guiding me to recognize that God had been so displeased with the animalistic nature of the majority of humans who lived prior to the time of Moses that God recognized the need for a spiritual "intervention"; and this is why God chose *wise and inspired* prophets (particularly Moses) to broadcast God's message to the masses. Since the majority of humans were so barbaric, God did not expect to transform all of their *animalistic behaviors* instantaneously. God's first task, then, was to *curb* savagery by introducing the lessons in the Torah for the purpose of teaching humans those *actions* that would guide them to (peacefully and safely) live, interact, and thrive in stable civilized communities; thus, in essence, Judaism is concerned with improving the well-being of humanity by focusing on human *actions*. The goodness that has, subsequently, resulted from this Jewish concern for humanity is one of the *greatest gifts* that *any* religion has ever shared with this uncivilized and misguided world.

My dream has taught me that The Messianic Prophesies were, above all else, *forewarnings* that more of God's message would be revealed to humans when humans proved that they were, sufficiently, civilized to benefit from the remainder of His lessons. Although I acknowledge that many observant Jews disagree with my dream beliefs, I have, nevertheless, understood that *the primary and practical purpose for The Messianic Prophesies* was to alert primitive humans that God would reveal more to them about the purpose of existence (at an appropriate future time).

Christians trust that a willingness to, merely, recognize *the* ***value*** *of Jesus' divine wisdom* (which He shared for the purpose of "fulfilling" the "law and the prophets") is all that is necessary in order to understand that Jesus' message (at least in part) does fulfill God's Messianic Prophecies; thus, Christians believe that (1) Jewish unwillingness to appreciate the significance of Jesus' teachings yet (2) Jewish expectations for Jesus to fulfill every one of the scores of Messianic requirements are (in comparison) reasons that are too trivial to, unjustifiably, dismiss Jesus as a false prophet and, as a result, ***to reject ALL of Jesus' inspired truths***.

Isaiah 29: 9-16 at 11-13 forewarned: "For you, the revelation of all this has become like the words of a sealed scroll. When it is handed to one who can read with the request, 'Read this,' he replies, 'I cannot; it is sealed.' When it is handed to one who cannot read, with the request, 'Read this,' he replies, 'I cannot read.' The Lord said: …these people draw near with *words only,* and honor me with their lips alone, though their hearts are far from me, and their reverence for me has become *routine observance of the precepts of men*".

Christians, thus, fail to understand why any **truly** religious human would choose to ***totally*** *disregard the* ***truth****, wisdom, and value of Christ's message.* If Judaism had merely been willing to *unseal and read Jesus' scroll* rather than, steadfastly, observe the precepts of men, how could any "son or daughter of Abraham" not have recognized that Jesus' inspired words (at least, in part) fulfill God's promise?

Returning, once again, to the Ten Commandments discussion, what do you believe is the significance of the Third Catholic Commandment (and the Fourth Protestant Commandment), "Remember the Sabbath Day to keep it holy"?

The Ten Commandments reveal conditions that existed in the world prior to the time of Moses. There was killing, adultery, false witness, theft, dishonoring of parents, and the coveting of neighbors' possessions. Life was clearly desperate, and most humans were required to work and/or slave until they dropped dead from exhaustion; that is, until…Moses received God's commandments.

Exodus 20: 8 chronicles God's directive regarding the Sabbath, "Remember to keep holy the Sabbath day. Six days you may labor and do all your work, but the seventh day is the Sabbath for the Lord your God. No work may be done, then, either by you, or your son or daughter, or your male or female slave, or your beast, or by the alien who lives with you. In six days, the Lord made the heavens and the Earth, the sea and all that is in them; but on the seventh day, He rested. That is why the Lord has blessed the Sabbath day and made it holy".

Moses' stern mandate at Exodus 35: 2: "… the seventh day shall be sacred to you as the Sabbath of complete rest to the Lord. Anyone who does work on that day *shall be put to death*" proved, indeed, to be the blessing which transformed Hebrew communities. An ***enforced*** *day of physical rest* enabled all to recover from the hardships of their labors and (as a result) to--quite willingly--learn, embrace, and, thus, be civilized by the 613 commandments in the Torah. Despite strong initial opposition from the wealthy and powerful, God's commanded day of rest, *accompanied with mandatory moral and religious instruction*, proved to so dramatically increase productivity and reduce barbaric behavior, during the other six days of each week, that even those rulers were, admittedly, pleased that God had provided a means for civilizing most of their subjects (and His children).

The concept of *keeping the Sabbath day holy* proved to be such an effective tool for civilizing humans that Christians, too, willingly observed that Commandment's mandate until the middle of the Twentieth Century because (until then) most states had adopted "Blue Laws" which restricted Sunday business hours and prevented all other pastimes, including sporting events, from beginning before two o'clock so that no alternative activities would create a time-conflict with Sunday's last church services. Since then, however, "Blue Laws" have, regrettably, been repealed; and the majority of Christian families have, gradually, chosen to use Sunday hours to rest, complete chores, or engage in social activities rather than observe The Third Catholic Commandment (and The Fourth Protestant Commandment).

It is unfortunate, then, that while many people recognize the importance of regularly engaging in physical activities in order to remain vigorous as they age, too few, any longer, acknowledge the need for maintaining their *spiritual **fitness*** as well. They fail to understand that (just as it is challenging to remain physically fit without regularly exercising) it is far more difficult for Christians to find and enter the Heavenly "pathway" without committing themselves to regularly scheduled and *guided* spiritual activities (which include Church attendance on the Sabbath).

Although there are examples in the Bible where Jesus said that those who believe in Him shall achieve eternal salvation, belief in Jesus is not *the sole requirement* for entry into Heaven because what Jesus had *truly* meant is expressed in John 5:51 when He explained, "I tell you the **truth**, if anyone *keeps My word*, he will never see death," and John 14:23 when he advised, "If anyone loves Me, he will *obey My teaching*. My Father will love him, and We will come to him and make Our home with him." At Matthew 7:21, Jesus warned, "Not everyone who says to Me, 'Lord, Lord,' shall enter the kingdom of Heaven, but *he who does the will of My Father….*" At verse 24, Jesus adds, "Therefore whoever hears the sayings of Mine, and does them, I will liken him to a wise man who built his house on rock…."; and at verse 26, Jesus concludes, "But everyone who hears these sayings of Mine and does not do them, will be like a foolish man who built his house on sand…". ***All humans*** who have lived their lives in a manner that is *reflective of **Christ's teachings*** "would have built their houses on rocks" and, thus, will certainly be loved by Jesus' Father in Heaven. Christians, nevertheless, recognize that it is difficult (if not impossible) for humans, who do not build their spiritual "houses on rocks", (by living their lives in a manner that is reflective of Jesus' and God's teachings) to successfully enter that "pathway" which leads to Heavenly ascension.

The reason, then, that all humans should devote time to, steadfastly, ***train*** *themselves* (1) to recognize the distinctions between good and evil, (2) to repent for their sins, and (3) to, thereafter, attempt to be as good as possible is because humans are spiritual beings who exist within primate bodies which are driven by animalistic instincts, urges, and desires (all, of which, are manifestations of Original Sin). God's purpose for creating such a reality is to help God identify those impulses which dominate and, thus, define each soul. God's hope is that humans develop such *strong spiritual goodness* that they are able to *utilize and control* their life essential animalistic talents rather than *be* ***ruled*** *by them*; as a result, when humans allow themselves to succumb to their bodies' impulses and cravings (and permit those sinful impulses and cravings to sculpt their identities), they (like Adam and Eve) fall victim to their Original Sin and, thus, fail God's test.

The influences of Original Sin are so strong that the most difficult mission facing all humans is, **truly**, that task of ***developing sufficient spiritual strength*** for the purpose of utilizing and controlling their life essential animalistic talents rather than being ruled by them. Since God has granted humans the ***spiritual*** *freedom* to, willfully, choose to be either good or evil (for the purpose of allowing humans to sculpt those, unique, spiritual identities that will determine their eternal destinies), it would be prudent for all humans to recognize the need to devote sufficient time and effort to learn how God's laws, and Jesus' lessons, teach them to be as good as possible; and keeping the Sabbath day holy is ***one*** *of the* ***more effective*** *means* for building that spiritual foundation which best directs Christians to live their lives in a manner that is reflective of Christ's teachings.

Can you share any insight as to why The Second Commandment is not the same for both the Catholic and Protestant religions?

The second *Protestant* Commandment exists because The *Protestant* Church, ***literally****, obeys* the admonition expressed by God at Exodus 20:3-4: "You shall not have other gods besides me. You shall not carve idols for yourselves in the shape of anything in the sky above or on the Earth below or in the waters beneath the Earth; you shall not bow down before them *or worship them*" ***despite*** the existence of other, conflicting, Biblical passages (in which God *specifically commands the creation of idols*) such as Exodus 25: 18-22 ("make two cherubim of beaten gold....") and Numbers 21: 8-9 ("and the Lord said to Moses, 'Make a seraph and mount it on a pole, and if anyone who has been bitten looks at it, he will recover'. Moses accordingly made a bronze serpent and mounted it on a pole...").

The Catholic Church, instead, interprets the instruction at Exodus 20: 4 to, merely, be an admonition against *the* ***worshipping*** *of all false and pagan gods*; thus, The Catholic Church chooses to ***utilize*** Christian saints, martyrs, idols, statues, images, and art as ***aids*** for the purpose of better helping Christians **link** to those spiritual tethers and frequencies which (to paraphrase Psalm 143: 8) show Christians and Jews "*the way* in which they should walk and lift their souls" because (while the Catholic Church understands that God forbids the ***worshipping*** of saints, martyrs, idols, statues, images, and art work), the Catholic

Church does not believe that God forbids the ***beneficial use*** of saints, martyrs, idols, statues, images, and art work.

By analogy, the easiest way to comprehend The Catholic Church's reasons for including saints, idols, martyrs, statutes, and art in their religious activities is by recognizing and understanding the most effective memorization and learning strategy--a method which succeeds by utilizing as many senses as possible:

Sight is, most often, the first sense employed because reading new information is, usually (in this modern era), the *initial* learning step. The second activity (saying the words aloud) causes the vocal cords and auditory nerves to vibrate; and *the vibrations of both the speaking and hearing senses amplify sight's ability* to facilitate retention. The strongest reinforcing step occurs, next, when the sense of *touch* is added; and that is accomplished when the words to be learned are, repeatedly, rewritten (until a *habit* has been conditioned). It is, also, helpful, whenever possible, to ***associate*** that which is being memorized to, other, more familiar (and easier to recall) odors, symbols, objects, statues, works of art, persons, stories, and/or experiences. Finally, the same steps must be ***repeated*** until such time as *automatic responses*, *recollections*, and *habits have been, effectively*, ***conditioned*** and, resultantly, prove that the memorization (and/or learning) process has succeeded.

Both the Catholic and Protestant religions employ ***most*** *of the senses* that are involved in this learning strategy whenever they share God's and Jesus' lessons with their followers. Parishioners sing praise to God (and Jesus) and read the Holy Scriptures aloud. By so doing, Christians utilize *sight*, *speech*, and *hearing* as tools for the purpose of helping them to better internalize Biblical lessons. When congregates utter the words, "May peace be with you," to one another while shaking hands, that symbolic *touching* gesture reinforces worshippers' inclinations to allow themselves to become conduits for God's energy for the purpose of willfully, and instinctively, sharing their spiritual goodness with others.

The Eucharist, the focal point of all Christian services, successfully connects communicants with Jesus' righteousness because those worshippers are able to ***symbolically embrace Christ***, and *accept Jesus' goodness within their souls*, when they employ the sense of *touch* while participating in the Sacrament (1) by drinking wine--or grape juice--that is representative of Jesus' blood and (2) by consuming a wafer which is representative of Jesus's body. John 6: 54-56 states, "He who feeds on my flesh and drinks my blood has life eternal, and I will raise him up on the last day; for my flesh is real food, and my blood is real drink. The man who feeds on my flesh and drinks my blood *remains in me, **and I in him***". There is no better way for Christians to be transformed by ***the most perfect spiritual virtues*** than by, *repeatedly*, (1) participating in the Eucharistic Ceremony, (2) opening their hearts and *feeling* Jesus' goodness, and (3) (because of the beneficial effect of *habit conditioning*) retaining ***His goodness*** within them always.

Roman Catholics, Eastern Christians, Lutherans, Anglicans, and Methodists (among other Christian denominations), also, incorporate the *sense of smell* in portions of their church services. The traditional explanation for the inclusion of incense, for example, is that the resultant smoke which wafts into the air, *symbolically*, represents prayers rising to Heaven. Moreover, when incense is, repeatedly, included in the Communion Ceremony, its fragrance can trigger, *automatic*, ***associative** responses* which help some communicants, eventually, *sense* Christ's presence and goodness whenever they *smell* burning incense (even when not praying or in church); hence, incense is, yet, an additional *learning and conditioning tool* which helps

Christians (1) connect with Christ's righteousness and (2) link to those spiritual tethers and frequencies that show Christians "*the way* in which they should walk and lift their souls".

For comparable reasons, The Catholic Church chooses to teach its followers about the blessedness of venerated saints and martyrs (not for the purpose of worshipping those saints and martyrs as gods but, instead, for the purpose of revealing *clearly identifiable examples* of the types of life-long human goodness that has, successfully, linked with the most desirable Heavenly rooms); thus, the Catholic Church chooses to venerate *only* those righteous humans who have demonstrated that they have ***transcended the limits*** *of the physical world, in some* ***miraculous*** *way*, and, by having done so, *bridged the barrier* which exists between Earth and Heaven (the physical world and the spiritual world).

The ***symbolic act of embracing the virtues*** which characterize particular saints' lives is, thus, an excellent means for Catholics *to identify and connect with* ***optimal*** *forms of goodness* (since those examples of righteousness illustrate how some ***special*** *humans* have sculpted spiritual frequencies which connect, directly, to the most desirable Heavenly rooms). Because saints, martyrs, statues, idols, and works of art can, by means of (1) *reinforcement and* (2) *association*, also, help Christians *identify (and link with)* the purest forms of Heavenly goodness, the Catholic Church believes that it makes sense to utilize the ***learning benefits*** that saints, statues, idols, works of art, and ***all other reinforcing images of goodness*** provide.

What does not make sense, however, is the manner by which the Protestant Church, steadfastly, fails to, any longer, utilize these *most beneficial and helpful religious learning aids* yet, instead, willingly *accommodates* many, far more dubious, quasi-Protestant activities such as: snake handling; fraudulent healing; *yelling* and *screaming* God's words;

embracing music that merely entertains by appealing, primarily, to animalistic impulses; glorifying clergymen who exploit God's message for the sole purpose of enriching themselves; and tolerating those cabals of clergymen who have transformed their religious denominations into non-religious (and even anti-Christian) *political and secular Humanistic* platforms.

What, then, is your interpretation of the Second Catholic Commandment (and the Third Protestant Commandment) from Exodus 20: 7: "You shall not take the name of the Lord, your God, in vain, for the Lord will not leave unpunished him who takes His name in vain"?

From the earliest age, I had been instructed by my mother that a Bible should be handled carefully and regarded with great reverence--not only because a Bible is a compendium of God's and Jesus' teaching, but because it is also one of the most important *tools* which can be utilized to help Christians communicate directly with their Creator. I was taught that, over time (and after much penitent prayer), a Bible can be infused with the type of, *talismanic*, *spiritual ether* which strengthens that link to God, Jesus, and the Holy Spirit and, thus, helps *sincere* Christians create a more direct connection with Heaven.

This understanding has (1) conditioned me to feel, *only*, the most *reverent emotions* when I am ever near a Bible and has (2) helped me to grasp the importance of certain *Christian power words* that have the capacity to generate such *meaningful spiritual vibrations* (by, almost magically, affecting how energy travels through space) that they, too, can enhance and strengthen the connection between physical world energy and spiritual energy. The most important ***power words*** of all, of course, are "***God***", "***Jesus***", "***Christ***", "***Lord***", and "***Our Father***". When Christians *restrict* the utterances of these words to *praying, blessing, and glorifying those names*, there is, ***at least, the possibility that God might*** **hear His name and, perhaps,** *be more receptive to listening and responding to those prayers.* Even when God is not listening, the *reverent use* of those ***power words*** will, at the very least, facilitate humans to connect with those spiritual frequencies and tethers that are *most directly* linked to God's goodness.

If, on the other hand, the words "***God***", "***Jesus***", and "***Christ***" are voiced inappropriately (in casual, irreverent, and meaningless ways) or vainly (as a part of vulgar curses or insults), such otiose utterances weaken the effectiveness of those ***power words*** and cause a ***disconnection*** *from God and Christ* (the ***true punishment*** alluded to in Exodus 20: 7) because such irreverence ***guarantees*** *that God and Jesus will* ***never*** *be listening.* (This means that the resulting spiritual connection for all persons who choose to regularly take the Lord's name in vain cannot possibly be any more operational than the telephone connection of two tin cans linked by a long string).

It is odd, then, that the words "***God***", "***Jesus***", and "***Christ***" are so often, inappropriately, included in insults and uttered as curses which are voiced when a speaker's intention is to cause harm. Most likely, it would seem that diabolical tethers are, mischievously, influencing misguided humans for the purpose of disconnecting them from God's grace. If so, Christians should, steadfastly, resist such diabolical influences and, instead, make every effort (1) to ensure that these **Christian power words** are never, inappropriately, uttered anywhere (or by anyone--including members of the entertainment industry), and (2) to acknowledge that misuse of the most significant words in the Christian belief system should always be recognized as an, unacceptable, insult to all Christians.

The two questions that remain, then, are: (1) why is the *vain utterance* of any word (even when it is God's name) a sin, and (2) why would any human face punishment, in any way, for, merely, improperly articulating a word? If, for example, a person (who speaks only a foreign language) were to utter English words which take the Lord's name in vain (yet has no understanding of the meaning of those words), would sin (or a violation of The Second Commandment) have occurred? The answer, clearly, is "No". Those utterances would have, simply, been insignificant sounds that were caused by empty, vibrating airwaves. Clearly, sin cannot occur when there is an absence of meaning and willful intent; and meaning and *willful intent* exist only at that wellspring where the spiritual soul and human consciousness create, what humans perceive to be, **true reality** (that ***ground zero source*** from which human realization of existence emerges). This is why it is most important for all humans to understand that, more than anything, it is a person's ***willful*** *thoughts* (no matter how quiet and subtle they may be) which sculpt most of that person's spiritual frequency (because thinking is a non-stop activity). This, too, is why Proverbs 23:7 in the King James Version reminds humans that *sin starts in the mind* because *we are what we think*: "For as he thinketh in his heart, so is he". Too many misguided humans choose to take the Lord's name in vain for the purpose of *demonstrating their contempt for (not only the Christian religion but for) all worldly goodness*. Regrettably (for them), a person's inner secrets mark that person forever; thus, it makes better sense for everyone to have *only* the purest types of secrets. This ***truth***, then, should make it easier for all humans to comprehend why a person's *intentional* ***(yet*** *irreverent, negligent, vain, and/or evil) utterances* have the *potential* to mark that person's soul, forever, as well.

Finally, why do you believe that the Fourth Catholic Commandment and the Fifth Protestant Commandment (which is proclaimed at Exodus 20: 12: "Honor your father and your mother that you may have a long life in the land which the Lord, your God, is giving you") has been included as one of The Ten Commandments?

While many Christians have interpreted this Commandment to be an instruction for children to remain respectful, loving, obedient, and grateful to their parents, I have always, ***also***, believed that this Fourth Commandment is an instruction directed toward adult children for the purpose of urging them to care for their elderly fathers and mothers when those parents are no longer capable of providing for themselves. The obvious reason is that (until very recently) there had been no governmental aid, or societal programs, which assisted seniors in times of their greatest needs. That burden fell, solely, upon close relatives; and, regrettably, it appears that, prior to God's issuance of the Ten Commandments, far too few parents were honored with the types of care that would have ensured them "*a long life in the land which the Lord...God" has given.*

For most of my life, I believed that I lived among civilized people who, willingly, honored this Commandment and, humanely, aided (rather than barbarically neglected, abused, and discarded) their elderly *fathers and mothers*. I maintained that *naïve* belief until such time as I assumed the role of *sole caregiver* for both of my parents and, sadly, became a first-hand eyewitness to the alarming, un-Christian-like, mistreatment that too many dependent *fathers and mothers* were receiving from custodial care providers, the medical community, and (in some cases), even, their own children.

My first suspicion was aroused when I recognized that too many seniors were dying in their seventies and eighties even though the majority of elderly persons do not suffer and die from terminal diseases such as congestive heart failure, cancer, and diabetes. Since it had been relatively easy for me to help my father remain entirely independent until his death at eighty-nine and my mother until her death at ninety-eight, I realized that many of the, ***non-terminal**, causes* of senior deaths were avoidable. I understood, for example, that since many life-extending drugs can prolong lives for decades (when prescription schedules are followed), too many seniors must be dying, merely, because they do not properly follow those regimens. I recognized that relatively minor infections (such as urinary tract infections, gum and teeth infections, toenail infections, and influenza), when ignored, initiate a series of physiologically debilitating chain-reactions which ***always*** result in death. Dehydration and malnutrition, if unheeded, also trigger the same deadly results. Although seniors seldom lose their appetites for tasty food, they, nevertheless, do stop eating when (1) preparing food or (2) chewing becomes too difficult for them; thus, whenever *proper food* is prepared for them and pre-cut into tidbits, they, once again, willingly eat and drink as much as always. In addition, too many elderly persons die from complications which result from falls; and the majority of those falls occur either because those seniors (1) had been disoriented by too many, unnecessary and over-prescribed, pain medications, (2) had neglected to eliminate unsafe conditions in their homes, or (3) (by having failed to remain physically active), had lost too much of their body strength. Despite the fact that most of those types of deaths are preventable, too many seniors have, nonetheless, been dying, unnecessarily--most frequently because they have no children, family members, or friends to provide, essential, life-preserving aid.

What is most puzzling, then, is the fact that many seniors (who have children and other family members available to provide help) are, nevertheless, dying from those same *avoidable causes*; thus, it can easily be inferred that their deaths occur, primarily, because too many of their children, intentionally, choose to disregard the instruction of the Fourth Catholic Commandment (and the Fifth Protestant Commandment).

In certain instances, neglectful behaviors are justified because some sons and daughters may live too far away to provide daily care; or some children may already be overburdened, for example, by (1) family needs, by (2) the necessity to hold second jobs, or because of (3) their own ill-health issues. Such *legitimate and unavoidable reasons* for failing to aid senior parents will, in most instances, excuse those children from being regarded, by God, as sinful violators of the Fourth (or Fifth) Commandment.

In other instances, however, when children are so lazy and indifferent that they are not concerned about the welfare of anyone other than themselves, their negligent failure to provide even minimal effective aid *assures* their parents' premature deaths (because too many sons and/or daughters (1) elect to avoid essential work and obligations, and (2) choose to refrain from utilizing their bodies and minds--and the gift of "consciousness"--in an appropriate manner that would please God). It should always be remembered, then, that since God expects all humans to develop and utilize their physical, mental, and spiritual God-given abilities, the refusal to perform (or a carelessness in the performance of) moral, spiritual, and legal obligations are examples of **slothful behavior** *and* are the most significant proofs of sinful ingratitude for God's gift of consciousness.

When children, deliberately, decline to be as conscientious and self-disciplined as possible toward their own dependent parents, those behaviors reflect intentional choices to remain foolish and uncaring for the purpose of pursuing only self-indulging, animalistic pleasures. Because, willful, **slothful** behavior causes humans to neglect God's and Jesus' teachings, Thomas Aquinas observed that **sloth** "...is evil in its effect, if it so oppresses man as to draw him away entirely from good deeds" (especially toward a son's and/or daughter's own dependent parents); thus, **sloth** is that controlling urge which best explains why some children elect to forsake (and, thus, sin against) their parents at those times when their parents are most in need.

The more serious violation of this Fourth Commandment occurs when some, heartless, children choose to hasten the deaths of their parents by, intentionally, causing harm to those vulnerable seniors in order to *greedily* assure themselves the largest inheritances possible. Those sinful children recognize that the longer their parents remain alive, the greater the financial drain on their potential bequests; thus, impious children scheme to accelerate death by (1) altering or replacing prescribed medicine, (2) ignoring their parents' infections, (3) failing to immediately seek emergency care when such assistance is obviously necessary, (4) neglecting to provide food and drink in the optimal, life-sustaining, manner, (5) arranging conditions so that falls are inevitable, (6) disorienting their parents with unnecessary narcotics, and (7) choosing to engage in any (and all) other diabolical behaviors which accelerate death. Since such elder-abuses that result in death are, in **truth**, nothing other than premeditated murders, the willful choices to violate the Fourth Catholic Commandment (and the Fifth Protestant Commandment), in such diabolical ways, are the most grievous and mortal of all sins; thus, regardless of how well elderly parents may trust their children, it would, nevertheless, be prudent for seniors to conceal the terms and conditions of their wills from all of their children as long as they remain alive.

Regrettably, in *far too many* instances, the misbehavior of ungrateful children is minor, however, in comparison to the horrors that greet vulnerable seniors who must rely upon custodial care service providers such as nursing homes and extended care facilities for help because too many nursing homes, regrettably, tailor their care plans for the sole purpose of maximizing insurance payments (regardless of whether those methods of care furnish the most appropriate forms of assistance).

During the last four months of my mother's life, my own ill health became so debilitating that I was no longer able to continue to *properly* provide the aid that my mother required; and I was forced, regrettably, to place her in nursing homes. Nevertheless, I continued to spend most daytime hours visiting and assisting her throughout those last few months of her life; and it was during those months that I, shockingly, witnessed far too many un-Christian-like transgressions.

When instances of mistreatment were too serious to ignore, my only alternative was to *attempt* to relocate my mother; but I was unable to prevent her from receiving similar harm in all three nursing facilities (including the final, Catholic nursing home--a facility where no nuns, priests, or other **true** Christians were actively involved for the purpose of insuring proper Christian care (most likely because of the dramatic decline in the overall number of nuns available to help). The Catholic Order of Nuns had, instead, merely (1) employed the very same staff members who traveled from one nursing home to another and (2) relied upon the same administrators whose primary talents were, puzzlingly, the abilities to maximized earnings--*even for non-profit organizations*). Lamentably, I was unable to locate a safe Christian harbor anywhere. Although my mother's, horror-filled, end-of-life experience was a single incident, it is, nevertheless, *doubtful* that she had been the only elderly person who has ever been harmed and neglected by nursing home personnel.

When my mother moved to her second nursing home, she was still able to walk independently with, and without, a rollator walker. Despite the fact that her insurance was billed for twice-a-day physical therapy sessions, all three nursing homes refused to allow her to walk; thus, after three months of daily-double physical therapy, those sessions only caused her to completely lose all ability to walk safely and independently. On one occasion, after I had been with her for most of the day, I left for a brief period. When I returned unexpectedly, I found her tied to a chair. She died from *complications* which resulted from a broken hip (after a fall accident) that would have never occurred had she been provided ***proper*** *physical therapy* and allowed to continue using her rollator walker.

My mother's insurance was also billed for daily oxygen use, and she was forced to be connected to an oxygen tank that, continually, restrained and imprisoned her even though she did not, in **truth**, require oxygen. The pulse/oximeter (a very inexpensive index finger gauge) that was used to justify oxygen-use billings was broken and regularly registered the *same low reading* (even when on my finger). Although I made frequent requests for a properly working oximeter, that malfunctioning, inexpensive, gauge was never replaced.

Her insurance was also billed for daily occupational therapy sessions for the alleged purpose of training her to swallow food correctly in order to prevent aspirational pneumonia. That type of pneumonia occurs when food, liquid, or vomit is misdirected into the lungs (because of an improperly operating gag reflex--a frequent side effect caused by unnecessarily administered narcotics) and triggers a lung infection which makes breathing so difficult that death ensues. When seniors die from pneumonia while in hospitals and nursing homes, aspirational pneumonia is, too frequently, the cause--often because patients are, slothfully, force-fed while in horizontal positions which, thereby, causes food to, *unavoidably*, be misdirected to the lungs rather than the stomach. The correct ways to prevent aspirational pneumonia are to ensure (1) that patients are *always* in upright positions while eating, (2) that *only* the proper types of safe food are provided, and (3) narcotics are administered *only when* ***absolutely*** *necessary*. Regrettably, those precautions are frequently disregarded; and aspirational pneumonia, *inevitably*, ensues.

My mother's occupational therapy provided no benefit because her ability to properly swallow was, soon, nearly lost (rather than improved). The occupational therapist's instructions were so ineffective (and so completely confused my mother) that she learned, instead, how *not* to swallow correctly; thus, had her death not resulted from her fall, my mother would have, almost certainly, soon thereafter, died from aspirational pneumonia.

It is even possible that the staff *intentionally* caused, first, my mother and, then, me to contract the worst norovirus (one which caused **constant** diarrhea and vomiting) that I have ever experienced. The staff had made no effort to prevent my mother and me from contracting the disease because (1) they took no precautions to ensure that her food and beverages (and the aides who prepared and delivered the food) were not contaminated with the virus, (2) they continually positioned her between sick patients for extended periods of time until she was also sick; and (3) they made no effort to warn me of her illness until I was infected with the virus as well). Because of the extreme symptoms, I was forced to stay away for three days and, thus, was unable to observe how badly she was mistreated; however, I did visit her, briefly, on the fourth morning of my illness (until eleven a.m.) and returned, *unexpectedly*, at six p.m. only to find her (**quite literally**) swimming in body waste from her neck to her ankles (because she had not been attended to--or provided food or liquids--in any way (during the height of her illness), for the entire time of my absence). I insisted that my mother be sent to an emergency room but was met with such strong resistance that (because of my ill condition) I finally, yet regrettably, acquiesced to the head nurse's assurances that the nursing home's doctor could provide, comparable, medical care. Sadly, even though my mother was in desperate need of intravenous fluid, the staff doctor only ***pretended*** to give her fluid (because no fluid ever left the intravenous bag and entered her body--even after I, repeatedly, insisted that he return to correct the problem). My mother was still so healthy that she, miraculously, recovered despite all of those obvious efforts to cause her harm.

I, immediately, hunted for another facility, but my search was made difficult because the administrative staff at my mother's nursing home intervened, each time, by networking with the next facility and encouraging that facility to refuse my mother's request for transfer. I was able to, finally, relocate her, *only*, after I returned my mother to my home, immediately had her rushed by ambulance to an emergency room--which then admitted her to an ***extended*** *hospital stay* for treatment of bedsores, dehydration, malnutrition, a urinary tract infection, aspirational pneumonia, and bruises. (All of those life-threatening conditions had developed after only a few weeks of nursing home care at the ***total*** *charge* of more than one thousand dollars a day). When I scoured the nursing home for my mother's clothing, many of her possessions, including her new (expensive) nightgowns and day clothes, were missing. The nursing home, when confronted with evidence, did agree to reimburse the cost of those items for which I could provide recent receipts; all else remained lost or stolen.

The treatment my mother received from her final nursing home was, lamentably, not better. Although my mother never drank alcohol or took narcotics in her entire life, the night nurse continually drugged her, so severely, that the resultant disorientation was an additional reason why my mother fell and broke her hip just days before her medical insurance payments would have expired and been replaced, thereafter, with Medicaid stipends (which amounted to less than one-half of the insurance payments). It was during those final weeks when my mother told me that she was being beaten by the night attendants who, when questioned, explained the bruises as having resulted from falls and accidents. Although it did not occur to me at the time (because my ***only** concern* was keeping my mother healthy and alive), I did notice that every item that I had left in my mother's room was rifled and placed elsewhere. I was oblivious to the fact that the nurse and nurses' aides were regularly searching for hidden cameras and/or microphones. Since my mother had, unnecessarily, been drugged with narcotics, it is reasonable to infer that she, most likely, was no longer being given her prescribed, life-saving, medications as well.

Although I had resisted agreeing to a Living Will with Advanced Directives which, in essence, grants permission to "pull the plug", *allegedly*, for the purpose of preventing prolonged suffering, I ***finally*** consented to the hospital and nursing home staffs', non-stop, insistence *after* my mother survived her hip surgery at the age of 98. I did not realize that the ***truthful*** *intention for the Living Will* was to use that consent as a legal justification to euthanize my mother because, as soon as I agreed to the Advanced Directive, all life preserving medical care and treatment was immediately stopped (without my knowledge or willful approval). Within days, she was moved to an emergency room and, then, to an end-of-life suite because all treatment (including proper medicine) was discontinued.

Every day, I am haunted by the regret that I was not well enough (or wealthy enough) to *effectively* confront and thwart such evil. While in my vulnerable state of ill health, I was forced to watch caregivers torture and murder my mother; and, other than briefly delaying her death, there was nothing that I could do to prevent any of their sinful crimes.

Prior to witnessing my mother's ***non-stop*** nursing home abuses, I had always held the highest opinion for those nurses, nurses' aides, and doctors who, *I had believed*, altruistically chose to devote themselves to senior-care. I understood how difficult and challenging it had to be for workers to constantly tolerate seniors' erratic behaviors, to regularly clean body waste accidents and change adult diapers, and to continually witness and experience the heartbreak of non-stop suffering and death. Initially, I even believed that my mothers' abusers were decent human beings because they always knew the correct things to say and always claimed to have my mother's best interest at heart. Had I not spent so much time at the nursing homes and witnessed their behaviors (when they thought no one was watching), I would have never realized how, ***totally***, **indecent** too many of those ***phony*** caregivers actually were.

I now realize that senior (and end-of-life) care is an employment field which ***must*** attract a disproportionate number of sadists, sociopaths, functioning psychopaths, and murderers because there is no other job, anywhere, that provides such a non-stop opportunity to abuse, torture, and murder a large number of human beings *without* ***any*** *fear of repercussions* (such as investigations and punishments).

You are painting nursing home conditions with too broad a brush and making it seem as though everyone involved in senior-care is an abuser or a murderer. That is too unfair because the overwhelming majority of caregivers deserve to be regarded with praise and gratitude--not condemnation. Why are you being so critical?

It is difficult to imagine how anyone could work in a nursing home, for even a short period of time, without witnessing (and, thus, being aware of) non-stop criminal misconduct. Conditions appeared, to me, to be even more heinous (and out-of-control) than those exposed by Upton Sinclair when his 1906 book, *The Jungle*, revealed details and examples of abuses in Chicago's meatpacking industry which (1) included the preparation and sale of diseased, rotten, and contaminated meat and (2) so enraged the entire country that it led to the ***immediate*** *adoption* of the1906 Meat Inspection Act and the Pure Food and Drug Act. The senior-care industry requires comparable, ***immediate,*** *investigation and legislation* as well. Only then, will it be possible to identify and separate those caregivers who are truly altruistic from those who are not. Thousands of claims for elder abuse remain open (at any given time) throughout this country (yet are not being properly, or timely, investigated) because the appropriate state agencies *continually* **claim** that they are understaffed. Since nursing home associations are some of the most reliable (and generous) of all political campaign contributors, states' inability (and/or unwillingness) to properly investigate (and regulate) the nursing home industry remains highly suspicious. Nursing home owners and administrators have to be made accountable (and criminally prosecuted) for ***ALL instances*** of senior neglect, torture, and murder.

If such an investigation is initiated, where do you believe the majority of blame lies?

The most remarkable revelation is that the overwhelming majority of nursing home abusers are women. Previously, while discussing abortions, I noted that it was questionable behaviors, decisions, and urges that caused unwanted pregnancies (and the subsequent "choices" to abort); thus, I warned that such *regrettable behaviors, decisions, and urges* could continue to predominate and, thus, *might* sculpt those women's spiritual frequencies for the remainder of their lives. That, sadly, seems to be **true** for *far too many* senior-care workers.

What is most disheartening is the fact that, at least for the duration of my mother's tragedy, all of the nurses and nurses' aides who tied her to chairs; refused to allow her to walk and, thus, caused her to lose the ability to walk; negligently (or intentionally) exposed her to a norovirus; fed her while in horizontal positions; neglected to clean her, remove body waste, and provide her liquids when she was desperately ill; failed to replace her malfunctioning oximeter; caused her to very quickly develop bedsores, dehydration, malnutrition, aspirational pneumonia, a norovirus infection, and a urinary tract infection; drugged her with narcotics; either stole or were responsible for the disappearance of my mother's possessions; beat her; and--very possibly--stopped providing her essential medications were ***(entirely)*** African-American women. I *now realize that* ***those savages***, *intentionally, murdered* "that ***very nice*** woman"--my mother.

Are you suggesting that African-American nurses and nurses' aides were behaving as racists and, intentionally, tried to harm your mother (or worse)?

I have no understanding as to why any nurses and nurses' aides would pretend to be so caring yet *deliberately* choose to neglect and abuse vulnerable seniors. Perhaps, their rationalizations are comparable to those of the slothful and heartless sons and daughters who, willfully, choose to ignore the Fourth Catholic Commandment (and the Fifth Protestant Commandment). Chillingly, however, I did not observe a single instance where African-American seniors were similarly mistreated.

Although I had been aware that *many* African-American caregivers lived in the same neighborhoods and, in some cases, were family members of the region's most hardened criminals (those miscreants who have been terrorizing society with drug dealing and non-stop crimes of violence such as murder, rape, assault, aggravated robbery, and carjacking for decades), I (much like the rest of civilized society) had, foolishly, been willing to cast a blind-eye to the fact that many African-American caregivers are not only the mothers, daughters, wives, and sisters of some of the most evil human beings on the face of this Earth but (at least, in some instances) are, also, the primary molders of their sons', husbands', and brothers' criminal mentalities. That *frightening* ***realization*** suggests that if the activities of senior caregivers were to ever be properly investigated and exposed, the number of incarcerated women might quickly rise to equal that of incarcerated men because there is the *possibility* that any thorough investigation could, conceivably, uncover evidence of the greatest mass murder in world history.

Are you, then, stating that African-American women are the only persons responsible for nursing home abuses?

Of course not--comparable levels of elder care abuse, ***most likely***, *exist* (even in nursing homes with very few African-American workers) because (*and this fact is worth repeating*) senior and end-of-life care is an employment field which *must* entice a disproportionate number of sadists, sociopaths, functioning psychopaths, and murderers since there is no other occupation, anywhere, which provides non-stop opportunities to abuse, torture, and murder large numbers of human beings without ***any*** *fear of punishment*.

You have made the point that criminal investigations of nursing homes must begin. How do you suggest that might be done?

It is absolutely necessary that all persons involved in ***any aspect*** of the medical field (including doctors) should be required to, regularly, submit to polygraph examinations in order to maintain their professional certifications (for the purpose of **guaranteeing** *professional integrity*). Their verbal assurances, alone, should ***NEVER*** be trusted.

Such a requirement would meet with extreme opposition. The Constitution grants protections against self-incrimination, illegal searches, and all comparable and inappropriate governmental intrusions. Why should medical personnel not be equally protected?

All Constitutionally protected rights have reasonable limits. The right to free speech, for example, does not grant an individual the privilege to falsely shout "fire" in a crowded theater when there is a near certainty that some people would be injured or die in the inevitable stampede to escape; and the right to bear arms does not grant a citizen the entitlement to own a nuclear bomb. No constitutionally protected right has ever been written for the intended purpose of facilitating evil. Since elder-caregivers (and doctors) always know the correct things to say, a polygraph examination *should*, in most cases, merely provide proof that their behaviors do, in fact, mirror their statements.

Most objections would result because polygraphs are known to provide imperfect and, sometimes, incorrect results. Such findings would never be admissible evidence in courts of law, so why should careers and reputations depend upon the results of polygraph testing?

Such objections are quite valid. Citizens should strongly object to virtually all "Big Brother-type" intrusions because free societies are, almost always, expected to insure the fundamental right of personal privacy (*please convey this message to the tech industry*). There are, nevertheless, instances when that right must be balanced with other, more important, rights. For example, the F.B.I. and the C.I.A., for purposes of maintaining national security and integrity, have, successfully, been relying upon the polygraph testing of their employees for years; and although it is **true** that such findings should never be used as evidence in courts of law, lie detectors ***must be*** the primary tool used to ensure integrity in professions where the lives of vulnerable humans are at risk.

The two primary reasons that polygraph findings have been regarded as unreliable, are (1) decades ago, the American market was flooded (perhaps intentionally) with a large number of foreign made, defective, machines whose incorrect results caused harm to too many innocent individuals and (2) there are many ways for both examiners and examinees to cheat and, thus, corrupt polygraph results. Neither of those reasons is, any longer, a valid justification to ignore the value that a *properly administered* lie detector test can provide.

What, in your opinion, needs to be done to ensure correctness in any polygraph-testing program?

First, far greater attention must be placed upon the design, manufacture, and (particularly) testing of all polygraph machines for the purpose of ***ensuring*** *the greatest likelihood of valid results*. Second, steps must be taken to prevent all known forms of cheating from occurring.

What steps must be taken to prevent cheating?

To begin, since it is known that polygraph results can be corrupted when an examinee is under the influence of certain drugs, the simplest way to prevent that method of cheating is to also require a blood (*and* urine) test in order to screen for all illicit drugs. If drug testing is a mandatory requirement for professional athletes (people who merely play games), there is no good reason why the *combination* of drug testing and polygraph examination should not be an essential, contract, requirement for all people who are responsible for the lives of vulnerable human beings.

The second most frequent form of cheating occurs when examinees conceal sharp objects in their mouths or between their toes for the purpose of triggering reactions, at inappropriate times, in order to demonstrate a pattern of incongruous responses (for the purpose of invalidating the entire test results). The easiest ways to thwart such deception are to require the examinees to (1) submit to mouth and toe examinations and (2) to wear hospital gowns (as they would when taking CAT scans and MRI's). A similar cheating strategy involves the coating of fingertips and sensor points for the purpose of dulling all emotional responses; thus, fingertips and sensor points should also be examined and cleaned.

The most frequent, and diabolical, form of cheating occurs when ***examiners*** *rig* their machines to either (1) trigger or (2) suppress responses at critical moments throughout the testing. Regardless of the credentials of the examiners, there is a great deal of dishonest money that can be earned by all examiners who have the abilities to *guarantee* the results that the examinee (or some third party) seeks. It is absolutely essential, then, that (1) all examiners are, themselves, frequently polygraphed and that (2) their equipment is, regularly, subjected to unannounced inspections. There would never be a need for polygraph testing if all examinees and examiners chose to live as honorable Christians; the problem, regrettably, is that too many people living in this modern era (and this ***free*** society) choose not to.

Those persons who might be guilty of misconduct would, obviously, quit their jobs before they would allow themselves to be polygraphed. Would not a massive job shortage in the elder care industry result?

One way or another, polygraph testing would put an end to elder care abuse and murder. The worst abusers would, wisely, leave their jobs; however, those nurses and nurses' aides who value the middle-class standard of living that their jobs provide would (from the outset), instead, choose to *properly* perform their jobs' responsibilities. Caregivers (including doctors) who refuse testing should ***immediately*** lose their professional certifications (until such time as they agree to be tested--and pass their tests). Additionally, all who decline examinations should be obligated to ***immediately repay*** *the costs of their training* (in those instances when training expenses had been paid with taxpayers' dollars and/or tax-exempt dollars). Finally, all persons who refuse to be tested (or fail their tests) should be excluded from future access to governmental support programs such as welfare, food stamps, housing, and medical assistance. Although such a Victorian Era-type penalty might seem harsh, that consequence is, nevertheless, *appropriate* because (1) all failures and (2) all refusals to be subjected to polygraph examinations (for the purpose of insuring professional integrity) are de facto admissions of criminal misconduct.

That possibility would surely create a dramatic personnel shortage because a large percentage of people would no longer choose to work in the eldercare field. Where, then, would you expect to find a sufficient number of caregivers?

I would suggest that before scientists race to land humans on Mars and design flying and self-driving cars, the scientific community should, instead, create smart, interactive, and wearable robots or (when absolutely necessary) smart, interactive, robotic wheelchair assistants for seniors (and all other disabled people) so that seniors are able to remain independent for additional decades. When that happens, far fewer caregivers will be required. The primary function of all wearable robots should be to help seniors safely walk (*without **any** possibility* of falling) even in instances when seniors lose consciousness. In addition, wearable robots should be able to: (1) constantly, yet unobtrusively, interactively respond to voice commands; (2) monitor all body functions such as heart rates, blood pressures, lung functions, and oxygen levels; (3) continually interface with (and send results to) hospital data-collection monitors; (4) unobtrusively provide oxygen in those instances when oxygen is required; (5) have the ability to defibrillate and/or resuscitate stopped hearts; and, in instances when medical crises might occur, wearable robots should be sufficiently intelligent to (6) immediately summon ambulances and unlock doors and/or (7) automatically convey seniors to self-driving cars and direct those cars to the nearest emergency rooms. Additionally, wearable robots should be able to interact with other robots that are capable of properly dispensing prescribed medicines and food at correct times. Another great health benefit would result if wearable robots could regularly, yet unobtrusively, draw, and completely analyze, blood samples in order to identify all possible maladies and chemical imbalances (at their inceptions). While the primary purpose of robots would be to allow seniors to live, independently, in their own homes for many more years, robots could also be utilized in nursing homes and assisted care facilities. Wearable robots, then, should be designed to recognize, chronicle, and notify authorities of all instances of elder abuse and/or neglect (particularly beatings) whenever abuse and/or neglect occurs.

The toughest remaining design challenges would be: (1) conceiving simple ways for seniors to put on and take off their wearable robots; (2) creating redundancies and contingencies for the inevitable instances when robots malfunction; (3) crafting the easiest automatic charging processes possible; (4) aiding seniors in personal tasks such as dressing, undressing, washing, and shaving; and (5) most importantly, assisting seniors' efforts to safely eliminate body waste, change disposable diapers, and keep private body areas clean and free from infection. An automatic bidet-type toilet seat might be an effective solution.

Would not the cost of such robots and toilet seats be prohibitive?

Wearable robots and bidet toilet seats would, *dramatically, decrease costs* because medical and **testing** expenses rise, astronomically, during the last few years of life (primarily because caregivers, so skillfully, exploit Medicare's and other health insurance systems' benefit plans). My mother's insurance was charged far more than one thousand dollars a day (*in **total** expenses,* by every nursing home,) for, non-stop, abuse and improper treatment. Well-designed, wearable robots would eliminate many of those costs and, dramatically, reduce all others. Additionally, when seniors, finally, do die from non-abusive and non-neglect *natural* causes, their wearable robots would, repeatedly, be refurbished and recycled.

In summary, the instruction of the Fourth Catholic Commandment (and the Fifth Protestant Commandment), **"*Honor your father and your mother that you may have a long life in the land which the Lord, your God, is giving you*",** *will only, finally, become a reality for most mothers* *and fathers* if (and when) well-designed wearable robots and/or robotic assistants are made available to ***all*** *dependent seniors.*

Now that your discussion of the Ten Commandments and the Seven Deadly Sins is completed, many non-Christians, anti-Christians, and make-believe Christians might condemn some of your analyses for employing what, to them, could seem to be un-Christian-like tones and beliefs. How do you justify the harshness of some of your observations?

At the beginning of this discussion, I explained that I was agreeable to revealing how my dream knowledge has helped to mold *my real life convictions* as long as it is understood (1) that I am sharing the personal viewpoints of a human being and (2) that my understandings should never be perceived as the teachings of a modern-day prophet. The reason for sharing my insights is based upon my belief that the greatest obstacle facing the long-term viability of the Christian Church is the absence of modern-day relevancy. While Christ's parables are filled with allusions which afforded clear understanding to His contemporaries (most of whom lived in agrarian societies), the importance and the meanings of Christ's allegories do not always have the same, present day, impact because they seem less germane to modern situations. I have, thus, examined ***some*** *contemporary behaviors* in a manner that ***I believe*** would concern Jesus if He were alive today; and I utilized my dream knowledge ***to speculate*** how Christ would have, most likely, responded to those modern transgressions. (My criticism of the behaviors of *some* nursing home workers, for example, is not too dissimilar to Jesus' criticism of the behaviors of the moneylenders in the Temple).

Despite the fact that Jesus made clear that His intention was not to condemn the world but, instead, to save it, both Jesus and God are, nevertheless, sufficiently omniscient to perceive all **truth**; therefore, ***my primary intention has been to reveal THAT REALITY which Jesus, God, and the Holy Spirit actually perceive***. Two additional purposes for my analyses have been (1) to explain why Matthew warned at 7: 13-14: "The gate that leads to damnation is wide, the road is clear, and many *choose* to travel it. But how narrow is the gate that leads to *life*, how rough the road, and *how few there are that find it*"; and (2) to clarify why it is ***senseless*** for humans to connect with tethers which lure them to damnation rather than those righteous Judeo-Christian tethers that shepherd them to the "gate that leads to life".

Notice how, in this modern era, virtually all Christian concerns about human misconduct (no matter how correct and justified) are, *successfully*, being branded as *hate speech*. Christian beliefs have, effectively, been silenced by successful, non-stop, ***diabolical***, (and, as yet, unchallenged) anti-Christian, non-Christian, and make-believe Christian propaganda agendas; and the consequence is that too many humans have been falsely portrayed as victims for the sinister purpose of deceiving them to, foolishly, descend to those pathways which directly lead to eternal damnation.

In summary, my analyses have attempted (1) to provide the best reasons for humans to examine and reflect upon the ways that they have chosen to live their lives and (2) to help them realize that Jesus' greatest gift to humanity has been to show humans "***the way***" to their spiritual salvations (by revealing those human qualities and behaviors which best assure Heavenly ascension). My hope (like those of the Doomsday Prophets) is that I have, successfully, (1) reminded all humans of their primary spiritual purpose, (2) provided them the insight and motivation to live the remainder of their lives in "ways" that would please God, and, thus, (3) helped *all humans* to better understand how to, continuously, harbor God's goodness within their hearts and souls. My prayer is that God will be so pleased with the life choices of ***all*** of His children that He will be able to bestow His love and blessings upon ***everyone*** because He will, finally, be able to recognize that ***all*** human souls are vibrating on the same wave-lengths as the ***peaceful Christian TRUTH frequencies*** which are tethered directly to the most desirable Heavenly rooms.

Made in the USA
Monee, IL
08 November 2021

8cfb6dc9-35e9-4859-b5dc-941669ac4f31R02